Human Sexuality
G.E. Segment 3

Richard Blonna
William Paterson University

Jean Levitan
William Paterson University

THOMSON

WADSWORTH

Australia • Canada • Mexico • Singapore • Spain • United Kingdom • United States

Human Sexuality
Blonna & Levitan

Executive Editors:
Michele Baird, Maureen Staudt &
Michael Stranz

Project Development Manager:
Linda de Stefano

Marketing Coordinators:
Lindsay Annett and Sara Mercurio

Production/Manufacturing Supervisor:
Donna M. Brown

Pre-Media Services Supervisor:
Dan Plofchan

Rights & Permissions Specialists:
Kalina Hintz and Bahman Naraghi

Cover Image
Getty Images*

© 2006 Thomson Wadsworth, a part of
the Thomson Corporation. Thomson,
the Star logo, and Wadsworth are
trademarks used herein under license.

Printed in the
United States of America
1 2 3 4 5 6 7 8 08 07 06

For more information, please contact
Thomson Custom Solutions, 5191
Natorp Boulevard, Mason, OH 45040.
Or you can visit our Internet site at
www.thomsoncustom.com

ALL RIGHTS RESERVED. No part of
this work covered by the copyright
hereon may be reproduced or used in
any form or by any means — graphic,
electronic, or mechanical, including
photocopying, recording, taping, Web
distribution or information storage and
retrieval systems — without the written
permission of the publisher.

For permission to use material from this
text or product, contact
us by:
Tel (800) 730-2214
Fax (800) 730 2215
www.thomsonrights.com

The Adaptable Courseware Program
consists of products and additions to
existing Thomson products that are
produced from camera-ready copy.
Peer review, class testing, and
accuracy are primarily the responsibility
of the author(s).

Human Sexuality
/Blonna & Levitan
ISBN 0-495-28096-8

International Divisions List

Asia (Including India):
Thomson Learning
(a division of Thomson Asia Pte Ltd)
5 Shenton Way #01-01
UIC Building
Singapore 068808
Tel: (65) 6410-1200
Fax: (65) 6410-1208

Australia/New Zealand:
Thomson Learning Australia
102 Dodds Street
Southbank, Victoria 3006
Australia

Latin America:
Thomson Learning
Seneca 53
Colonia Polano
11560 Mexico, D.F., Mexico
Tel (525) 281-2906
Fax (525) 281-2656

Canada:
Thomson Nelson
1120 Birchmount Road
Toronto, Ontario
Canada M1K 5G4
Tel (416) 752-9100
Fax (416) 752-8102

UK/Europe/Middle East/Africa:
Thomson Learning
High Holborn House
50-51 Bedford Row
London, WC1R 4LS
United Kingdom
Tel 44 (020) 7067-2500
Fax 44 (020) 7067-2600

Spain (Includes Portugal):
Thomson Paraninfo
Calle Magallanes 25
28015 Madrid
España
Tel 34 (0)91 446-3350
Fax 34 (0)91 445-6218

*Unless otherwise noted, all cover images used by Thomson Custom Solutions have been supplied courtesy of Getty Images with
the exception of the *Earthview* cover image, which has been supplied by the National Aeronautics and Space Administration (NASA).

Custom Table of Contents

chapter *one*

Exploring Healthy Sexuality

Student Learning Objectives

After reading this chapter, students will be able to

- Define *human sexuality*.

- Define *health* and *wellness*.

- Describe the key components of healthy sexuality.

- Explain how the six dimensions of health and wellness impact one's sexuality.

- Compare and contrast behaviors that enhance or inhibit healthy sexuality.

- Describe the key sources of sexual information.

- Evaluate sources of sexuality information.

- Describe the major findings of the key researchers of sexuality over the past 100 years.

- Describe the components of informed decision making.

- Understand some of the health challenges to sexuality.

Test your understanding of these objectives by taking the end-of-chapter quiz, available online at **http://health.wadsworth.com/blonna1.**

activity teaser: *How "real" are the relationships we see on TV? Find the answer in the Personal Exploration Activity on page 10.*

case study 1.1

Maria

Maria, age 25, identifies as Puerto Rican American.

Maria is a full-time, commuter student in her senior year. She is engaged to Nick, a 22-year-old Italian American, also completing his senior year. Maria was finishing up her final project in Dr. Blonna's Human Sexuality class and came in to discuss her paper.

"I'll never forget this conversation," Dr. Blonna recalled, "because it came from such an unlikely source that it was striking. Maria was the quintessential urban woman; tough, street-smart, wise beyond her years, with a cynicism born from years of living in northeastern New Jersey."

I just finished writing my paper and took some time to think through some of the assessments that I took and the work that we did in class this semester. I can't believe how much I've changed in just 16 weeks. I took this class because I was curious about my sexuality and my relationship with Nick. I was mostly interested in the, you know, the sexual behavior part. I thought that maybe I could learn a few ways to spice up our sex life.

I can't believe how much more I learned about my sexuality and how I never realized how much a part my health played in it. I never even realized what health really was and how things like my spirituality, fitness, and environment influenced it. I took a couple of fitness and body image assessments, and it made me realize that I have never really been comfortable with my body. I guess that is why I have had such a hard time really relaxing with Nick when I am naked and enjoying sex even though he's told me a thousand times he loves my body and likes me just the way I am.

Dr. Blonna asked Maria to tell him about the other parts of her assessment, her spirituality and environmental health.

I rediscovered my spirituality this semester. I guess I had lost touch with it because I'd spent a lot of time over the past few years questioning my faith and the church I grew up in. You helped me realize that it is normal to question our faith and that faith transcends any specific religion. You also made me realize that it was important to not give up my faith as I sorted through my spiritual beliefs and tried to find a connection to something that worked for me. I've kind of started that by doing more things that connect me with nature. I haven't given up on my religion, but I find I am able to think about it differently outdoors than by sitting in church. Nick and I have started getting away from the hustle and bustle of the city on weekends. We've started to drive to the mountains and take long hikes in the woods. We've found some really amazing places within 2 hours from home that are quiet, peaceful, and beautiful. We really felt that "connection" you talked about in class. We've even gone to the beach in the winter and had the whole place to ourselves. Sometimes we just walk hand-in-hand for miles without even saying a word to each other. It's like some bond has developed that transcends us. I don't know, it sounds crazy but it's made me appreciate everything a little more.

I guess that I can see the holistic thing you've been talking about in class and in the textbook. I mean, like I am getting in shape by doing all of this walking and nature stuff. My relationship with Nick has never been better. We have this new connection, and I've got to admit we've found that some of these places are great for spontaneous sex. I also think I am beginning to find some kind of rekindling of my spiritual self. Being outside, quietly taking it all in, feeling in touch with my body, feeling sexy toward my man, all of this stuff just seems to make me feel some connection with something bigger than myself.

Critical Thinking

Maria and Nick are able to escape from the hustle and bustle of their everyday environment and spend time walking in the woods or along the beach. What other strategies could be used to make sure that health needs are met when such escapes are not possible?

Use your Virtual Workbook to explore your answer to this question at **http://health.wadsworth.com/blonna1.**

Maria's case illustrates how one's health plays a crucial role in healthy sexuality. The interplay of the different dimensions of health manifests itself in many ways in our sexuality. As you can see with Maria, often the dimensions of health overlap. Where does our environmental well-being end and our spirituality begin? Where does our physical health stop and our emotional health start? Maria so eloquently describes the interconnections between our health and our sexuality.

As we continue living in the 21st century, students may be struggling to sort out the conflicting messages about "healthy sexuality." Compared to students growing up in the previous century, so much more information is open and accessible. There are choices that are better understood, with the power of the Internet to answer questions that in previous generations may not even have been asked. More and more, individuals are demanding their rights to be who they are in terms of their sexuality.

Sexuality remains a critical force shaping our lives. It is part of how we see ourselves and impacts our **self-esteem.** It is ever-present as we relate to others on both romantic and platonic levels. Students, as well as the population at large, are constantly confronted with media messages on enhancing sexuality through the use of various products. Sexual themes remain prominent in all forms of entertainment, including books, film, television, and music.

As health educators, we hold to the position that good decision making is grounded in having accurate information, an opportunity to develop a personal value system, and discussion of possible and probable outcomes of behavior. We advocate the accompanying opportunity to become aware of the variety of sexual lifestyles and concerns of those who are unlike ourselves.

Self-esteem A way of looking at oneself; may be high or low

Our Sexual Climate

To try to figure out how best to make healthy personal decisions in a climate of contrasts is confusing and problematic. Americans talk about sex and sexuality all the time. It is a favorite subject of the media. Some conservative media pundits criticize our culture for its overemphasis on sex. They claim that sexual themes dominate our culture and the media and that the government has gone too far in allowing the free expression of sexuality. Some liberal commentators say exactly the opposite. They claim that our culture is sexually restrictive and downright puritanical. As examples of a restrictive culture, they cite the continued demand for abstinence-until-married sexuality education in the schools, restrictions on reproductive rights, and resistance to the legalization of domestic partnerships/gay marriage. Still others claim that our culture sends mixed messages about sexuality. It is used to market and sell almost everything, yet most schools are not allowed to teach about sexuality in a comprehensive, forthright way.

The reality is that government and society influence our sexuality in many ways, some positive, some negative, and some ambiguous. We are sexual beings from conception to death, and our sexuality evolves and grows regardless of official sanctions or restrictions. We learn about sex whether we do or do not have sexuality education in our schools. It is not a question of *whether* we learn. It's more a matter of the *quality* of what we learn. A key to understanding sexual learning is to realize that we learn about sexuality and what it means to be a man or woman even if no one ever sits us down and has a heart-to-heart talk about the "birds and the bees." And that classic explanation of where we came from is only a small part of understanding ourselves.

Quality sexuality programs result from well-thought-out curricula, with goals and objectives for student learning. Curricula are based on accurate information, in which the pursuit of knowledge is encouraged rather than restricted. Students have a chance to examine their values and the factors that contribute to healthy and appropriate personal decisions. Eighteen states plus the District of Columbia require schools to provide sexuality education: Delaware, Georgia, Illinois, Iowa, Kansas, Kentucky, Maryland, Minnesota, Nevada, New Jersey, North Carolina, Rhode Island, South Carolina, Tennessee, Utah, Vermont, West Virginia, and Wyoming (Sexuality Information and Education Council of the U.S. [SIECUS], 2001). Other states have varying requirements, from sexuality "units" within health education programs, to focusing on HIV/AIDS but avoiding much discussion about the broad aspects of sexuality. Some topics may even be prohibited from discussion. For example, 15 states do not require schools to provide STD, HIV, and/or AIDS education: Alaska, Arizona, Arkansas, Colorado, Hawaii, Idaho, Louisiana, Maine, Massachusetts, Missouri, Montana, Nebraska, South Dakota, Texas, Virginia—and of those, Arizona, Louisiana, Mississippi, and Texas require that such education teach abstinence but not prevention methods (National Abortion and Reproductive Rights Action League [NARAL], 2001). In our information-rich culture, such censorship further highlights the conflicts students face when attempting to move toward sexual health.

In many ways the sexual learning that takes place outside any classroom is far more influential, as it is constant, both verbal and nonverbal, and often insidious. Students can easily relate the types of misinformation they acquired from friends throughout their childhood and simultaneously often report that their parents didn't talk with them about sexuality issues. In reality, though, parents convey information, impart values, and serve as **role models** whether a formal, face-to-face, serious conversation ever takes place between parent and child. A frown or a raised eyebrow can convey disapproval just as a nod, smile, or laugh indicates support. To be silent on an issue, to omit sexuality from the daily discourse in our lives, to never bring up sexuality as part of the conversation around the dinner table sends a strong message about its being a taboo subject.

Some of what we see and learn, unfortunately, does not present the healthiest picture of sexuality. Sometimes our parents, caregivers, friends, teachers, and media figures do not provide us with the best role models or information for healthy sexuality. The sexual scripts we receive may not promote healthy relationships and in some cases may actually jeopardize our lives. For example, if women are taught that they must be thin to be sexually attractive, what connection might that "lesson" have to eating disorders such as anorexia and bulimia? If men are taught that they are entitled to sex and that women want to be dominated, what connection does that "lesson" have to dating violence and rape? Sometimes the very people and institutions charged with teaching us and nurturing us fail or, worse yet, sexually abuse us.

So what is human sexuality? **Sexuality** is a broad term that refers to all aspects of being sexual. Many people think human sexuality refers to sexual behavior—what people do, how often they do it, and so on. Although sexual behavior is an important part of being sexual, human sexuality encompasses much more than that. Sexuality involves our genetic inheritance, our anatomy and physiology, and the reality of being a sexual creature in a biological sense. It also encompasses our thoughts and feelings about our body and what it means to be a man or a woman. It involves our ethics, values, and the cultural mores we've assimilated through our family, ethnic group, and religious affiliation.

Our sexuality extends beyond the self to encompass our friendships, intimate relationships, and sexual relationships. Lastly, our sexuality does not exist in a vacuum. It is influenced by and influences our environment. Our institutions (schools, governments, and so on), neighborhoods, communities, campuses, states, and countries, and their policies, help shape the person we are and our options as a sexual being.

Role model A person whose behaviors are imitated by others

Sexuality A broad term referring to all aspects of being sexual

Factors That Contribute to Our Sexuality

Our sexuality is influenced by many factors throughout our lives, each impacting our development in similar or unique ways. No researcher or theorist has the widely accepted, definitive explanation for how each of us becomes who we are. Some rely heavily on biology, looking to our genetic inheritance as a prescription for how we will develop. Others hold the culture and the socialization process to be the critical forces that shape our lives. Some believe the psyche processes information as a result of experiences perceived as positive or negative, which in the end cause the individual to become the person he or she is. Finally, some maintain that the person we are is a result of the interaction of heredity/genetics, family socialization, culture, and personal experience.

Without being able to clearly determine which factor is most influential, we do know that we all receive strong and perhaps conflicting messages about sexuality from family, friends, school, media, religion, and the culture. **Sexologists,** those who study sexuality through various rigorous research methodologies, provide input into our knowledge base. Developing a healthy sexuality involves processing that information and, as individuals, internalizing that which is useful.

Family

The family has historically been viewed as a critical force in our development. The examination of family influence can focus on both genetic predispositions as well as scripted ways of behaving. Are our ways of being due, therefore, to "nature," "nurture," or combinations of both? From a biological perspective, family represents those to whom one is related "by blood," and, consequently, we may be like our parents and siblings. Complicating that perspective, however, are the various reproductive technologies available today, redefining aspects of the biological connection to parents.

Are we the persons we are because of how we were reared? In a social sense, the term *family* has taken on broader connotations as people's living arrangements take on a variety of forms. Divorce, remarriage, stepfamilies, blended families, and single families introduce new models. The traditional **nuclear family,** consisting of a married man and woman and their biological children, represents less than half of all households in the United States today. The primary caregiver thus may assume a greater role in a child's development than previously. The challenge comes in trying to evaluate the impact of various family arrangements on a family's members.

The impact of parental influence on sexuality is still open to debate. For example, the societal concern with homosexuality has led courts—almost exclusively, until more recent times—to award children to the heterosexual parent in custody cases resulting from divorce. The concern is that gay or lesbian parents will influence their children to be gay or lesbian. That the heterosexual parents of the gay and lesbian adults were unable to influence their children's orientation is not given the same credibility. As we will discuss later, good parenting skills, rather than the parents' sexual orientation, are key to raising healthy children. The family influences the development of healthy sexuality in numerous ways. Through family, we learn gender roles and expectations, are taught about love and affection, learn patterns of touch, develop a sense of our physical selves, and assume patterns of social interaction. In each of these areas, our experiences can lead to healthy or unhealthy development. In some areas of parenting, a number of approaches can lead to healthy sexual development.

It is generally accepted that parents should be loving and supportive toward their children. Children who receive physical affection will, in turn, be more likely to be able to give affection to others. Embedded in such general advice, however, are individual patterns that may be criticized. For example, research has shown that boy children stop receiving physical

Sexologists Specialized researchers of sexual subjects from a variety of disciplines including psychology, biology, medicine, nursing, and health

Nuclear family A family made up of the mother, father, and their children

Children learn about sex from their families without it ever being mentioned.

affection earlier than girls, who may continue to be hugged and kissed throughout their lives. Does the change in the type of touch boys receive impact their adult patterns?

In terms of **gender role** expectations, most parents reinforce gender-stereotyped behaviors very early on. Boys are expected to play aggressively and to enjoy trucks, Legos, action figures, and the like. Girls get socialized to plan for motherhood, beauty, and domestic tasks. The women's movement of the late 1960s and early 1970s questioned the impact of gender stereotyping on the healthy development of boys and girls. Over 30 years later, television commercials for children's toys reveal little departure from the traditional gender role expectations. Toy manufacturers, in their defense, claim they are marketing to the children who will buy their products. When they have attempted to market toys in a more gender-neutral manner, their efforts have not been successful. Families have different views on what is socially acceptable and what toys they want to purchase, yet children seem to develop their own preferences regardless.

> **Gender role** The different behaviors and attitudes that society expects of females and males

Friends

One's peer group has always maintained a powerful role in shaping our attitudes and values about sexuality. Depending on the friends with whom we socialize, we have various experiences at different ages. Teens may refer to others as "being in the fast crowd"—which may mean that more sexual activity and drinking take place. Kids may refer to others as "geeks" or "nerds"—meaning that, though smart, they seem to lack social skills and have interests that are "not cool." Regardless, peer pressure, social judgments, and opportunities all interact to influence healthy development. At the same time, those very influences can leave a negative mark dominated by low self-esteem, depression, and feelings of inadequacy.

Most students report that the bulk of their sexuality education comes from talks with friends. They say that some friends passed along accurate information, and others spoke with authority while dispensing inaccurate information. Students have reported that, as children and teens, they saw sexually explicit pictures, magazines, and videos at a friend's home—all supposedly belonging to "my friend's dad." The sneaking around and the searching through hidden material convey a message about sexuality.

As sexuality educators, we have volumes of accurate information available to our own children. Nonetheless, we have been confronted at times with "What do you know?!" and "Why do you have to have all this stuff around?" In some cases, one's friends are perceived as more knowledgeable than parents.

Culture

> **Culture** The sum of the learned set of rules governing the behavior of people, often focused on the influences of race, class, religion, and ethnicity

Anthropologists have defined **culture** as anything and everything that humans learn. Implied within that is a learned set of rules for appropriate behavior. In practice, when addressing issues of culture, what actually may be under study are influences of race, class, religion, and ethnicity.

All cultures have established rules to regulate sexual activity (Mindlin, Wallace, & Kapell, 2002). Some are viewed as restrictive, and others are seen as permissive. Even though Western cultures share certain traditions and values—such as patriarchy, monogamy, having children within marriage—actual behavior varies from one group to another.

As the United States becomes an increasingly pluralistic society, it is forced to confront what may seem to be "foreign" practices. For example, female genital mutilation or female genital cutting (discussed more fully with female anatomy and physiology in Chapter 2) is a custom practiced primarily in parts of Africa.

case study 1.2

Karen, with Eyes Wide Open

Karen, age 24, is white.

I remember, as a kid, traveling with the "in crowd" in middle school. There was a group of about 25 of us, and we started having boy-girl parties around the sixth grade. A couple of girls were considered the "pretty ones," and they had the boyfriends. I always got invited to the parties but ended up "watching" rather than participating. There were kissing games, close dancing, and the girls with developed chests invariably let some of the boys "cop a feel." I remember my mother, in particular, being very concerned that certain kids were "bad influences." Despite her reservations about some of my peers, I wasn't being approached, so there were no decisions for me to make. I was watching and learning . . . just not being asked to participate.

I had one friend who my mother worried was a "bad influence." Her parents were divorced, her father was out of the picture, and she was living with her elderly grandparents. One weekend she invited me to join her on a visit to her mother's apartment in the city. My friend confided that her mother had two different boyfriends; in retrospect, I realize that she slept with both of them. I remember feeling uncomfortable watching my friend's mother walk around the apartment in her underwear, sit on her boyfriend's lap, and kiss him. Somehow I knew that my own mother would have been very upset if she knew what type of education I was getting!

Critical Thinking

Karen was aware that her mother disapproved of her friend. How might a parent encourage better communication so that a child's observations and concerns could be discussed?

Use your Virtual Workbook to explore your answer to this question at **http://health.wadsworth.com/blonna1.**

Today, U.S. health care providers find themselves caring for girls and women who have undergone this mutilating experience.

Newspapers and magazines will report on international cases where punishments are meted out for those individuals whose sexual behavior violates the established culture. One case involved a couple living on the run in England. The woman was afraid that her father or brother was going to kill her because she had defied her culture by choosing her partner. Western ideas of falling in love, being able to decide whom to marry, and the like, were in direct conflict with her Muslim upbringing, which dictated that the bride's father arrange the marriage, with her input having little or no value. In 2003, pressure from outside nations resulted in a Nigerian court saving a woman from being stoned to death. She had given birth to a child as a result of being raped, yet her village court had labeled the crime adultery, requiring her to be punished.

Both cases confront students with cultural practices different from what is common in the United States. Our cultural beliefs have also been cited as justification for involvement in war and have made us the target for terrorism abroad and at home. The wars in Iraq and Afghanistan, the terrorist attacks of 9/11, and the subsequent vulnerability we have felt on our home soil have changed us all forever.

Although the first World Trade Center attack of 1993 and the subsequent bombing of the Alfred P. Murrah Federal Building in Oklahoma City in 1995 put us on notice to the possibility of major terrorist activity on American soil, the events of 9/11 were so horrific, they could not be ignored and will never be forgotten. Repeated television coverage of the terrorists flying American commercial airplanes into the World Trade Center, the Pentagon, and a lonely field in the middle of Pennsylvania brought the horror into everyone's lives. For those with family members and friends working at the various sites, the intensity of their grief was magnified.

The authors work at a university where the World Trade Center and skyline of Manhattan were visible from the highest point on campus. Our students were directly involved with 9/11, some by working and volunteering at the site, and oth-

7

ers connected to those who died. We will never forget that day, how students, faculty, and staff wandered around campus screaming and sobbing, frantically trying to place cell phone calls to loved ones. Dr. Blonna's son, a freshman at the time, recalls sitting on top of the roof of his dormitory building watching in disbelief as the World Trade Center ruins over 25 miles away smoldered long into the night. Students were crying and trying to console each other as they tried to make sense of what had happened earlier in the day.

The impact of that day lingered over the campus for the entire semester like a thick fog. Many students, faculty, and staff barely survived the semester, sometimes just going through the motions. Many class sessions started out with a moment of silence to honor the dead, the missing, and the heroic rescuers. Many professors, like Dr. Blonna, started each class by getting students to form a circle, hold hands, and share their strength with those who were less hardy. Some of our students remain in therapy, a few years after the events of 9/11. Researchers estimate that tens of thousands of New Yorkers suffered from posttraumatic stress disorder (PTSD) in the months following the attack on the World Trade Center (Seong-Ngoo, 2002). Additionally, about 17 percent of the United States population *outside* New York City reported symptoms of PTSD 2 months after the terrorist attacks (Manisses Communication Group, 2002).

Events such as the terrorist attacks of 9/11, war, and chronic and traumatic stress changed the campus and outside culture (Lane, 2002). On campuses around the country, grief counselors were brought in to help students cope with their losses. Campus counseling centers were inundated with students, faculty, and staff seeking help. Students from around the country made a pilgrimage to New York City to help out any way they could (Kirgiss, 2002).

Loss, grief, and fear brought on by the aforementioned events have changed our collective culture and have many implications for personal wellness and sexuality. They affect our trust, our ability to form intimate loving relationships, and our sexual desire (Davey, 2002; Dettmer, 2001). Studies have shown that blood levels of testosterone, the hormone of sexual desire, diminish in response to such events (Tsigos & Chrousos, 1996). Debra Straw (2001), a professor from Burlington, Vermont, writing in *Community College Week*, describes this so eloquently in the following passage: "One young woman, normally an A student, told me last week that she has been getting B's and that she has been taking depression medication and getting therapy as a direct result of what has been happening in the larger world. These young people now live in fear and uncertainty. Their American Dream seems to have been blown away" (p. 3).

The terrorist attacks of 9/11 threatened the diversity that is so vital to a well-rounded college experience (Garmon, 2001). Terror, fear, anger, and suffering impacted the previous level of acceptance and understanding of students from different cultures, particularly those of the Middle East. Some campuses across the nation reported backlash against Middle Eastern students, professors, and staff, and Islamic studies and culture (Boulard, 2001). This creates a campus climate that is not healthy and safe. We firmly believe that for healthy sexuality to occur, one's environment must be safe and conducive to a free expression of ideas and lifestyles. When tolerance and acceptance are replaced by intolerance and rejection, everyone suffers.

Popular Culture

Terrorism and threats of war, however, do not seem to interrupt popular culture's fascination with sexuality. Television programs in the early 2000s increasingly have brought the viewer into the lives and bedrooms of dating couples. People meet on television, date in front of a camera, get sexually involved in front of a camera, and even marry, sometimes to someone either picked by their parents or voted on by viewers. Even the mainstream program *The Today Show* has succumbed to having couples compete for being married on the show, with Internet voting on the clothes to be worn, ring to be purchased, hairstyle and dress for the bride, among other wedding-related activities.

While television has become more direct about sexual humor and sexual content, it has also taken greater responsibility in discussing sexual issues in a more forthright manner. Cable television can be credited for leading the way for greater openness; competition for viewers has brought the traditional networks along. For example, the History Channel developed a few multipart series on sexuality, looking at sexuality in the 20th century and another beginning in ancient times. Viewers can also find segments on sexual issues on such news programs as *20/20*, *Dateline*, and *Primetime*, along with a variety of topics covered by public television stations.

"Reality TV" programs are very popular and bring the viewer into the lives and bedrooms of dating couples.

The sexuality of the rich and famous continues to be scrutinized. The years 2002–2003 were witness to Michael Jackson, the pop singer, coming under intense scrutiny for his interest in children, with possible charges of sexual abuse. Catholic priests across the United States were brought to task for the years of sexual abuse covered up by the church hierarchy. Rabbis were arrested for soliciting sex online. As always, the romantic lives of politicians were fair game for media scrutiny. When JonBenet Ramsey was murdered in the late 1990s, not only were people upset at the horror of the death, but they also frequently reacted to the mature look given to this young model and beauty pageant contestant.

A cursory examination of popular magazines today will reveal more and more skin, especially that of women's bodies. The *Sports Illustrated* Swimsuit Issue (winter 2003) is not that different in appearance from a *Playboy* magazine printed decades earlier. Both have well-written articles of interest, yet the sensual photography of the female models makes the magazines big sellers. The lingerie company Victoria's Secret distributes catalogues and designs store windows displaying female underwear in a seductive manner. Abercrombie and Fitch in fall 2003 distributed the *A&F Quarterly—The SEX ED Issue* in which the clothing was the centerfold, with naked male and female models in seductive poses filling the catalogue. The content and images were provocative enough that a paper sleeve surrounded the catalogue, and its purchase was limited to those 18 and older.

Popular music, particularly that focused on youth, has lyrics about sexuality that are explicit, direct, and often angry. Whereas country singers have long shared the details of dysfunctional relationships, the Dixie Chicks raised some eyebrows when they sang about the murder of a man with a history of beating his wife. Rappers sing and shout about reactions to body parts and sexual activity. Women get referred to as "bitches," and young kids will sing along to songs focused on oral sex and sexual intercourse.

U.S. culture is saturated with sexual messages, yet at the same time political leaders debate whether or not honest, factual, information dare be presented to youth.

All That Glitters Is Not Gold

The goal of this activity is to stimulate you to take a critical view of ideas and actions related to sexuality that are presented in the media as normal and healthy. Your task is to determine whether they are healthy or unhealthy for relationships and whether they fit your values.

Gather a few of your friends together to watch one of your favorite television shows that deals with romantic relationships. *Friends* and *Sex and the City* are the kinds of shows that fit well with this activity. Your task while watching the show is to individually list the relationship behaviors as either healthy/realistic or unhealthy/unrealistic. Examples to watch for are couples talking at the same time and never listening to what the other says, one partner treating the other with respect, and similar behaviors. When the show ends, compare your list to the lists of your friends. Do you all see the behaviors in the same way, or do your friends see something as healthy when you think it is unhealthy? If you find differences, explore the reasons for your views with your friends. Ask your friends what healthy/realistic behaviors they would like to have in a loving relationship. Do they think the behaviors we watch in the media hurt the way we relate to one another?

K–12 Schools

Schools are charged as the institutions primarily responsible for transmitting knowledge and helping children learn about the world. As a logical extension, schools are to play a key role in sexuality education. Even so, the debate has raged for decades regarding the role schools should play, the depth of information they should convey, at what ages children should learn information about sexuality, and how, if at all, schools can teach in a "value-free" way. Programs that have been successful have been conducted by working closely with parents, clergy, and community leaders to develop curricula that are acceptable. The efforts in this regard far exceed those in other subject areas such as English or history. Research shows that most parents support sexuality education in the public schools.

The National Guidelines Task Force, under the auspices of SIECUS (1997), identified six key concepts that should be part of comprehensive sexuality education programs: human development, relationships, personal skills, sexual behavior, sexual health, and society and culture. A broad spectrum of professionals, including the American Medical Association, National Education Association, U.S. Centers for Disease Control, and Planned Parenthood Federation of America, to name a few, published *Guidelines for Comprehensive Sexuality Education*, which expands on the teaching of 36 sexuality-related topics presented from an age-appropriate perspective (SIECUS, 1996).

Since the *Guidelines'* publication in the early 1990s, however, opponents to comprehensive sexuality education have seen their position supported with federal funding for programs that teach abstinence until marriage. There is little doubt that concerns about sexually transmitted disease (STD) and HIV infections among young people have fueled the abstinence education movement. In 1997, the federal government earmarked multimillion-dollar grants to the states for the development of **abstinence-based curricula** (see Table 1.1). Such funding was both continued and increased in 2002, with presidential and legislative support.

Nonetheless, the Kaiser Family Foundation (2000) conducted a national study finding that the overwhelming majority of parents, teachers, principals, and students want some form of sexuality education taught in secondary school. The ma-

Abstinence-based curricula
School programs that advocate not having sex before marriage

Table 1.1 Federal Guidelines for Abstinence Education

"Abstinence education" means an educational or motivational program which:

A. Has, as its exclusive purpose, teaching the social, psychological, and health gains to be realized by abstaining from sexual activity.

B. Teaches abstinence from sexual activity outside marriage as the expected standard for school-age children.

C. Teaches that abstinence from sexual activity is the only certain way to avoid out-of-wedlock pregnancy, sexually transmitted diseases, and other associated health problems.

D. Teaches that a mutually faithful monogamous relationship in context of marriage is the expected standard of human sexual activity.

E. Teaches that sexual activity outside of the context of marriage is likely to have harmful consequences for the child, the child's parents, and society.

F. Teaches young people how to reject sexual advances and how alcohol and drug use increases vulnerability to sexual advances, and

G. Teaches the importance of attaining self-sufficiency before engaging in sexual activity.

Source: Cited in the *Federal Register, 62* (March 13, 1997), 49.

jority of parents wanted students to learn about HIV/AIDS and other STDs, the basics of pregnancy and birth control, how to deal with the pressure to have sex, the emotional issues and consequences of being sexually active, how to use and get birth control methods and abortion, and issues related to sexual orientation.

The Office of the Surgeon General (2001), under the guidance of then-surgeon general David Satcher, issued a report *The Surgeon General's Call to Action to Promote Sexual Health and Responsible Behavior.* The report summarizes scientific findings about various educational efforts and asks that a mature national dialogue on issues of sexuality, sexual health, and responsible sexual behavior begin. Satcher, along with the professionals from various disciplines who collaborated on the report, recognize that the rates of STDs, HIV/AIDS, unintended pregnancies, sexual violence, and so on, make sexual health an obvious part of public health priorities. The report wisely calls for a variety of educational venues representing the diversity of our culture to positively address sexuality education.

College

Young or old, resident or commuter, full-time or part-time, college students realize that college impacts sexuality in many ways. A college campus is a unique environment. Unlike high school, college is a place of limitless intellectual and personal freedom, where ideas and the pursuit of knowledge reign supreme. It is a place where knowledge, attitudes, and behavior are supposed to be examined and challenged. It is also a place of great personal and intellectual diversity, where people of all walks of life come together to learn and grow. For many of us it is the first time we have ever experienced such freedom and diversity.

The freedom and diversity of college extend into our sexuality. Away from home and in a new environment, we are exposed to people, ideas, experiences, and situations that challenge us and help shape us as sexual beings. The combination of personal freedom and the opportunity to try out new ideas, behaviors, and lifestyles is exciting. Our college years are a time of great personal growth. Many of us develop intimate, loving, sexual relationships in our college years that remain with us for a lifetime.

College life also is a time for making choices. The decisions we make also can remain with us for a lifetime. Our decision-making ability is put to the test on a regular basis. Sexual choices are among the most important decisions we have to make. Decisions about who we are and what it means to be men and women, who we are attracted to, how we want to live and express our sexuality, what our sexual needs and wants are, and how we will fulfill them are but a few of the decisions we will make during our college years.

Evaluating Sexuality Research

Research Methods and Sources of Information

Sexology The discipline that scientifically studies sexuality

As we strive toward a personally healthy sexuality, a critical task for all of us is to evaluate the information we receive. **Sexology,** the discipline that scientifically studies sexuality, is often conducted by researchers, some of whom refer to themselves as *sexologists*. Because the field of sexuality is truly interdisciplinary, researchers may primarily identify as biologists, psychologists, sociologists, anthropologists, health educators, nurses, historians, physicians, and more. Wiederman (2001) identifies 19 professional journals whose primary focus is publishing research on human sexuality. In addition, professional organizations in the field also publish newsletters and reports, which add to the knowledge base.

It has often been difficult for researchers to secure adequate funding for sexuality research. Government funding has been most available if the research agenda can be closely demonstrated to impact public health. To some, however, the very study of human sexuality is suspect; others can appreciate the need to know and how much there is to learn. Table 1.2 profiles some of the more prominent research and researchers. The studies were conducted in different ways—some through questionnaires, some through interviews, some by observation, and so forth—although it would be fair to argue that better funding may have yielded broader samples and more comprehensive information.

As mentioned, a growing number of professional journals are focused on sexuality research. At the same time, there are limitations on the types of research conducted. Although a wide variety of questionnaires have been designed and administered, most sexuality research involves surveying selected populations. Often university academics rely on the input of students, groups who are at the very least better educated and literate. In contrast, it would be far more difficult to assess information from populations who may not speak English, trust researchers, or even communicate about sexuality issues.

Ethical and practical considerations also impact what kinds of research are conducted. Observing and surveying children may be problematic, as parental permission must be secured; determining when an issue may be most related to the developmental stage of the child can become political and contentious. Some research is best conducted as a longitudinal study, where a population can be examined over time; the costs associated with such a design, however, can be prohibitive. In other cases, topics such as understanding sexual functioning related to a particular disease may pose challenges in securing an adequate sample size.

Because disciplines have their own established perspectives, the research presented may have other limitations or biases. Key criteria separate good research from poor research. Issues such as bias, sampling issues, honesty, and access all contribute to the quality of sexuality research findings.

Table 1.2 Contributions of Experts on Sexuality

Researcher(s)	Research	Years	Comments
Richard von Krafft-Ebing	*Psychopathia Sexualis*	1886	Viennese psychiatrist who introduced Victorian public to fetishism, sadomasochism, transvestism, homosexuality
Havelock Ellis	*Psychology of Sex*	1897–1910	Challenged negative views toward masturbation and narrow definitions of normal behavior
Alfred Kinsey and associates	*Sexual Behavior in the Human Male* *Sexual Behavior in the Human Female*	1948 1953	A pioneer undertaking involving thousands of males and females interviewed about their sexual behavior
William Masters and Virginia Johnson	*Human Sexual Response* *Human Sexual Inadequacy*	1966 1970	The first research efforts to photograph and physiologically record thousands of instances of sexual arousal, orgasm, masturbation, and coitus. Followed by brief effective treatment for sexual problems.
Morton Hunt	*Sexual Behavior in the 1970s*	1974	Showed consistencies and changes in sexual behavior a generation after the Kinsey findings
Philip Blumstein and Pepper Schwartz	*American Couples*	1983	Study of sexual and affectional behavior of couples
Shere Hite	*The Hite Report on Female Sexuality* *The Hite Report on Male Sexuality* *Women and Love* *Good Guys, Bad Guys*	1976 1981 1987 1991	Although statistically unrepresentative, an early attempt at qualitative research yielding valuable insights to behavior
Popular culture	Magazine surveys: *Redbook, Cosmopolitan, Playboy*	1980	Surveyed more than 100,000 readers; findings often apply more to magazine's readers than to all adults
Richard Green	*The "Sissy Boy" Syndrome*	1987	Controversial study on the origins of homosexuality
Edward Brecher	*Love, Sex, and Aging*	1984	One of the first large-scale scientific studies of sexuality in older people
John Money Anke Erhardt	*Man and Woman, Boy and Girl* *Gay, Straight and In-between*	1972 1988	Now-controversial study of gender anatomy, and identity. Attempted definitions of the biological and psychological determinants of sex, sexuality, and gender.
Edward Lauman, John Gagnon, Robert Michael, and Stuart Michaels	*The Social Organization of Sexuality: Sexual Practices in the United States*	1994	Comprehensive examination of practices within social settings and their meanings

(continued)

Table 1.2 Contributions of Experts on Sexuality *(continued)*

Researcher(s)	Research	Years	Comments
Vern and Bonnie Bullough	*Sin, Sickness, and Sanity; Women and Prostitution: A Social History; Cross Dressing, Sex, and Gender*	1957– present	Review of extensive historical data on a variety of subjects
Michel Foucault	*The History of Sexuality*	1980	Argues that sexuality is socially constructed, including orientation
Centers for Disease Control	Youth Risk Behavior Surveillance System (YRBSS)	1999, 2002	Federally sponsored ongoing research conducted in collaboration with federal, state, local, and private sector agencies to examine health risk behaviors of youth to develop better health programs. Specific attention paid to tobacco and drug use, diet and exercise, violence and injury, and sexual behaviors connected to STD/ HIV and unintended pregnancies.

When applying research findings to one's personal life, practical questions to consider include the following: Are you like most people? If not, how aren't you? If you are part of a sexual minority—identifying, for example, as bisexual—how does this affect your lifestyle? If some expert claims that a sexual behavior is problematic and you engage in it, will your behavior change? Should it? Who *is* this expert when it comes to helping you make decisions about your sexuality?

Sexuality Researchers

Because of the interdisciplinary nature of the field of sexology, individuals and teams of researchers have conducted research exploring various aspects of sexuality. Some of the prominent names in the field have examined human sexual response and subsequently developed strategies to help people respond more fully and positively. Others have focused their work on patterns of behavior, differentiating for gender, race, culture, and ethnicity, where possible. Theorists have worked on questions of gender, orientation, and identity. Others have looked at relationship patterns. Almost all traditional styles of research have been utilized over the years to help provide a fuller understanding of human sexuality. Descriptive research formats have been widely used to survey a myriad of attitudes, values, and experiences. Experimental designs have yielded better understanding of sexual functioning and dysfunction. Qualitative research, in which individuals have been interviewed in depth, has provided the richness and contexts that statistical reports omit.

Each "expert" or group of experts has brought valuable data, theories, and insights into our understanding of human sexuality. What is critical to understand, however, is that the richness and diversity of human sexuality have also posed obstacles to any one theory explaining "it all." A conference held at the famous Kinsey Institute in 1998 brought researchers from different backgrounds together in an attempt to encourage discourse and bridge the gap between those who postulated from a biomedical perspective and those who represented the social constructionist perspective. The participants focused primarily on sexuality across the life cycle, sexual orientation, sexual risk taking, adolescent sexuality, and pol-

sex in society 1.1

Criteria Associated with Good Research

We are bombarded with sexual information every day. Countless studies and reports are released and presented by the media. "Experts" report new findings that challenge our notions about sexual issues. Here are some guidelines for evaluating sources of sexual information and research:

1. **Evaluate the researchers.** Reputable researchers are well known in their fields, have some kind of university or agency affiliation, and are members in good standing in professional organizations, and their research is not connected to or funded by for-profit businesses.
   - Who did the research?
   - Was the study done by reputable researchers?
2. **Evaluate the researchers' track record.**
   - Have they conducted scientific studies before?
   - Is their previous research respected and accepted in the field?
3. **Evaluate the sample.** Two issues related to the population studied will tell you the most about the quality of the study: sample size and randomness.
   - How large is the sample? (In general, the larger the sample, the better the study.)
   - Were the samples chosen randomly (subjects chosen at random from a larger pool of eligible), or were the subjects taken from a convenience sample

(an intact group; students in a certain class—prison population, army recruits, subscribers to a certain magazine, and so on)?

4. **Evaluate the methods.** In general, first-person observable reports (person-to-person interview or direct observation) are better than other ways of gathering data (such as mailed questionnaires and telephone interviews). Sexuality research is unique, though. Anonymity protections in many situations will help guarantee better results. Unfortunately, when facing a questioner, respondents may be sensitive to reactions to their answers and consequently give desired answers rather than honest ones.
   - How was information about the subjects obtained?
5. **Evaluate replication.** Studies that are replicated with different samples and come up with similar findings are more likely to stand the test of time. Research linking smoking to lung cancer, for instance, has been replicated with samples from different countries over the past decade and yielded similar results.
   - Has the study been replicated with a different population resulting in the same findings?
6. **Examine the impact.** Read reviews and reports of the study in reputable journals.
   - Have other researchers in the field received the study well?

icy and culture. Although the work of the researchers added greatly to our understanding of human sexuality, there evolved no shared definition of sexual theory or consensus of perspective (Weis, 2002).

A Wellness Approach to Understanding Sexuality

One way to explain and understand our sexuality is to look at it from a more holistic approach. Think of how Maria from Case Study 1.1 described how the dimensions of health affected her sexuality. A person cannot study something such as body image, for example, without looking at issues related to individual personality, family and peer influences, and societal expectations. The focus of this textbook is on healthy sexuality and strategies for maximizing our sexual potential.

Healthy sexuality enables a person to develop to the fullest potential. It requires being knowledgeable. It involves personalizing information and using it to make informed decisions about your life and the world around you. Making good decisions about yourself and others is an essential part of healthy sexuality.

Healthy sexuality The safe and open exploration and development of our potential as human beings

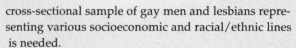

sex in society 1.2

Diversity in Sex Research

One of the long-standing criticisms of many human sexuality studies is the lack of diversity in their subjects. Most of the classic studies in the field have focused on white, heterosexual, middle-class subjects. The two best-known sexuality works—Kinsey's studies of male and female sexual behavior and Masters and Johnson's work on sexual response—are both based on such a sample. Both were conducted decades ago, when diversity received much less attention. The lack of diversity seems to affect three distinct minority subgroups: lower socioeconomic status populations, racial minorities (blacks, Asians, and Hispanics/Latinos), and gays, lesbians, and bisexuals. To complicate matters, although these three categories of populations are underrepresented in major studies of sexual response and behavior, they are overrepresented in other types of sex research, such as those focusing on STDs and teen pregnancy.

The problem may represent a lack of aggressive recruitment of nonwhite, non-middle-class, nonheterosexual subjects in major sexuality research (particularly studies that are privately funded) and an overreliance on sampling from public clinic populations (people with STDs, family planning), which tend to have higher minority representation.

Studies of gay, lesbian, and bisexual populations also have been clouded by methodological problems associated with sampling. Studies of gay men draw heavily from men who frequent gay bars, subscribe to gay publications, are incarcerated, or attend gay public events. Less is known about lesbian women. A true cross-sectional sample of gay men and lesbians representing various socioeconomic and racial/ethnic lines is needed.

Methodological issues related to sampling and sample size have been cited as the primary problems related to obtaining more diverse samples. It is harder to target recruitment efforts for lower socioeconomic status, minority, and gay/lesbian populations. Targeting narrow segments of these populations (for example, gay men attending gay bars) is easier and has a higher-yield recruitment than mainstream sources such as newspapers, random-digit telephoning, and the like. Narrowing the scope of recruitment, however, means that sampling may miss a true cross section of the population targeted for study.

Can these studies accurately reflect human sexual behavior and response if they omit large segments of the population? Are there differences between and among various racial and ethnic groups, socioeconomic segments, and different sexual orientations that might lend greater insight into the true nature of human sexuality?

Finally, newer research has attempted to draw conclusions and examine differences in attitudes, values, and behaviors of groups drawn from a broader range of backgrounds. Students must remember, however, that the United States has increasingly drawn immigrants into our midst who do not answer surveys, may not speak English, or even feel that sexuality is a topic to be discussed with anyone outside the immediate family circle.

It involves our personal level of well-being, the health of our relationships with others, and the nature of the environment in which everything occurs. The best way to conceptualize this approach to understanding human sexuality is to use a health and wellness model to describe it.

Health Total mental, physical, and social well-being, not merely the absence of disease

Holistic health The process of moving toward optimal functioning across the physical, social, spiritual, emotional, and intellectual dimensions

Health and Wellness Defined

In 1947 the World Health Organization (WHO) defined **health** as "the state of complete mental, physical, and social well-being, not merely the absence of disease" (p. 35). WHO's definition was the first globally accepted conceptualization of health and stood the test of time for more than a decade.

Although multifaceted, this definition of health was flawed, according to members of a new movement called **holistic health.** The holistic health movement came into being in the 1960s as an attempt to expand the view of health that WHO had promulgated.

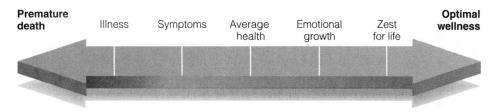

Figure 1.1 *Health and Wellness Continuum* Health can be viewed as a continuum. Where we are on the continuum at any given time is strongly influenced by our lifestyle.

One of the early pioneers in the field, Halbert Dunn (1962), believed that the WHO vision of health characterized it as a static state. Rather than call health a state of well-being, Dunn preferred to view it as a continuum. Developing and maintaining a high level of health means moving toward optimal functioning. Health is a conscious and deliberate approach to life and being, rather than something to be abdicated to doctors and the health care system. Like your health in general, your sexual health is viewed as moving along a continuum, reaching optimal states as a result of your decisions and behavior (see Figure 1.1).

In addition, Dunn recast the notion of well-being to revolve around functioning. How well does the organism function? Dunn viewed functioning as evidence of well-being. Although people will have setbacks in their quest for optimal functioning, the direction in which their lives are moving becomes an important criterion for evaluating their well-being. In this movement, daily habits and behaviors, and overall lifestyle, assumed primary importance.

Originally, the scope of well-being was limited to three dimensions: physical, social, and mental. Adherents of holistic health argued that the mental dimension has two components: the intellectual (rational thought processes) and the emotional (feelings and emotions). Each of these domains deals with a different aspect of psychological well-being. A final dimension, the spiritual, was added because it was thought that humans could not function optimally in a spiritual vacuum. Therefore, the holistic definition of health has five dimensions: physical, social, emotional, intellectual, and spiritual.

In the 1970s and 1980s, the definition of health was expanded once again by the wellness movement (Ardell, 1985). Adherents defined **wellness** as "an active process of becoming aware of and making choices toward a more successful existence" (National Wellness Institute, 2002). Added to the previous dimensions was that of environmental health. Currently, some authors are adding vocational/occupational health to the definition, arguing that one's environment includes the work site and accompanying health issues related to job and career.

What is critical to wellness is to understand that it is a process of becoming healthier. The journey (becoming the best one can be) is more important than the ending. The process of wellness involves becoming increasingly more aware of health and making healthy choices. Success is individually determined and is based on the ability to live life to its fullest.

A key element of the wellness model is striving for balance. When all of the six dimensions are at high levels and in balance, we have optimal health and well-being. When the dimensions are out of balance or one is severely lacking, we have lower levels of health and well-being. Figure 1.2 illustrates this concept.

Wellness The state of optimal health and well-being

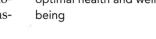

The components of wellness

Figure 1.2 *Six-Dimensional Wellness Model* Wellness is a multifaceted phenomenon.

Source: Adapted with permission from Bill Hettler, M.D., 1979; http://hettler.com, 2003.

The average college campus offers many opportunities for engaging in regular physical activity.

Physical well-being A component of wellness reflected in how well the body performs its intended functions

Body composition The fat and nonfat components of the human body; important in assessing recommended body weight

Intellectual well-being A component of wellness referring to the ability to process information effectively and rationally

The Six Dimensions of Wellness

The first dimension, **physical well-being,** is reflected in how well the body performs its intended functions. Absence of disease—although an important influence—is not the sole criterion for health. The physical domain is influenced by one's genetic inheritance, nutritional status, fitness level, **body composition,** and immune status, to name just a few.

Intellectual well-being is the ability to process information effectively. It involves the capability to use information in a rational way to solve problems and grow. It includes issues such as creativity, spontaneity, and openness to new ways of viewing situations. To maintain a high level of intellectual well-being, one must seek knowledge and learn from one's experiences.

Emotional well-being means being in touch with one's feelings, having the ability to express them, and being able to control them when necessary. Optimal functioning involves the understanding that emotions are the mirror to the soul. Emotions help us get in touch with what is important in our lives. Our emotions make us feel alive and provide us with a richness of experience that is uniquely human.

Social well-being involves being connected to others through various types of relationships. Individuals who function optimally in this domain are able to form friendships, have intimate relationships, give and receive love and affection, and accept others unconditionally. They are able to give of themselves and share in the joys and sorrows of being part of a community. This community includes both formal and informal networks. Formal networks include organizations such as churches, professional organizations, fraternities, sororities, and campus groups requiring official membership, dues, and standards. Informal networks such as an intramural sports team do not have rigid rules for membership. In a sense, your social networks are a big part of your environment.

Environmental well-being involves high-level functioning on two levels. The most immediate environment, the **micro-environment,** consists of school, home, neighborhood, and work site. The people with whom we interact in those places link the environment to the social aspects of our health. This environment greatly affects our health and personal safety by influencing whether we are at risk for and fear issues such as theft, crime, and violence. The quality of our air and water, noise pollution, crowding, and other issues that impact our stress levels are also affected. Our social support system is also part of this environment.

The **macro-environment,** the level of well-being at a larger level-state, country, and the world at large—also affects our wellness. The impact of things discussed earlier in the chapter—the wars in Iraq and Afghanistan, the terrorist attacks of 9/11, and other things such as violence, international disputes, racism, sexism, heterosexism, ageism, and so on—all influence us daily to some extent. When we authors were in college, the Vietnam War was going on. College-age men started each day reading the newspaper to see what draft numbers

Friendships are an important part of social well-being.

were being called up (there was a draft, and all draft-eligible men were issued draft numbers) and whether any of their friends were killed or missing in action. Decisions that our political leaders make, such as engaging in wars or determining where we store radioactive wastes, affect the way we think and live our lives. Our ability to stay focused and whole is constantly challenged by the media, which bring the entire world and its problems into our living rooms each night. We need to learn to think globally, act locally, and be happy despite the myriad of problems in the world.

Spiritual well-being involves feeling connected to something beyond oneself. One way to express spirituality is by participating in organized religious activities. This usually means believing in a supreme being or higher supernatural force and subscribing to a formalized code of conduct to live by. In a secular sense, spirituality could manifest itself through connection to something greater than oneself. Whether it is being part of a community, working to save the environment, helping feed the needy, or being committed to world peace, the underlying feeling is a perception of life as having meaning beyond the self.

Finally, **occupational/vocational well-being** involves issues related to job wellness. Occupational/vocational well-being encompasses everything from the safety of our particular work site to the nature of your career. Work site well-being includes physical (air, water, physical plant, machinery, and so on) and social (relationships with coworkers, management, health and wellness facilities and activities) factors. Our personal wellness is affected by the health of our work site. Employers and work sites vary tremendously in relation to health. Some strive for optimal levels, encouraging employees to take advantage of a myriad of health-enhancing programs and services, whereas others meet the minimum acceptable standards for health and safety set by the government.

Besides the specific health of the workplace, different jobs/careers pose varying threats to our well-being as a result of the nature of the work. Some jobs such as police and military service are risky because of possible exposure to hostile combatants. Other occupations such as firefighters, emergency medical service workers, coal miners, and oil rig operators are risky because they place employees in dangerous environments. Other occupations entail high stress due to deadlines, competition, or other factors.

Wellness and Human Sexuality

Our sexuality both contributes to overall health and well-being and is affected by it. High-level sexual health can be a positive force in our lives. It contributes to the full functioning of our body, mind, spirit, and social relationships. When we are engaged in healthy sexual activity and have a healthy outlook concerning our sexuality, we can maximize our potential as men and women. Conversely, our sexuality is affected by our overall level of health and well-being. Sexual response (from desire to arousal and orgasm) is greatly influenced by our overall level of well-being. We simply are less interested in sex and perform poorly when we have low-level health and wellness.

The important thing is to be moving toward optimal health, even if you never achieve it. If your current level of health is lower than you would like, the main thing is to take steps to improve. The experience and process of improving, the journey, is as important as the current level of functioning.

Many of us have limitations that keep us from achieving the high levels of health that others enjoy. A wellness perspective of health and sexuality helps us accept our limitations and maximize the potential within us. You may never have the body of the man or woman of your dreams, but you can enjoy healthy sexuality if you strive to be the best you can be.

Emotional well-being A component of wellness that refers to being in touch with one's feelings, having the ability to express them, and being able to control them when necessary

Social well-being A component of wellness that involves connection to others through various types of relationships

Environmental well-being A component of wellness that reflects our ability to function in our immediate environment, such as home, school, and work, as well as being able to deal with the world at large

Micro-environment The part of one's environment that is immediate and includes living situation, campus, neighborhood, home, and work site and family, friends, and associates who populate these places

Macro-environment The environment that extends beyond the micro and includes one's city, state, country, and the world at large

Spiritual well-being A component of wellness that involves feeling connected to something beyond oneself

Occupational/vocational well-being A component of wellness that reflects our ability to use our unique skills/talents to work that is meaningful and rewarding. Our values are expressed through involvement in paid and nonpaid activities that are personally rewarding for us and make a contribution to the well-being of the community at large.

case study 1.3

Donna's Journey to Sexual Health

Donna, 40, is white.

I'm 40 years old, and I like myself. I accept myself. I can be who I am. But it wasn't always like that. As I look back, I realize that my sexuality has played a very significant role in my life. Sexuality is a significant part of everyone's life, yet if you stray from the center, the average, the expected, then the journey at the very least has more bumps in it than for most.

We can get into a whole list of identities—woman, daughter, lover, student. I see labels as political designations. You try them on to see which ones fit. Can you find "one" that encompasses a total human being? I don't think so. In the last 5 years I've taken "transgendered" as one of my primary identities, yet I am also a mother of two boys. I am committed to a woman as a partner. I am a recent college graduate with a full-time job that isn't what I've always hoped to be doing with my degree, but it pays the bills. And when I clear out some of my debts, I hope to pursue graduate school at some point.

I've always been "inappropriate." My mother was always into dressing me to be the pretty little girl, and in 6 seconds I would destroy her efforts. I wanted to climb trees, play in the dirt, and have fun—all sorts of things you couldn't do in a dress. My hair was always very long to please my mother. My way to manage that was to always keep it in pigtails. Once on my own, I started dressing in drag, with short hair and men's clothing. I came out to my family when I was 16, but to my painful surprise found the reception in the lesbian community most unwelcome. Being butch and dressing like a man back in the 1970s was not "politically correct."

I remedied my sense of not fitting in and trying to sort everything out by marrying a man and trying to live as a heterosexual woman. I was very successful at that game for close to 20 years, being the dutiful wife and mother.

Today it's a 50–50 shot as to whether people think I'm a man or a woman. It used to bother me a lot when people were confused. Now, I find it amusing and really don't care. I have a job where I can be free to be who I am, sharing the ups and downs of my life with people who are friends. I don't fit neatly into the transgendered community, nor do I have "gender dysphoria." My body is my body, and I accept it. I wear men's clothing primarily because they fit better, both body and psyche. I build muscle in "male-patterned" ways, my voice has gotten deeper over time, and my neck is thick. The blood tests I've had in the past all indicate "normal hormone parameters" for a woman.

I feel that I've experimented a lot to find out what is most comfortable and to learn who I am as a sexual person. Not that my journey has ended, but I better understand the road to healthy sexuality. And self-acceptance is a great place to start.

Critical Thinking

How does Donna illustrate some of the problems associated with trying to attach a label to someone's sexuality?

Use your Virtual Workbook to explore your answer to this question at **http://health.wadsworth.com/blonna1.**

High-level *physical well-being* can make us feel better about our bodies and provide the energy and capacity to maximize sexual pleasure and functioning. High-level cardiovascular fitness and muscle tone can enhance sexual functioning and pleasure. When our bodies are healthy and optimally functioning, we feel better about how we look and move and have higher self-esteem—two elements critical to healthy sexuality.

High-level *emotional well-being* can help us understand and cope with the myriad of feelings that being sexual creates. It helps us cope with the emotional roller coaster that most of us face when confronted with issues such as gender identity, sexual orientation, puberty, dating, and preventing unintended pregnancy. A high level of emotional well-being helps us understand and accept our emotions related to these and other sexual issues.

High-level *intellectual well-being* helps us process sexual information, think critically, and make sound decisions regarding our sexual health. The ability to sort through the often-conflicting barrage of sexual information and advice requires an ability to seek out information, evaluate facts, seek clarification of unanswered questions, solve problems, and relate this information to our own needs, wants, and values.

High-level *social well-being* enhances our sexuality and provides a safe forum to explore it and share it with others. Having solid friendships, intimate relationships, and sexual partnerships with people we care about, love, and trust allows us to explore our developing sexuality in a safe way.

Our sexual health is based in our ability to form healthy relationships with others. *Intimacy* is the ability to be open and honest and to feel close with another person. It enhances relationships but is not part of all the relationships we form. For example, you may be open and honest with a college roommate with whom you live day to day. In contrast, you may not find it appropriate or feel comfortable discussing personal concerns with colleagues at work. Relationships that involve an obvious power dynamic—such as boss and employee—often dictate that we are prudent in what we disclose and how intimate we become.

The expression "blood is thicker than water" has been used to explain the support we often expect from family. Friends may come and go, but your family is always your family. In truth, some people have wonderfully intimate relationships with family, whereas others have disengaged from their family or contact them only in times of need. When one's sexual lifestyle is perceived at odds with family expectations, family ties may be strained or severed, with friendships providing the intimacy and support needed.

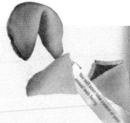

healthy sex hints 1.1

Making Informed Decisions

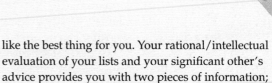

The following is a simple decision-making model that may help you make better decisions about your sexuality.

1. *Establish your goal.* Try to put in a broader context the decision you are making about an issue. ("How will this decision affect my goal?")
2. *List the pros and cons.* In two columns on a sheet of paper, list the consequences of saying either yes or no to the question you are trying to make a decision about. Don't scrimp. Put down all of them, no matter how trivial they might seem.
3. *Prioritize the pros and cons.* Rank the pros and cons from most important to least important.
4. *Weigh the pros and cons.* Although one column might be greater than the other (many more pros than cons, for instance), the top one or two items on the shorter list might carry much more weight.
5. *Ponder the results.* Examine the lists, and discuss them with one or two people whose opinions you value.
6. *Listen to your instincts.* Sometimes something may seem to be right for the average person but not feel like the best thing for you. Your rational/intellectual evaluation of your lists and your significant other's advice provides you with two pieces of information; your gut-level intuition provides you with another.
7. *Decide.* Action is important. You must make a decision and move on with your life.
8. *Give it time.* Once you make a decision, give yourself time to experience the effects of that decision. At first it may seem that you made the wrong decision. Only time will tell.
9. *Reevaluate.* Go through this model again to reevaluate your decision once a sufficient amount of time has passed.
10. *Don't beat yourself up!* You are human! Sometimes you will make the wrong decisions. Learn from your mistakes, and try not to make the same ones twice. Persecuting yourself and putting yourself down are not productive and will not help you make better decisions.

Someone once noted that if heterosexual women could relate to their male partners and hold them to the same expectations they have for their female friends, romantic relationships would be in a better state. This observation points to the subtle ways by which we change the script when we look toward developing healthy romantic relationships. Identifying what is unhealthy in someone else's relationship is often easier than seeing the weaknesses in one's own relationships.

High-level *environmental well-being* extends from our personal living space, to our school and work space, to the world beyond. As such, it is often the one area of our health where there is the least personal control. As we age and become independent, our environment extends beyond the family into the immediate community. Community standards for safety and support vary from place to place. Official government, police, and school policies on diverse issues such as treatment of known sexual offenders, sexual harassment in the community, gay rights, sexual abuse, prostitution, prevention and treatment of sexually transmitted diseases, and so on, all influence one's sexual health. Unofficial community standards interact with official policies to create a climate within a community that either supports sexual development and expression or sets up barriers to it.

A primary environment for college students is the campus. Campus policies, especially for residential students, have a great impact on issues related to sexual health. Colleges are becoming increasingly aware of the necessity of formalizing policies on issues such as the prevention and treatment of students with HIV/AIDS, sexual harassment and assault, sexual health services, and so on. The American College Health Association (1996) provides guidance on developing these policy issues. See Table 1.3 for a sample college policy regarding AIDS.

The focus on *occupational/vocational well-being* can be subsumed within a broad definition of *environment*. The jobs and careers we choose reflect who we are as people. They also set the stage for meeting partners and developing relationships that give our lives meaning. As a nation, we are spending increasing amounts of time related to work, both on the job and in commutation. Some individuals find themselves with 2 or more hours needed to "get to work," followed by a full work day, then the advisable 7 hours of sleep, needs for exercise, quality time with family, and so forth; as a result, stress overload becomes "mathematically" apparent. Chemical and radiation exposure at work, along with overall safety of the workspace, affects health in general and aspects of sexual health in particular. Fertility can be affected. Pain and injury can certainly impact sexual functioning.

High-level *spiritual health* connects us with a higher power. It puts our sexuality in a broader context, providing a different perspective from which to view ourselves and our behavior. It also links our lives with a broader purpose and historical continuity that reaches beyond the self and mere personal fulfillment. We feel as though we are part of something that transcends our present place and time.

healthy sex hints 1.2
Creating Healthy Environments

- *Help create a healthy sexual environment within your community.* Be a role model for healthy sexuality. Lead by example, whether through words or actions.
- *Get involved in organizations that actively champion sexual rights.* If you can't or don't want to get publicly involved with them, support organizations financially. Make a contribution to acknowledge and support their work.

- *Be an advocate within any organization in which you are involved, such as youth sports, church or temple, fraternity/ sorority, and the like.* If you see or hear things that work against creating or maintaining a healthy sexual environment, speak out.

Table 1.3 Excerpts from a University AIDS Policy

The staggering implications of this country's most life-threatening disease, AIDS, have become part of our nation's consciousness. We must now make the necessary preparations to protect the rights of both those students who have been exposed to or infected by HIV as well as the noninfected members of our University community. Above all, we must train all members of the University community to have a humane, well-informed reaction to those whose lives have been compromised by being exposed to or infected by the virus.

AIDS Advisory Board

WPU [William Paterson University] responded to the AIDS crisis by creating a presidentially appointed 6-member AIDS Advisory Board in 1987. The primary goals of this committee are as follows:

1. To encourage the faculty to include discussions of the social, medical, and economic effects of AIDS in their classes.
2. To offer our students a comprehensive roster of referral sources for their own educational advancement and, if necessary, their own health concerns.
3. To train peer educators to address the social forces that promote behavior that could make them susceptible to HIV infection (alcohol abuse, drug abuse, STDs, etc.).
4. To provide speakers for educational programming.

Guidelines

1. The initial admission decision for applicants will not take into consideration whether the applicant has a positive test to the virus thought to cause AIDS (a + HIV antibody test).
2. Students with the HIV infection will be afforded the same living arrangement as are all other residential students, except in specific cases where the health of the infected student is in jeopardy. Since this virus can be transmitted only by intimate sexual contact and/or by sharing contaminated blood products, the University feels separate housing accommodations are not justified. Individual decisions will be made on a case-by-case basis. It should be noted that the infected student stands a far greater chance of having his/her health compromised by a non-infected roommate through the transmission of the common airborne viruses than would the noninfected student of acquiring HIV through casual contact with his/her infected roommate.
3. Students with HIV infection will be afforded normal classroom attendance, working conditions and participation in cocurricular and extracurricular activities in an unrestricted manner as long as they are physically and psychologically able to do so.
4. Students with HIV infection will have access to all public facilities open to the University community.
5. Programs will not be implemented to require screening of students with HIV infection.

Institutional Responsibility/Confidentiality of Information

The American Council on Education (ACE) recommends that institutions have the responsibility to provide the following:

1. A comprehensive program of education about AIDS.
2. A training program that includes not only information about AIDS but a clear representation of the University's AIDS policy.
3. A system of encouraging people with the HIV infection to inform those who are appropriate of their condition.
4. A means of counseling people with the HIV infection about the facts of the disease and what has to be done to avoid transmission.
5. Regular assessment (every three months) of students with HIV infection to determine health status and psychological needs.

Although this University may be unaware that infected students may be unreasonably engaged in conduct that threatens the health of others, we will attempt to offer protection to the community at large while still protecting the rights of the person with HIV.

Section 504 of the Federal Rehabilitation Act of 1973 prohibits discrimination against individual(s) with disabilities. No qualified student with disabilities at William Paterson University is to be excluded from participation in, be denied benefits of, or be subjected to discrimination under any program or activities of the university community.

The knowledge that a given individual is carrying HIV could have such a profound and possibly irrational effect upon the recipient of this information who then might take steps that could easily compromise the campus life of the individual in question. The likelihood is that such information could not legally be placed in any non-medical files

(continued)

Table 1.3 Excerpts from a University AIDS Policy *(continued)*

without the expressed written permission of the student, according to the Family Education Rights and Privacy Act of 1974. This Act would probably apply to any verbal communication as well, and thus confidentiality must extend to faculty, administrators, other students and even partners.

The diagnosis of HIV or AIDS would occur at a hospital as part of a complete medical work-up and then be reported to the New Jersey State Department of Health, which then should forward the information to the Centers for Disease Control in Atlanta. The hospital or the student may report back the results of such testing, which are confidential, as part of the student health record. Often, a student would continue outside health care and not report to the Student Health Service. Education and counseling are available through the health center and counseling center when requested.

Source: Student Handbook, William Paterson University, 1998–1999. Reprinted with permission.

Health Challenges

As we've pointed out in this chapter, wellness functions along a continuum, with various dimensions impacting our sexual health throughout our lives. Ideally, college students and young adults are not confronted with serious health challenges. In reality, some already have or will find themselves managing chronic, sometimes debilitating illnesses and/or disabilities. Some of those illnesses and disabilities directly affect sexuality, whereas others may do so indirectly. Students have reported problems with substance abuse, eating disorders, and gambling. Others break bones, injure backs, and have accidents that may leave them in a wheelchair. Managing bouts of depression, having panic attacks, or being diagnosed with an obsessive–compulsive disorder all take their toll on socializing and getting close to others. For those who contract an STD such as genital warts, which is viral and long-term, the issue of how and what to tell a future partner adds to the regular issues related to dating.

We take the position that sexual health requires understanding ourselves and others—the people intimately in our lives and those in our communities. Toward that end, when an individual is confronted with health challenges, the specific condition can become a limitation. Although we all have limitations of one kind or another, health challenges become most limiting when they *define* us rather than being viewed as a *part* of who we are. Optimal sexual health requires that we be able to identify available resources and strategies to enable the highest levels of functioning possible.

Table 1.4 provides some of the resources available. Increasingly, the Internet has provided the much-needed link for those who previously may have felt isolated from information and support.

Table 1.4 Resources Available to Support Health Challenges

Professional Journals
Journal of Sexuality and Disability
Sexuality and Disabilities

Selected Web Sites and Phone Numbers
Sexuality and Disability Webliography: www.bccpd.bc.ca
A Web site of suggested readings compiled by the Wellness and Disability Initiative.

Spinal Cord Injury: www.sexualhealth.com
A Web site with information and resources on sex and disability.

Mental Health: http://Ulifeline.org
A Web site designed for college students. Sponsored by the Jed Foundation, named for a college student who committed suicide. The site has linkages to resources related to mental health, suicide prevention, drug abuse, and more.

Depression and Bipolar Support Alliance: www.dbsalliance.org
Web site support for those living with mood disorders.

STDs
American Social Health Association: www.ashastd.org
Provides information and resources about sexually transmitted diseases.

National AIDS hotline: (800) 342-2437

Gay Men's Health Crisis line: (212) 807-6664; www.gmhc.org
These two resources focus primarily on HIV/AIDS.

Chronic Illness/Cancer
Chronic Fatigue: www.chronicfatiguesupport.com
A Web site sponsored by ProHealth, Inc., with an expert medical advisory board.

Testicular Cancer Resource Center: http://tcrc.acor.org
Provides information for patients, caregivers, and physicians.

Susan G. Komen Breast Cancer Foundation: www.komen.org
Provides breast cancer research funds as well as educational and support services.

Drug Use
Bacchus & Gamma Peer Education Network: www.bacchusgamma.org
This is an association of college and university peer education groups focused on alcohol and other safety issues for students.

Alcohol hotline: (800) ALCOHOL

Alcoholics Anonymous: http://alcoholics-anonymous.org
The white pages of phone books list local chapters.

Cocaine hotline: (800) COCAINE

Narcotics Anonymous: www.wsoinc.org
The white pages of phone books list local chapters.

Eating Disorders
National Eating Disorders Association: www.NationalEatingDisorders.org
Provides educational and treatment information on eating disorders.

National Association of Anorexia Nervosa and Associated Disorders (ANAD):
www.anad.org
Provides hotline counseling, education, and referrals.

Your responses to the Personal Assessment, Thought Questions, and Test Yourself! quiz questions can be logged online in your Virtual Workbook at **http://health.wadsworth/Blonna1.**

Personal Assessment

1.1 Wellness Lifestyle Questionnaire

Because sexual health cannot be separated from overall health, we would do well to attend to all the dimensions of our well-being. As you answer the items, try to think about how each may have an impact on your sexual health.

Please circle the appropriate answer to each question and total your points as indicated at the end of the questionnaire. Circle 5 if the statement is *always* true, 4 if the statement is *frequently* true, 3 if the statement is *occasionally* true, 2 if the statement is *seldom* true, or 1 if the statement is *never* true.

1. I am able to identify the situations and factors that overstress me.	5	4	3	2	1
2. I eat only when I am hungry.	5	4	3	2	1
3. I don't take tranquilizers or other drugs to relax.	5	4	3	2	1
4. I support efforts in my community to reduce environmental pollution.	5	4	3	2	1
5. I avoid buying foods with artificial colorings.	5	4	3	2	1
6. I rarely have problems concentrating on what I'm doing because of worrying about other things.	5	4	3	2	1
7. My employer (school) takes measures to ensure that my work (study) place is safe.	5	4	3	2	1
8. I try not to use medications when I feel unwell.	5	4	3	2	1
9. I am able to identify certain bodily responses and illnesses as my reactions to stress.	5	4	3	2	1
10. I question the use of diagnostic X rays.	5	4	3	2	1
11. I try to alter personal living habits that are risk factors for heart disease, cancer, and other lifestyle diseases.	5	4	3	2	1
12. I avoid taking sleeping pills to help me sleep.	5	4	3	2	1
13. I try not to eat foods with refined sugar or corn sugar ingredients.	5	4	3	2	1
14. I accomplish goals I set for myself.	5	4	3	2	1
15. I stretch or bend for several minutes each day to keep my body flexible.	5	4	3	2	1
16. I support immunization of all children for common childhood diseases.	5	4	3	2	1
17. I try to prevent friends from driving after they drink alcohol.	5	4	3	2	1
18. I minimize extra salt intake.	5	4	3	2	1
19. I don't mind when other people and situations make me wait or lose time.	5	4	3	2	1
20. I walk four or fewer flights of stairs rather than take the elevator.	5	4	3	2	1
21. I eat fresh fruits and vegetables.	5	4	3	2	1
22. I use dental floss at least once a day.	5	4	3	2	1
23. I read product labels on foods to determine their ingredients.	5	4	3	2	1
24. I try to maintain a normal body weight.	5	4	3	2	1
25. I record my feelings and thoughts in a journal or diary.	5	4	3	2	1
26. I have no difficulty falling asleep.	5	4	3	2	1
27. I engage in some form of vigorous physical activity at least three times a week.	5	4	3	2	1
28. I take time each day to quiet my mind and relax.	5	4	3	2	1

29. I am willing to make and sustain close friendships and intimate relationships.   5   4   3   2   1

30. I obtain an adequate daily supply of vitamins from my food or vitamin supplements.   5   4   3   2   1

31. I rarely have tension or migraine headaches, or pain in the neck or shoulders.   5   4   3   2   1

32. I wear a seat belt when driving.   5   4   3   2   1

33. I am aware of the emotional and situational factors that lead me to overeat.   5   4   3   2   1

34. I avoid driving my car after drinking any alcohol.   5   4   3   2   1

35. I am aware of the side effects of the medicines I take.   5   4   3   2   1

36. I am able to accept feelings of sadness, depression, and anxiety, knowing that they are almost always transient.   5   4   3   2   1

37. I would seek several additional professional opinions if my doctor were to recommend surgery for me.   5   4   3   2   1

38. I agree that nonsmokers should not have to breathe the smoke from cigarettes in public places.   5   4   3   2   1

39. I agree that pregnant women who smoke harm their babies.   5   4   3   2   1

40. I believe I get enough sleep.   5   4   3   2   1

41. I ask my doctor why a certain medication is being prescribed and inquire about alternatives.   5   4   3   2   1

42. I am aware of the calories expended in my activities.   5   4   3   2   1

43. I am willing to give priority to my own needs for time and psychological space by saying no to others' requests of me.   5   4   3   2   1

44. I walk instead of drive whenever feasible.   5   4   3   2   1

45. I eat a breakfast that contains about one-third of my daily need for calories, proteins, and vitamins.   5   4   3   2   1

46. I prohibit smoking in my home.   5   4   3   2   1

47. I remember and think about my dreams.   5   4   3   2   1

48. I seek medical attention only when I have symptoms or think some (potential) condition requires checking, rather than have routine yearly checkups.   5   4   3   2   1

49. I endeavor to make my home accident-free.   5   4   3   2   1

50. I ask my doctor to explain the diagnosis of my problem until I understand all that I care to.   5   4   3   2   1

51. I try to include fiber (whole grains, fresh fruits and vegetables, or bran) in my daily diet.   5   4   3   2   1

52. I can deal with my emotional problems without alcohol or other mood-altering drugs.   5   4   3   2   1

53. I am satisfied with my school/work.   5   4   3   2   1

54. I require children riding in my car to be in infant seats or in shoulder harnesses.   5   4   3   2   1

55. I try to associate with people who have a positive attitude about life.   5   4   3   2   1

56. I try not to eat snacks of candy, pastries, and other "junk" foods.   5   4   3   2   1

57. I avoid people who are "down" all the time and bring down those around them.   5   4   3   2   1

58. I am aware of the calorie content of the foods I eat.   5   4   3   2   1

59. I brush my teeth after meals.   5   4   3   2   1

60. (*for women only*) I routinely examine my breasts.   5   4   3   2   1

    (*for men only*) I am aware of the signs of testicular cancer.   5   4   3   2   1

How to Score

Enter the numbers you've circled next to the question number, and total your score for each category. Then determine your degree of wellness for each category using the wellness status key.

Emotional health	Fitness and body care	Environmental health	Stress	Nutrition	Medical self-responsibility
6 _____	15 _____	4 _____	1 _____	2 _____	8 _____
12 _____	20 _____	7 _____	3 _____	5 _____	10 _____
25 _____	22 _____	17 _____	9 _____	13 _____	11 _____
26 _____	24 _____	32 _____	14 _____	18 _____	16 _____
36 _____	27 _____	34 _____	19 _____	21 _____	35 _____
40 _____	33 _____	38 _____	28 _____	23 _____	37 _____
47 _____	42 _____	39 _____	29 _____	30 _____	41 _____
52 _____	44 _____	46 _____	31 _____	45 _____	48 _____
55 _____	58 _____	49 _____	43 _____	51 _____	59 _____
57 _____	59 _____	54 _____	53 _____	56 _____	60 _____
Total _____	Total _____	Total _____	Total _____	Total _____	Total _____

Wellness Status

To assess your status in each of the six categories, compare your total score in each to the following key:

0–34 Need improvement; **35–44** Good; **45–50** Excellent

Source: Gordon Edlin and Eric Golanty: *Health and Wellness,* 5th edition, © 1998, Sudbury, MA: Jones and Bartlett Publishers. www.jbpub.com. Reprinted with permission.

Thought Questions

1. What is human sexuality? What are its components?
2. What is the definition of *health* according to the World Health Organization?
3. What complaints did the wellness movement have with the WHO conceptualization of health?
4. What is the definition of *wellness*? What are its six components?
5. Define healthy sexuality, incorporating the elements of wellness.

Test Yourself!

1. Which generalization about sexuality in our culture is most accurate?
   a. Our culture is clearly becoming more sexually permissive, as reflected in the content of our television programming.
   b. Our culture is clearly becoming more sexually restrictive, as evidenced by growing financial support for abstinence-until-marriage education.
   c. Our cultural climate has not changed significantly for decades.
   d. Sexual messages in our culture are contradictory and diverse.

2. Guidelines developed for comprehensive sexuality education programs highlight the importance of teaching about all but which of the following?
   a. Abstinence-until-marriage strategies
   b. Human development
   c. Relationship skills
   d. Society and culture

3. In evaluating sexuality research, which among the following is least important?
   a. The size of the sample responding
   b. The gender of the researcher
   c. The professional affiliation of the researcher
   d. How the information was gathered

4. The criticism that there has been a lack of diversity in research subjects is highlighted by the fact that
   a. most subjects are white, heterosexual, and middle class.
   b. most research is conducted on the East and West coasts of the United States.
   c. more research has been conducted on women than men.
   d. few subjects are over 35 years of age.

5. According to Dunn, personal well-being is connected to
   a. regular visits to physicians and other health practitioners.
   b. personal habits and lifestyle.
   c. the health of your parents and other relatives.
   d. age and ethnic background.

6. John feels depressed a lot and is told about a Web site where college students can get information about mental health, along with a referral. By checking the site out, he will be attending to which aspects of his well-being?
   a. Physical and spiritual
   b. Emotional and intellectual
   c. Emotional and physical
   d. Intellectual and environmental

7. Sarah has decided to move into a campus apartment with friends. Her decision should improve which components of her well-being?
   a. Physical and social
   b. Environmental and emotional
   c. Social and environmental
   d. Emotional and physical

8. Students who exercise regularly are more likely to
   a. feel better about their bodies.
   b. get better grades.
   c. have more friends.
   d. gain weight over time.

9. Increasingly, college campuses have policies focused on sexuality-related issues. Policies related to all but which of the following should be expected?
   a. HIV/AIDS
   b. Sexual assault and date rape
   c. Sexual harassment
   d. Premarital sex

10. The model for making informed decisions recommends all but which of the following strategies?
    a. Identify the pros and cons.
    b. Weigh the pros and cons.
    c. Rate what is most important to least important.
    d. Think about what is right, not what your gut instincts tell you to do.

Media Menu

You can link to the following online tools by visiting
http://health.wadsworth.com/blonna1.

Film

Research Methods

 InfoTrac Activity

Kempner, M. E. (2003, February–March). True integration of prevention programs requires broad focus on sexual health. *SIECUS Report, 31*(3), 5.

 Web Resources

American Association of Sex Educators, Counselors, and Therapists

www.aasect.org/

Professional organization devoted to the promotion of sexual health by the development and advancement of the fields of sex therapy, counseling, and education. There is a selection of associated Web links and the "contemporary sexuality" section providing general items of interest on sexuality.

Go Ask Alice

www.goaskalice.columbia.edu/

Columbia University's Health Education Program, offering information and e-mail advice on sexual health, sexuality, communication, and relationships. The primary goal is to make health and wellness a life priority for students, staff, and professors.

Sexuality Information and Education Council of the U.S. (SIECUS)

www.siecus.org

National nonprofit organization that promotes comprehensive education about sexuality and advocates the right of individuals to make responsible sexual choices. This site details information on sexuality, contraception, and sexual abuse and assault.

The Society for the Scientific Study of Sexuality (SSSS)

www.SexScience.org

The Society for the Scientific Study of Sexuality is dedicated to advancing knowledge of sexuality. It believes in the importance of both the production of quality research and the application of sexual knowledge in educational, clinical, and other settings. The site provides links to professional meetings, journals in the field, other SSSS publications, professional contacts, and more.

Discovery Health

http://health.discovery.com/

This the Discovery Channel's health Web page. It has excellent sexual health information (click on sexual health icon on the left side). It also offers an array of online health assessments through the following link: http://health.discovery.com/tools/assessments.html.

National Wellness Institute (NWI)

www.nationalwellness.org/home/definitionofwellness.asp

Founded in 1977, the National Wellness Institute has steadfastly provided health promotion and wellness professionals unparalleled resources and services that promote both professional and personal growth. Besides a membership division, NWI hosts the National Wellness Conference. Held annually in Stevens Point, Wisconsin, at the University of Wisconsin for over 25 years, it is the most highly acclaimed conference for wellness and health promotion professionals.

The Sexual Health Network

www.sexualhealth.com

The Sexual Health Network is dedicated to providing easy access to sexuality information, education, mutual support, counseling, therapy, health care, products and other resources for people with disabilities, illness, or natural changes throughout the life cycle and those who love them or care for them.

Bill Hettler Home Page

http://hettler.com/

Bill Hettler has been providing wellness/health promotion consultations and presentations since 1972. He serves as president of the board of directors and is one of the cofounders of the National Wellness Institute, Inc. He is probably best known as one of the creators of the National Wellness Conference. This week-long conference has influenced the lives of thousands people for more than 20 years.

Online Health Assessments

http://health.discovery.com/tools/assessments.html

Take as many of the additional assessments as you wish. Make sure to explore all of the available assessments under all three menus (general health, personality, nutrition).

References

American College Health Association. (1996). *Policy guidelines for HIV/AIDS on campus.* Washington, DC: Author.

Ardell, D. (1985). *The history and future of wellness.* Dubuque, IA: Kendall/Hunt.

Boulard, G. (2001, December 24). After September 11th students find themselves under a magnifying glass. *Community College Week, 14*(10), 2–4.

Davey, J. (2002, September 30). One day in September. *Community College Week, 15*(4), 4.

Dettmer, J. (2001, October 29). New York shows strength in adversity. *Insight on the News, 17*(40), 13.

Dunn, H. (1962). High-level wellness in the world of today. *Journal of the American Osteopathic Association, 61,* 9.

Garmon, J. (2001, December 24). Making sense, not war. *Community College Week, 14*(10), 4–6.

Henry J. Kaiser Family Foundation. (2000). *Sex education in America: A view from inside the nation's classrooms.* Chart pack. Menlo Park, CA: Author.

Kirgiss, K. (2002, February). Taylor-made service: After the terrorist attacks, 99 students from Indiana's Taylor University drove to New York to help however they could. *Campus Life, 60*(7), 62–64.

Lane, K. (2002, January 21). After the fall: Against the ruined backdrop of Ground Zero, the wounded Borough of Manhattan community college is struggling to rebuild. *Community College Week, 14*(12), 6–11.

Manisses Communication Group. (2002, September 16). Survey finds impact of September 11th stretches across the country. *Mental Health Weekly, 12*(35), 1–3.

Mindlin, A. C., Wallace, E. E., & Kapell, M. (2002). Cultural and religious determinants of sexual behaviors: A cross-cultural analysis of the available literature. *Michigan Academician, 34*(1), 6–8.

National Abortion and Reproductive Rights Action League Foundation. (2001). *Who decides? A state-by-state review of abortion and reproductive rights.* Washington, DC: NARAL and the NARAL Foundation.

National Wellness Institute. (2002). Definition of wellness [Online]. Available: www.nationalwellnessinstitute.home.

Office of the Surgeon General. (2001). *The surgeon general's call to action to promote sexual health and responsible sexual behavior.* Washington, DC: U.S. Government Printing Office.

Seong-Ngoo. (2002, May). Psychological burden after September 11th tragedy. *Student British Medical Journal, 138.*

Sexuality Information and Education Council of the U.S. (1996). *Guidelines for comprehensive sexuality education* (2nd ed.). New York: Author.

Sexuality Information and Education Council of the U.S. (1997). Guidelines for comprehensive sexuality education fact sheet [Online]. Available: www.siecus.org/pubs/fact/fact0003.html.

Sexuality Information and Education Council of the U.S. (2001, August–September). Issues and answers: Fact sheet on sexuality education. *SIECUS Report, 29*(6) [Online]. Available: www.siecus.org/pubs/fact/fact0007.html.

Straw, D. (2001, December 24). A separate peace in a wartime classroom. *Community College Week, 14*(10), 4–6.

Tsigos, C., & Chrousos, G. P. (1996). Stress, endocrine manifestations and disease. In C. L. Cooper (Ed.), *Handbook of stress, medicine, and health.* New York: CRC.

Weis, D. (2002, May). Another stab at sexual theory [a review of *The Role of Theory in Sex Research,* edited by J. Bancroft]. *Journal of Sex Research, 39*(2), 158–160.

Wiederman, M. (2001). Why understanding research? In *Understanding sexuality research.* Belmont, CA: Wadsworth.

World Health Organization. (1947). Constitution of the World Health Organization. *Chronicles of the World Health Organization, 1,* 29–43.

chapter *five*

Child *and* Adolescent Sexuality

Student Learning Objectives

After reading this chapter, students will be able to

- Compare and contrast a variety of theories of personality from birth through adolescence.

- Describe how the key aspects from various psychological theories impact sexual development.

- Discuss the effects of parenting practices such as bonding, toilet training, and nudity on healthy sexual development.

- Compare the biological consequences of puberty with the psychosocial aspects of adolescence.

- Describe the findings of a variety of studies concerning adolescent sexual behavior.

- Compare the adolescent sexual behavior of people in the United States with those from other cultures.

- Evaluate the positive and negative aspects of sexual activity during adolescence.

*Test your understanding of these objectives by taking the end-of-chapter quiz, available online at **http://health.wadsworth.com/blonna1.***

activity teaser: *How do you decide what sexual behavior is right for you? Find out with the Personal Exploration Activity on page 150.*

case study 5.1

Rebecca and Jake

Rebecca, 24, and Jake, 25, are white.

Critical Thinking

How do parents develop parenting strategies that bridge the gaps among how they each were raised, what they have learned to be healthy for their child, and what they are each comfortable with as parents?

Use your Virtual Workbook to explore your answer to this question at **http://health.wadsworth.com/blonna1.**

Rebecca and Jake became parents for the first time in their mid-20s. They both were so excited at the birth of Adam yet nervous at the same time about how to be good parents.

REBECCA: I grew up in a very puritanical household. My parents rarely touched or showed any kind of physical affection toward each other or my brother and me. I know they loved each other and us, but it just wasn't their way to express it physically, in public. Nudity also was not tolerated, and sex was never discussed. Being with Jake has taught me that the physical expression of affection and love is a natural and positive thing.

JAKE: I come from a very physical, touchy family. Our whole family loves to hug and kiss, and visitors rarely get in or out of the house without a big hug hello and good-bye. When Rebecca and I got together, differences in our attitudes about touch had to be worked out between us. I love being naked, and for me touch does not always mean "I want some sex." I felt it was really important that Rebecca commit to breastfeeding Adam . . . she knew the health benefits, but the reality of if at all seemed to scare her a bit.

We often just sit and look at Adam, our precious little baby. We want him to grow up healthy and comfortable with his sexuality. We've been taking turns getting up to change and feed Adam. When it's Rebecca's turn, she gets up, goes into Adam's room, and nurses him while rocking in the chair in his room. When it's my turn, I bring Adam into our bed and then put him back in his crib after nursing. We both love the skin–skin contact we share with the baby and each other.

REBECCA: Despite how tired we both are, we know that this phase of being parents is only the beginning. There will be so many more challenges down the line. What we know for sure is that we will work together to help Adam navigate through the sexual challenges of childhood and the teen years.

As you sit here reading, you may want to ask yourself, "How did I get to be the sexual person that I am?" You look a particular way and have your own unique thoughts, feelings, attractions, and needs. Despite what is often a cultural desire to protect children from things sexual, the reality is that profound aspects of sexual development occur in childhood and adolescence. How you are as an adult stems from the varied influences and experiences you have had "growing up." And as we explore adult issues in Chapter 6, you may want to question when, if ever, development *stops*.

Psychosexual development
Psychosexual development The blending of sexual aspects of one's development with other psychological factors

Psychosexual development is the process of becoming a sexual person. The term traditionally refers to the psychological aspects of sexual development. As we've mentioned throughout this text, though, to completely separate the psychological from the physical, intellectual, emotional, social, spiritual, and environmental facets of our sexuality is not possible. Most discussions of psychosexual development present it as an outgrowth of personality, with great emphasis placed on the first years of life. Although the classic personality theorists remain important as a foundation, current theorists and critics have examined the interplay of biological, psychological, social, and cultural influences on the overall development of sexuality. In addition, debates continue as to what is truly "healthy" for children and teens.

Personality *The collection of values, attitudes, and behavior that make us who we are*

Personality is the entire collection of one's thoughts, attitudes, values, beliefs, perceptions, and behaviors. Our personalities define how we see ourselves independently and within our environment. Personality is constantly evolving and is cumulative in nature. Your personality today is the sum total of all of the things you have experienced until this point in your life. Various theories have been proposed to explain how personality develops.

Traditional Theories of Personality

Behaviorism: John Watson

Behaviorism, developed by John Watson (1970), proposes that personality develops as a result of responses to general and specific stimuli. Behaviorists believe that at birth we are blank slates with no predetermined attributes. Our personalities evolve as the result of myriad interactions between stimuli (people, places, events, situations, images) and the responses they evoke. Responses can be either positive or negative and vary in strength. The more powerful the response, the more likely we will either embrace (positive response) or reject (negative response) whatever stimulus prompted it.

Let's use masturbation to explain how this stimulus-response model works. Imagine that when you were an infant, your mother caught you fondling yourself while lying on the rug in the living room in front of your grandmother. Your mother was upset and smacked your hand, saying, "Bad girl. Little ladies don't touch themselves down there." This negative reinforcement (slapping the hand away and saying "bad girl") in response to a stimulus (touching yourself) begins to shape how you feel toward masturbation. The specific context (in the living room, in a public setting, in front of Grandma) also contributes to shaping the behavior.

If this response is repeated over time, in similar and different contexts, it can either extinguish (get rid of) the behavior of masturbation or drive it underground and surround it with shame and guilt. The person then might practice the behavior in private and associate it with negative feelings.

Other personality theories stress developmental stages and tasks. These theories propose that personality develops in stages that build upon each other.

Behaviorism A stimulus-response theory of personality development grounded in the belief that human personality evolves as a result of the interaction between exposure to stimuli and the responses that this exposure evokes in the person. Watson is credited with the theory, expanded later by Skinner.

Humanism: Abraham Maslow

Abraham Maslow (1970) was one of the most influential humanists. The premise of **humanism** is that human beings are motivated by a desire for personal growth. Maslow believed that all humans are unique and are capable of growth and reaching their utmost potential in all facets of their lives. Humans are essentially good and are capable of making choices about the direction their lives will take. Maslow believed that all people are capable of reaching their highest potential if they progress through a series of stages of development that meet various basic human needs. Figure 5.1 presents Maslow's hierarchy of needs. As you can see, they reflect the physical, social, intellectual, emotional, spiritual, and environmental domains that characterize present-day wellness theory.

Before people can develop loving, intimate relationships, they must meet their most fundamental needs for survival and safety that form the basis of the pyramid. To get to the top, one has to pass through all of the previous levels, successfully meeting the needs of each stage before proceeding to the next. The top of Maslow's pyramid, self-actualization, represents the pinnacle of human development. People reaching the top are said to be fully self-actualized.

Maslow also believed that, as we work our way up this pyramid, we often encounter "peak experiences"—moments that crystallize what it means to be fully alive, to **transcend** mere existence. He felt that these peak experiences help us feel connected to the world around us, to be one with our universe.

Humanism A theory of personality development proposing that human personality development is shaped by innate desire and need for maximizing personal growth

Transcend To rise above or extend beyond ordinary limits

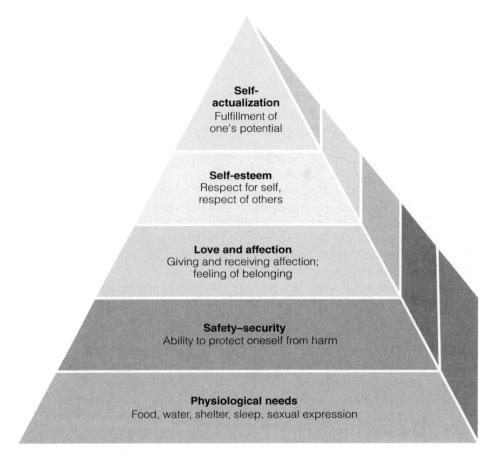

Figure 5.1 *Maslow's Hierarchy of Needs*

The following are characteristics of individuals who achieve self-actualization through transcendence:

1. Transcenders have more "peak" or creative experiences than others.
2. Transcenders are more responsive to beauty and more holistic in their perceptions of humanity and the world.
3. Transcenders are innovators who are attracted to the unknown, embrace change, and see themselves as the instruments of their transcendence.
4. Transcenders can fuse work and play. They are less attracted by the rewards of money and more motivated by the satisfaction of being true to whom they really are and serving others.
5. Transcenders are more likely to accept others with unconditional positive regard.

Psychoanalytic Theory: Sigmund Freud

Freudian **psychoanalytic theory** purports that personality develops as a result of a struggle between conscious and unconscious forces in our lives (Hall, 1954). These forces are directed by our **ego** (the rational, thinking mind), **superego** (the conscience), and **id** (the pleasure-seeking life force). The ego is conscious and based in reality, interweaving sensory perceptions with thoughts and memories. The superego, which is partially unconscious, is judgmental; it factors in our beliefs about right and wrong.

Psychoanalytic theory Also known as Freudian theory (after its founder, Sigmund Freud), describes personality development as outgrowth of interaction of id (pleasure-seeking, guilt-free), superego (the conscience, influenced by society and parents), and ego (rational, analytical mind driven by logical thinking)

Ego Rational, analytical facet of human mind, according to Freudian theory

Superego The conscience, influenced by society and family, according to Freudian theory

Freud called the fuel of this life force "libidinal energy." The id does not distinguish between right and wrong, good and evil. Whatever brings pleasure is good. The superego (in concert with the ego) is supposed to keep the id in check.

Freud believed that the transference of libidinal energy has direct consequences for our psychosexual development. He outlined stages of development, each with a set of needs to be satisfied:

Oral stage. The first, or oral, stage lasts from birth to the second year of life. During the oral stage, stimulation of the mouth through sucking, biting, and swallowing is the main source of erotic satisfaction. Inadequate satisfaction during the oral stage, according to Freud, would produce an "oral personality"—someone preoccupied with mouth habits such as overeating or smoking.

Anal stage. During the second, anal phase, from ages 2 to 3, libidinal energy shifts to the anus. During this stage, the child derives pleasure from anal stimulation and being in control of defecation. This provides the child's first real opportunity to assert some independence from parental control. This stage coincides with toilet training. Freud believed it is the holding back or letting go of bowel movements (personal control) that produces physical and psychological pleasure for the child. Rushing a child through toilet training (thereby limiting the ability to derive anal pleasure) or making too big a fuss over soiling the diapers or making a mess could result in fixation at this stage. People who are fixated at this stage are either anal-expulsive (dirty, extravagant, wasteful) or anal-retentive (excessively clean, neat, cheap, and compulsive).

Phallic stage. The third phase of development is the phallic stage, between the third and fourth years. During this time, libidinal energy shifts to the genitals, and the child derives erotic pleasure through fondling and exhibitionism. Freud also believed that during this time the child develops a sexual attachment to the opposite-sex parent and becomes fearful of the parent of the same sex. Named the **Oedipal complex** (after the Greek legend in which Oedipus killed his father and married his mother), this attachment, if handled calmly and without undue concern or punishment, gradually subsides as the child moves into the next stage, latency. Psychoanalytic theorists focus on the dynamics of this phase in their attempts to explain sexual orientation.

Latency stage. Freud believed that sexuality goes into a period of latency extending from age 5 until **puberty**. At this time, the child becomes more focused on nonsexual interests such as intellectual and social issues. Modern observance of young children and preadolescents clarifies the difficulties with accepting such a concept. Sexual exploration, sex games, and, for some, mature sexual involvement makes latency an archaic idea.

Genital stage. At puberty, genital sexuality reemerges, and the adolescent becomes sexually attracted to members of the opposite sex, a prerequisite for marriage and childrearing. Freud placed marriage as the culmination of normal psychosexual development.

Freud's theory is valued more for its place in history than its current usefulness. His work brought the importance of sexuality to an understanding of personality development, yet serious questions about his methods and biases have diminished the value of his work for contemporary analysis of sexual development. From a modern perspective, Freud was sexist and heterosexist, not understanding female sexual response or the healthy development of homosexuality and bisexuality.

Eight Stages of Development: Erik Erikson

Erik Erikson (1978) constructed a model of personality development that views it as the result of a struggle between opposing forces that present themselves in a series of stages that occur throughout our lives. Figure 5.2 shows Erikson's eight

Id Pleasure-seeking, guilt-free facet of human mind, according to Freudian theory

Oedipal complex A psychoanalytical term (named after Oedipus in Shakespeare's play) that describes the internal struggle that 3- to 4-year-olds face as they begin to identify more with their opposite-sex parent

Puberty Biological transition from childhood to young adulthood

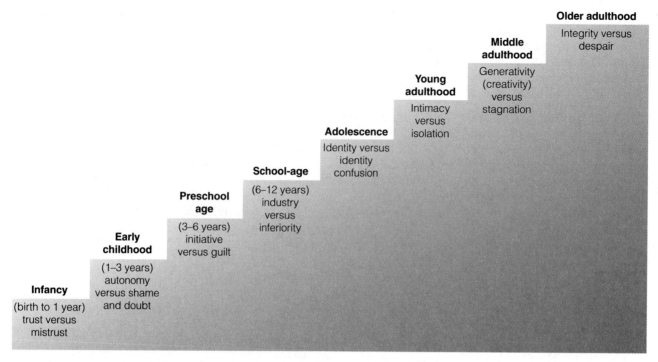

Figure 5.2 *Erikson's Developmental Stages and Conflicts*

stages of development. Instead of the struggle between the libidinal-driven id and the ego/superego, Erikson viewed development as a conflict between opposing psychosocial forces and qualities. According to Erikson, to continue to grow, we must resolve these crises.

Healthy personality development results from accomplishing the developmental tasks required for the stage and then moving on to the next one. In a sense, positive attributes win out over negative attributes, and the personality development moves to the next level. Inadequate task resolution results in thwarted development in that particular area. This leaves the person with a lack of certain skills and attributes that will be needed later in life.

For example, if, as an infant, one never successfully develops a sense of trust in oneself and others, the person will grow up with a stronger sense of mistrust. This stays with the person throughout life, limiting the ability to trust others, develop sustained loving relationships, and maximize the individual's potential as an adult. The inability to trust another person makes it difficult to develop intimate relationships based on faith and sharing deeply personal emotions.

Modern Theory

Feminist theory Theories that argue that personality and identity are socially constructed. What is "correct development" for boys is different from what is deemed "correct development" for girls.

It is important to understand that certain theorists provided the basis from which contemporary work has evolved. Today, some question the very foundations of traditional personality theory. **Feminist theory,** for example, posits that personality and identity are socially constructed. What is "correct development" for boys is different from what is deemed "correct development" for girls. Judith Lorber (2001) writes, "I am arguing that bodies differ in many ways physiologically, but they are completely transformed by social practices to fit into the salient categories of a society, the most pervasive of which are 'female' and 'male' and 'women' and 'men'" (p. 48). Feminist scholars challenge the culture to reexamine the power structure, encouraging broader developmental choices for both boys and girls.

As feminism worked to increase options for girls, others brought to light the need to reexamine how boys are raised, and the limitations placed on their development as well. Michael Gurian (1996), in *The Wonder of Boys*, writes:

> *It requires pretty effective blinders these days to think as I did in the early 1980's—that boys are boys and girls are girls predominantly because of environmental forces. It is more accurate to say that much of who we are is determined by body chemicals, brain differences, hormones, and by society's efforts to honor this biology through its socializing forces. (p. 5)*

Gurian is a firm believer that boys are hard-wired to be a particular way but can be raised to be confident, caring contributors to the culture at large.

The new area of research called **Queer theory** has expanded the scholarship that examines the development of sexual orientation. In particular, those identified with this movement challenge heterosexuality as the only valid "end point" of psychosexual development. They argue for a more fluid understanding of gender and orientation, and the role that power and politics play in development (Butler, 1999).

In 2002, Judith Levine raised the ire of many with her book *Harmful to Minors: The Perils of Protecting Children from Sex*. She writes that sex is and should be a positive and wonderful part of children's lives, and that cultural attempts to protect them from information and experiences was harmful to their health and development. She was both critical of conservatives who promoted abstinence-until-marriage ideology and curricula, as well as those who were advocating comprehensive sexuality education, which in her view was doing too little, too late.

Bookstores today are filled with shelves of books on parenting. Write parenting on the search line of a browser, and numerous references and selections for purchase will appear. Is there one book that is the ultimate guide for the development of sexually healthy children? Our response is no. Professionals do not agree. Theorists do not agree. Even family members do not agree. That said, it is important to understand that both scholarship and clinical practice have much to offer for better parenting. The realities and complexities of sexual development, however, do not lend themselves to easy guidelines and rules.

Queer theory Theories that look to explain sexual orientation and sexual identity without relying on heterosexuality as the norm

Early Development

Five common themes related to early sexuality transcend all of the theories about sexual development: bonding, other expressions of physical intimacy, self-exploration and masturbation, nudity, and toilet training. Even though theorists might differ in their interpretation and significance, most would agree that they exert a tremendous impact on sexual development. These critical sexual development issues surface during infancy and childhood and remain throughout life. How our caregivers initially handle these issues strongly influences the direction our development takes.

The major task of infancy, according to Erikson, is to develop a sense of trust. For trust to win out over mistrust is essential to continuing healthy psychological development in all of us.

Bonding

One of the earliest behaviors that helps foster trust and satisfies our most primal physiological needs is bonding. **Bonding** is a process of developing a close physical and psychological relationship with one's primary caregiver. Bonding be-

Bonding The close physical emotional attachment between infants and their primary caregiver(s)

*Bonding can take many forms.
Here a mom plays in the pool
with her child.*

Courtesy of the authors

tween mother and child begins almost immediately as the newborn and mother
are brought together to share the first moments of life. Bonding continues as
mother and child are brought together during feeding, diaper changing, and simple things such as smiling, talking to the child, and acknowledging the child
when approaching him or her.

Fathers also fulfill a bonding role. They are often present at the birth of the
baby and develop strong, close physical bonds with their children, sharing in
their care and feeding. The increased use of the word *parenting* rather than *mother-
ing* and *fathering* reflects social changes around the raising of children. Parents increasingly divide child-rearing responsibilities to fit with their work schedules
and time at home.

During the bonding process, infants learn to associate the mother and father
with fulfilling the most basic needs for sustaining life. Trust in the world as a
whole begins by trusting in mothers and fathers. Infants respond positively to
touch. **Thriving**—a term pediatricians use to describe physical and psychological
growth—is enhanced by touch and bonding. Failure to thrive has been noted in
infants who, among other things, have been deprived of sufficient physical nurturing during infancy. As children, these infants often lack the cognitive and
motor abilities of their peers.

Thriving Pattern of normal
weight gain, neuromuscular
development, and other
developmental attributes of
infants

Other Forms of Physical Intimacy

In addition to bonding as a contributor to the development of sensuality and sexuality, other forms of touch play an important part. Beyond the basic need of
touch for infants to thrive, touch is related to the development of sensuality. Our
entire skin surface is capable of acting as an erogenous zone. It is sensitive to
touch in all of its manifestations. Babies love to be held, stroked, and rocked. Although we can't interview them, we can tell this from the cooing sounds they
make, their facial expressions, and their continued responsiveness to our stroking
and hugging them. Our ability or inability to respond positively to physical intimacy is believed to be rooted in the time our parents spent touching and stroking
us as infants (Montague, 1986).

How we touch babies varies from generalized hugging and stroking to infant
massage and baby exercise. Infant massage strokes are similar to those used

with adults, but much gentler. Care must be taken to avoid sharp movements. Infants generally won't last through an entire full-body massage; they begin to wriggle and laugh. Beyond the closeness and benefits from touch that massage affords, research has identified additional health benefits that result from the effect massage has on the body. Infant massage has been found to help babies adjust their circadian rhythms and move toward better sleeping habits, as well as promote better health and development (Ferber, Laudon, Kuint, Weller, & Zisapel, 2002; Globus, 2002).

Unfortunately, many parents feel awkward or uncomfortable expressing themselves through touch and physical contact. Some of us have grown up in households where touch was withheld or minimized. Sometimes parents worry that their feelings (or their child's) are sexual, not sensual. Even though infants are capable of experiencing erotic pleasure, sensual pleasure shared with your child and sexual desire are different. Mature, parental sensual pleasure associated with hugging and stroking one's child is vastly different from sexually desiring that child. There is no intention of genital sexual contact, nor is there any desire to experience such behavior.

An aversion to touch is a learned behavior. As such, you can unlearn it and not make the same mistakes with your own children. In sharing the joys of touch with them, you can relearn the joys of physical closeness and sensuality.

Grandparents can lavish love and attention on their grandchildren, bringing extra sources of affection.

Spiritual and Emotional Wellness

Although we are not always cognizant of it as infants and children, we begin to develop a sense of connectedness or disconnectedness during this stage. Probably the earliest manifestation of spirituality is the bonding with primary caregivers. This is a powerful connection not only to other human beings but also to the world as a whole. Developing a sense of trust in ourselves, others, and the world as a whole begins with the skin-to-skin nurturing we receive from our parents in times of need. Parents and caregivers often describe the feeling of bonding and nurturing of an infant as one of the most profoundly spiritual feelings they have ever experienced. Many rediscover a sense of awe and faith in the power of love by connecting with and nurturing our children.

Infant and childhood emotional development forms the foundation for much of our adult emotional makeup. Basic personality constructs such as self-esteem, trust, happiness, and optimism begin to take shape during infancy and childhood. As Maslow and other developmental theorists point out, the ability to fully self-actualize as adults requires people to meet basic emotional needs early in life. It's harder to love others as adults if a person was not loved as an infant and if pieces of one's emotional development were left scattered on the floor of childhood and **adolescence.** Nurturing infants, children, and adolescents, attending to their needs, and providing a safe haven and outlet for their desires are all essential for their continuing emotional development and healthy sexuality.

Adolescence Time period representing the psycho-social transition from childhood to young adulthood

Self-Exploration and Masturbation

All infants discover the joys of genital pleasure inadvertently. They discover what it feels like to have their genitals rub against things in their immediate environment (crib, blanket, toys, diaper, clothing, their mother and father). If allowed to do so, infants between 6 and 12 months of age will touch their genitals. They will learn that they are capable of initiating the same pleasurable feelings they felt when rubbing against objects.

Masturbation Individual or mutual stimulation of genitalia by hand or using other objects

Sexologists have long debated whether this behavior should be considered **masturbation,** a form of "sexual" behavior. Although it is definitely sensual and erotic, it lacks the associated sexual connotations that older children and adults have concerning genital pleasuring. These associations are learned later. This genital play should be evaluated exactly for what it is—play (Kaplan, 1974). It feels good, and children become frustrated if their hands are kept away from their genitals.

Infant self-exploration and masturbation also lay the foundation for developing a broad continuum of sexual feelings and behaviors. Masturbation is a normal developmental act, one of the earliest forms of sexual activity. Most children discover masturbation quite innocently as a physical, not sexual, act.

Boys' penile erections often occur as sexual reflexes in response to a variety of stimuli ranging from self-touching to breastfeeding. Girls experience clitoral erection and lubrication under similar circumstances.

These earliest attempts at self-exploration teach us about our body and the potential it has for providing pleasure. Conversely, the body has the potential for negatively influencing sexual development if parents overreact to their children's attempts at self-stimulation. Adults who punish children for masturbating may be denying them valuable opportunities for learning about self-pleasuring and setting the stage for negative attitudes (shame, guilt, fear) about sex. Parents who say nothing about masturbation send negative messages through their omission. Children learn that these omissions represent areas that are off-limits for discussion.

Yelling at a child, slapping his or her hand away, admonishing the child for doing something "dirty"—these adult responses to masturbation convey strong negative messages. Negatively reinforcing a behavior that is pleasurable—self-exploration—creates a confusing mixed message. If it is more related to the timing of these acts (little Billy always seems to play with his penis when Grandma is sitting next to him), gently moving the child to a crib or playpen in another room might help. When children become verbal, caregivers might explain to them that playing with themselves under private conditions (such as in their own rooms) is OK but it is not all right in more public settings where it might offend others (such as Grandma or the neighbors).

Self-exploration, again, is normal. It cannot be carried to excess and is self-limiting if children are left alone. Adults should view it like other forms of play. It is amusing for a while, and then the child moves on to something else. If left alone, children will not sit in their rooms all day and play with themselves. Parents who cannot accept their children's self-exploration might discuss the matter with a counselor, priest, rabbi, minister, pediatrician, or sex therapist to get help in dealing with their feelings. Exploring their sexual fears and concerns will reassure them that this self-touching behavior will not misguide their children's sexual development.

Nudity

Infants and children are nudists at heart. Most infants and young children are perfectly comfortable lying and running around the house naked. They do not associate nudity with morality. To be naked to them is simply to be without clothes. Parents and other caregivers (and, later, society at large) teach infants and children that nudity has sexual overtones.

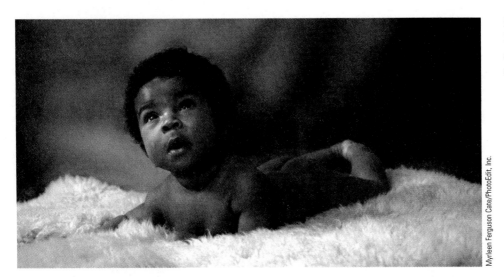

Babies are sensual creatures. They like to be nude and feel softness and textures of things such as sheepskin throws.

Myrleen Ferguson Cate/PhotoEdit, Inc.

Our culture, however, associates nudity with sexuality. In contrast, Scandinavian cultures have nude beaches that cater to families. Being naked with one's family is considered normal and healthy.

Unlike some other cultures that accept nudity as part of life and don't make a big deal about it one way or another, U.S. culture frowns upon most public displays of nakedness. We owe this to our Puritan heritage. When they came to America, the Puritans enacted many laws that attempted to curtail public displays of nakedness and sexual behavior. To this day, laws dating back to the early 1800s still are on the books concerning things such as proper swimming attire. The rigid views concerning sex and nudity grew out of Victorian England in the 19th century. In that formal, rigid culture, visions of naked flesh were linked to uncontrolled sexual desire and giving into the will of the devil. In an almost comical adherence to covering their exposed limbs, the Victorians went to extremes such as putting "skirts" onto the legs of pianos and chairs lest they offend and tempt their owners to engage in lewd behavior.

Even though most states allow private displays of nudity in nudist colonies, this behavior is the exception rather than the rule. Community opposition to nude beaches, clubs, and public displays of nudity is still strong. Women seem to bear a heavier burden than men in our culture. Men are almost always allowed to go topless in public, whereas female toplessness is considered lewd and almost always against the law.

Given our puritanical heritage and history of opposition to nudity, most Americans, not surprisingly, feel more comfortable with their clothes on than off. This collective discomfort with nudity affects our comfort level with our own bodies and our ability to relax and be sensual and sexual with others.

Understanding nudity and how we deal with it with our infants and children has many facets. How we handle nudity plays a big part in the kind of foundation we lay for our children's psychosexual development. Many parents fear being nude with their children. Their fears range from their baby "having an accident" (unintentional urination/defecation) to transmitting the wrong message about sex. In actuality, letting your child be naked or being nude with your child is perfectly normal and healthy.

Bonding is enhanced by nudity. The warmth and close, physical contact that can be achieved from skin-to-skin contact is unparalleled. Even partial nudity, torso to torso, conveys a special closeness that cannot be achieved any other way. Allowing your children to be nude while establishing reasonable parameters for family nudity seems to be a prudent, middle-of-the-road approach to this issue.

case study 5.2

The Family Bath

Cara and Charles are in their early 30s; she identifies as biracial and he as African American.

Critical Thinking

What are your views on family nudity? Do you think that parents and children "should" be comfortable seeing each other without clothes? Is it more appropriate to cover up at some point for healthy development?

Use your Virtual Workbook to explore your answers to these questions at **http://health.wadsworth.com/blonna1.**

Cara and Charles loved being naked and seldom wore a lot of clothes around the house when the children, Aisha and Rakeen, were little. As a couple, they had a ritual of bathing together as much as possible. Once the kids outgrew their infant tubs, each parent took turns being responsible for giving the kids a bath. Because the children were only 2 years apart, sometimes both kids were bathed together. On other occasions one parent or the other would get into the tub with the kids. Getting the whole family into the tub was just too crowded.

As a family, all four were able to enjoy being in water together when they visited the grandparents in South Carolina. Next to a small swimming pool was a tiny hot tub that fit four very comfortably. The freedom of being naked in the water, however, was replaced with the need to be in a bathing suit. Nonetheless, all four could enjoy the family time together in the water.

When Cara and Charles added a new addition to their home, they purposely spent the extra money so that a large bathtub could be installed. The ritual of bathing as a couple could now be continued without overlapping legs and arms. Even the faucet was out of the way! What was missing, however, was the family nudity. The kids, now 11 and 13, had no interest in getting in the water naked with their parents. While getting changed in front of the kids and being naked is still a pattern at home, Cara and Charles seem to be getting more unsolicited feedback about their own bodies. "Ewww . . . you have so much hair there! Am I going to get hair like that?" Or, "Mom, why do you have so many stretch marks over there? Do all moms get those?" The kids seem to have moved to greater body awareness, self-consciousness, and a general need *not* to see their parents naked. The family bath will have to be relegated to memory.

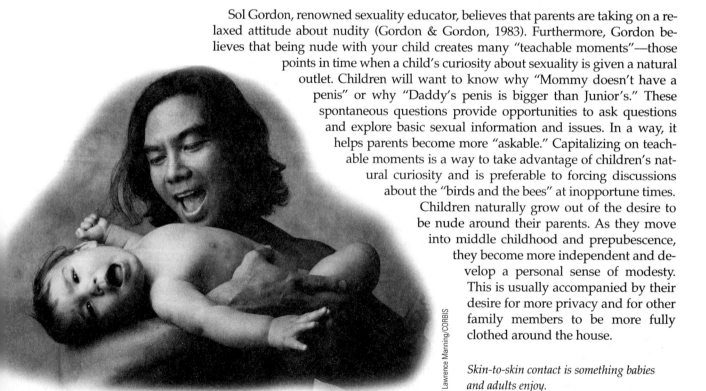

Sol Gordon, renowned sexuality educator, believes that parents are taking on a relaxed attitude about nudity (Gordon & Gordon, 1983). Furthermore, Gordon believes that being nude with your child creates many "teachable moments"—those points in time when a child's curiosity about sexuality is given a natural outlet. Children will want to know why "Mommy doesn't have a penis" or why "Daddy's penis is bigger than Junior's." These spontaneous questions provide opportunities to ask questions and explore basic sexual information and issues. In a way, it helps parents become more "askable." Capitalizing on teachable moments is a way to take advantage of children's natural curiosity and is preferable to forcing discussions about the "birds and the bees" at inopportune times. Children naturally grow out of the desire to be nude around their parents. As they move into middle childhood and prepubescence, they become more independent and develop a personal sense of modesty. This is usually accompanied by their desire for more privacy and for other family members to be more fully clothed around the house.

Skin-to-skin contact is something babies and adults enjoy.

Lawrence Manning/CORBIS

Toilet Training

The mastery of toilet training is essential in completing the developmental tasks of toddlers, as well as building a solid foundation for sexual health and positive psychosexual development. Toilet training is empowering for children. Along with mastering bowel control, they gain a measure of self-control, self-esteem, and independence. Wearing "big boy pants" is how one friend's son refers to his newfound freedom from diapers.

If parents or caregivers handle toilet training properly and do not rush their children, they develop a sense of pride in accomplishing something important to them. Toilet training is messy and involves a lot of time and work. Parents need to understand this and be careful not to punish their children or criticize them too harshly for the inevitable "mistakes" and soiled underpants they will encounter. Splitting the labor can help. When moms and dads (or other combinations of caregivers) work together, they each get a break from changing diapers and cleaning up messes.

Parents also need to accept that each child progresses through this stage on a different time schedule. When children are ready to give up diapers, they will. Adults can't rush the process or predict how long it will take. Trying to rush the child to fit someone else's time line (for example, the day care center will take only toilet-trained children) may not be the best strategy. Following these simple guidelines, your children can develop those all-important feelings of self-control and self-esteem (Gordon & Gordon, 1983).

Other Early Tasks

Another major developmental task of early childhood is learning to walk. Children who are helped with, but not overly protected from, the bumps and falls that are a normal part of learning to walk develop a sense of control over their environment. They learn about the literal "bumps and bruises" that are a normal part of achieving anything meaningful in life.

As children become more autonomous, they need to be able to explore their environment safely. To develop a sense of self-control and self-esteem, they need to have hazard-free environments and the freedom to explore them autonomously. Children whose exploratory play is restricted or unsafe may even become fearful of being alone or taking a risk later in life. Children who are overly protected and shielded from even the most minor stumbles have a harder time becoming autonomous.

Parents have to realize that boys and girls alike need to develop this sense of autonomy, and they are equally able to sustain the normal bumps and bruises inherent in developing autonomy. Traditional parents may feel a need to protect their daughters out of some ill-conceived notion of their frailty. Realize that the skills essential for developing autonomy are also critical for healthy sexual development. Although they are not overtly sexual in nature, these skills help build self-esteem and self-confidence that will influence the child's, and later the adolescent's, ability to make good sexual decisions and minimize unnecessary risk taking.

Development in Early Childhood

Self-exploration continues during early childhood (ages 3 to 5) and often extends to playmates. The more mobile child now begins to interact with other children more frequently. Games such as "doctor" and "nurse" typically provide opportunities for sex play and exploration. The availability of playmates often influences the nature of play. Same-gender versus opposite-gender exploration is a function of who is available to play with rather than representing any adult sexual orientation (such as heterosexual or homosexual).

Children continue to gain freedom and begin to be exposed to a variety of people and experiences as they further explore their environment. The major task at this stage corresponds to Erikson's developmental initiative versus guilt (refer to Figure 5.2). Children's actions are more purposeful as they evaluate their own competencies and initiate behaviors consistent with these limits. Children's likes and dislikes at this stage are more firmly established, and their behavior is more purposeful. They know what they want and use their greater mobility and freedom to pursue these desires. When this pursuit puts conflicts with how significant others want them to behave, they begin to feel guilt.

Children at this level struggle with their overwhelming preoccupation with self as they are increasingly exposed to other youngsters in a variety of play and social situations. They find themselves in situations with other youngsters that force them to share, take turns, and accommodate others. This socialization is a vital and necessary developmental step that will prepare children for the kinds of social interactions necessary for their future success in school.

As we pointed out in Chapter 4, gender identity is already strongly established by this stage. Little boys and girls know what being masculine and feminine means, and they continue to explore and refine these roles. The more freedom they are given to explore behaviors and roles, the greater opportunity they will

healthy sex hints 5.1
Becoming an Askable Parent

Becoming an askable parent is a lifelong process. A neon sign doesn't suddenly appear during adolescence signaling approachability. Being an askable parent is a reward earned after years of sending subtle messages about the desire to listen and willingness to help. The following are guidelines on how to be an askable parent:

1. *Start early.* Body language and nonverbal behaviors concerning bonding, nudity, and toilet training send messages about approachability.
2. *Don't worry about giving too much information.* Scientific evidence doesn't indicate that too much information too soon will overstimulate children. If a child is getting too much information, he or she will simply get bored, tune you out, and change the subject.
3. *Communicate even if you're not entirely comfortable about the topic.* If you are uncomfortable with a specific sexual issue, you can still address it openly and honestly with your children. The child might respond positively to your admission that you have difficulty talking about an issue.
4. *Admit your ignorance.* You don't know it all. Even the best teachers don't know everything about their sub-

ject. If your child asks a question you can't answer, admit it and offer to look it up. Better yet, look it up together.

5. *Realize that less is better.* Concise, simple answers that address the question at hand are better than long-winded answers.
6. *Don't worry about offering information that children can't understand.* If you make a mistake by being too technical, children will extract what they need or understand, and the rest will go over their head.
7. *Don't be afraid to make mistakes.* Everyone makes honest mistakes. Handle these as you would any other mistakes: Admit you were wrong, and try to correct the mistake, if possible.
8. *Relate your values.* Children want to know how you feel about sexual matters. Take every opportunity to share relevant values with them.
9. *Have a sense of humor.* Lighten up. Sexuality education gives rise to opportunities to laugh and learn at the same time. Children feel less inhibited about an adult's talking about sexual matters if sex isn't always portrayed as a deadly serious topic.

have in moving toward a more flexible gender identity. For instance, little girls who are allowed to play with boys and engage in active, physical play and sports might find that they enjoy this type of activity. Little boys who are allowed to play house and with dolls might find this an enjoyable addition to or replacement of more traditional roughhouse activities.

Development in Childhood

Children continue to explore and mimic gender role behaviors and scripts they learn from their parents and the culture. "Playing house" is a common script for 5- to 7-year-olds. The boys play the "daddies," and the girls play the "mommies." Often these games include kissing, hugging, cuddling, and lying on each other. Children at this age talk about people they love and will marry someday. Children often have a "special friend" to whom they are attracted and for whom they have loving feelings. Elementary school children exchange valentines and other symbols of endearment.

Children at this age also begin to develop their own language and sense of sexual humor. Jokes about bodily functions are common. These children have a great deal of interest in sounds and smells associated with bodily functioning. Children of this age are amused by riddles and rhymes that often are crude and sexually coarse.

healthy sex hints 5.2
Education for Children

Most parents and professional educators feel that children need to talk about sexuality issues in the home. Having the resources with which to do that in an informed way has been possible for many years. In addition, so much more is accessible over the Internet. Here is a brief list of helpful books for both parents and children.

Two by Deborah Roffman, published by Perseus Publishing:

Sex and Sensibility: The Thinking Parent's Guide to Talking Sense About Sex (2001)
But How'd I Get in There in the First Place? Talking to Your Young Child About Sex (2002)

Two by Debra Haffner, along with her daughter Alyssa Haffner Tartaglione, published by Newmarket Press:

From Diapers to Dating (1999)
Beyond the Big Talk: Every Parent's Guide to Raising Sexually Healthy Teens, from Middle School to College (2001)

Two by Robie Harris, published by Candlewick Press:

It's Perfectly Normal: Changing Bodies, Growing Up, Sex and Sexual Health (1994)
It's So Amazing! A Book About Eggs, Sperm, Birth, Babies, and Families (1999)

Robert Hatcher, Shannon Colestock, Erika Pluhar, and Christian Thrasher have a book designed for older adolescents and young college students:

Sexual Etiquette 101 and More (Bridging the Gap Communications, 2001)

These books are honest and forthright about sexuality information. Contacting the Sexuality Information and Education Council of the U.S. (SIECUS) or Planned Parenthood Federation of America will link parents to a wide array of books and pamphlets that address how to promote sexual health. Books and pamphlets have also been developed to help families learn and talk about adoption, gay, lesbian, bisexual and transgendered youth, intersexuality, sexual assault, disability, and other related topics.

By 8 or 9 years of age, children begin to become more segregated in their play. Boys tend to play with other boys, and girls with their girlfriends. Although they still have the same interest in the opposite gender, the socialization process begins to segregate them more and more. Formal activities such as team sports and school-based extracurricular activities are often segregated, sometimes formally but usually informally. Little girls who might have played touch football with the guys last season may try out for cheerleading this year. Boys who played sandlot baseball with the neighborhood boys and girls may sign up for Little League, while their female counterparts sign up for softball. Leagues in some towns encourage mixed-gender participation.

In addition to cultural influences that help shape boys and girls and influence which direction they might take regarding sports, economic and political factors play a big part. Often, funding for girls' sports and recreational activities does not equal that earmarked for boys. Consequently, girls haven't always been offered the same opportunities as boys to compete in youth sports. To attempt to rectify that, Title IX of the Civil Rights Act was passed to ensure parity in funding. The law refers to all benefits and activities available in schools. Most of the controversy regarding Title IX revolves around sports and athletic programs. Title IX has been instrumental in getting more girls and women involved in sports and athletic activities.

Development in Preadolescence

Many of the books available for children and teenagers reinforce the idea that children develop at their own pace. A new term, *tweens*, refers to children roughly between 10 and 12 who, although not teenagers, are confronting issues not commonly associated with young children.

Studies show that although segregation of the sexes is more pronounced during this time, feelings of desire and affection are strong. Most boys and girls of this age view relationships with other preadolescents as important and something they desire. Children in this age range are learning how to interact with members of the same and opposite sexes they find desirable. They are learning the scripts and rehearsing the behaviors necessary to make the transition from childhood to young adulthood. Adults may find some of the behavior amusing, yet the fact that we use the term *social skill* literally means that skill development is crucial.

Sixth-grade dances are good examples of this learning process. The room is filled with 11- and 12-year-olds who want to mix and mingle with girls and boys they are attracted to. What usually happens, though, is that boys line up along one wall and the girls the other. They horse around and act goofy but rarely cross the line and ask someone to dance. This is a transition, a rite of passage in American culture. The next year or the year after that, they will begin to cross the line and ask each other to dance. Some will even bring partners to the dance. For now, it is a stepping stone, an opportunity to try out another script.

Hedgepeth and Helmich (1996), as they developed materials for sexuality educators, have noted that young adolescents between the ages of 12 and 14 are dealing with the following developmental issues:

1. They're worried about their bodies.
2. They're engaged in a search for identity, including sexual orientation identity.
3. They are very centered on the self yet influenced by peer attitudes.

4. They intellectually understand that behavior has consequences but don't necessarily think the consequences will happen to them.
5. They're fearful of asking questions of adults that may make them appear uninformed.

Negative Influences

In today's world, children are exposed to sexual content in much more direct ways than their parents' and grandparents' generations. A parent who may be preparing dinner in a kitchen with the evening news on the television may inadvertently be exposing a child to stories of sexual abuse, abduction, and murder. Some children have interacted online with pedophiles, while some of those interested in children get picked up due to FBI sting operations. While the rates of reported cases of child sexual abuse have been declining ("Reports of Child Sexual Abuse," 2001), the raw numbers of children sexually abused in 1997 were estimated at 223,000. Beyond that are the numbers of cases that never make it into the databases of police departments, social service agencies, and schools.

In an attempt to teach children such skills as "Yell no!" and "Reach out to an adult you can trust," some schools began putting sexual abuse prevention programs into place during the 1980s. The thought was that teaching "good touch versus bad touch" would empower children to protect themselves. Those programs along with drug and HIV/AIDS prevention programs often took precedence over time devoted to more positive developmental lessons.

Increasingly, children also spend time online, checking out Web sites, going into chat rooms, and "IM-ing" (instant-messaging) their peers. As a result, some children have found unsolicited pornography attached to their e-mails. There are constant challenges to promoting sexual health in children. It is our position that parents must talk with their children and be aware of the myriad influences on their sexual development.

Intellectual Wellness

Individuals begin to learn about sexuality from the day of birth. Infants and children learn symbolically. They learn about what feels good through direct physical exploration. They learn about what is taboo by the reactions of significant others.

Children continue to grow as they become more verbal and are able to communicate by asking questions and seeking clarification. Development takes shape according to the answers received and the nonverbal messages attached to the information. If children grow up in a household where sexual questions are allowed and teachable moments are capitalized, the natural curiosity about sex is satisfied.

This learning continues through childhood and adolescence. What differs is the sheer quantity of information to which people are exposed and the sources from which it is derived. Infants and young children receive sexual information mostly from parents and other caregivers. By the time of adolescence, sexual information flows in torrents from sources ranging from parents to mass media to the Internet.

Today, more than ever before, many excellent sources of information about sexuality are available—books, recordings, educational television shows, Web sites, and more. Unfortunately, many poor sources of information and negative gender roles also bombard us daily. The ability to process all of this information and make sense of it is aided by our ever-growing intellectual development and rests on a foundation of "askable parents" and a school environment and curriculum that encourage questions and make information readily available.

Development in Adolescence

Adolescence denotes a period of years (roughly between 12 and 18). The major task associated with adolescence is to develop a self-identity (Erikson, 1978). Adolescence can be a time of great excitement and joy as individuals literally move from childhood to adulthood. During adolescence, both the body and the mind change and grow. They outgrow not only their old clothes but often their old ideas as well, and sometimes their old friends, as they struggle to come to grips with who they are and where they are going.

Experts have come to understand that the promotion of good health behaviors at this stage has a critical impact on adult lifestyles (Hatcher & Scarpa, 2002). Consequently, health programs directed at teens often focus on adolescent risk-taking behaviors with particular attention to tobacco and alcohol use, exercise and nutrition, sleep, accident reduction, and sexuality. Set up within the Centers for Disease Control (CDC), the Youth Risk Behavior Surveillance System has surveyed adolescents across the United States for the risk-taking behaviors felt to contribute to social problems, death, and disability (CDC, 2003). Its rich database has provided information from representative samples taken between 1991 and 2001 from students sampled from 50 states along with more intensive analysis of urban youth (CDC, 2003). Unfortunately, those surveys, discussed later, ask only eight questions about sexual behavior, with the questions having a strong focus on participation in sexual intercourse related to alcohol, condom use, and frequency within a designated time frame (CDC, 2003).

Puberty is the time of myriad physiological events that characterize adolescence. It is a time of profound physiological change as the body matures and becomes "reproductively ready" with fully adult genitalia, a reproductive system, and hormones coursing through the bloodstream, sending messages to the brain of arriving sexually.

Reproductive readiness Pubertal development resulting in full growth of genitalia and onset of fertility

Psychosocial readiness for sexual activity with another person takes a while to catch up to **reproductive readiness.** Adolescents become caught in a state of confusion as the body sends the mind messages about sex that the adolescent may not be ready to handle psychosocially.

The media likes to exploit this confusion and report about the problems and the failures associated with adolescence. We hear about teenage drug and alcohol misuse, HIV disease, teen pregnancy, satanic cults, and defiant behavior. Movies glorify adolescent rebelliousness and juvenile delinquency. In contrast, however, many teenagers navigate adolescence in a healthy, productive way with both peer and adult support systems providing guidance.

Michael Carrera, a respected adolescent sexuality expert, works to help teenagers emerge from adolescence as young adults who are strong, competent, and whole. Along with the Children's Aid Society, Carrera (2003) has developed a model for working with youth that has had demonstrable positive results on adolescent health. His program includes getting participants involved with work and money management, educational support that includes tutoring and test preparation designed to move students toward college, a family life/sex education program, involvement in the arts, and participation and development of lifetime individual sports. Simultaneously, students have access to comprehensive medical care including reproductive health care and mental health counseling. Students in his program, some 5,000 over 19 years, have shown lower pregnancy rates, delayed onset of intercourse, better sexual health behaviors, and higher graduation rates.

Physical, Psychological, and Social Wellness

Child and adolescent health is positively impacted by participation in exercise and organized sports. Historically, organized sports were seen as important for boys' development, yet of little interest to most girls. Title IX of the 1972 Education Amendments Act outlawed discrimination in secondary and postsecondary educational institutions receiving federal funding. Its impact on reducing gender discrimination in sports has been significant.

In 1971, 1 in 27 girls participated in high school sports compared to 1 in 2 boys. By 2001, the ratio for girls was almost the same as for boys, with 1 in 2.5 girls participating compared to the 1 in 2 ratio for boys (Lopiano, 2001). Participation in sports helps teens learn about teamwork, goal setting, and the pursuit of excellence. Physical activity can enhance self-esteem and improve body image. Research has also shown that teenage female athletes are less likely to get pregnant, delay their first sexual intercourse, and report that they had not had sexual intercourse compared to nonathletes (Lopiano, 2001).

Figure 5.3 highlights the physiological changes associated with puberty. In general, these can be grouped into changes associated with primary and secondary sex characteristics.

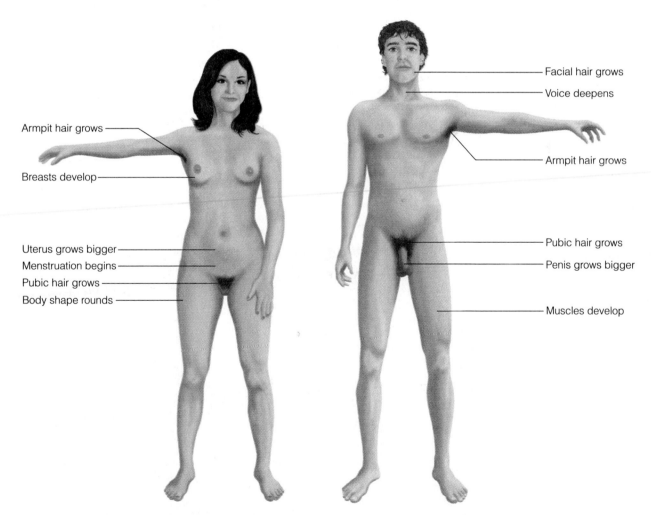

Armpit hair grows

Breasts develop

Uterus grows bigger

Menstruation begins

Pubic hair grows

Body shape rounds

Facial hair grows

Voice deepens

Armpit hair grows

Pubic hair grows

Penis grows bigger

Muscles develop

Figure 5.3 *Changes Associated with Puberty*

Primary Sex Characteristics

Primary sex characteristics
Growth of the sex organs

Primary sex characteristics are associated with the full growth and development of the sex organs. A boy's penis and testicles grow and reach full adult size by the end of puberty. The testes begin to produce sperm and androgens, and first ejaculation signals the onset of reproductive readiness.

In girls, the major internal (vagina, ovaries, uterus, and fallopian tubes) and external (labia, mons, clitoris) sexual structures reach maturity. First menstruation is the sign that puberty has arrived.

Secondary Sex Characteristics

Secondary sex characteristics Nongenital changes associated with puberty; include growth of pubic, facial, and underarm hair, breast development, increases in height and weight

Secondary sex characteristics are nongenital changes associated with puberty. Boys and girls both experience a growth spurt and begin to attain their subsequent adult height. They both grow pubic, underarm, and body hair. Although boys characteristically grow significantly more facial hair than girls do, this generally represents a continuum with a range of possibilities for boys and girls, from relatively hairless to very hairy.

Gonads The primary endocrine glands in men (testes) and women (ovaries) that influence sexuality

Body contours begin to develop. Girls naturally deposit more fat on their hips and breasts than boys do, but, as with facial and body hair, there is a wide continuum of growth possibilities for both boys and girls. The voice box in boys enlarges, creating a deeper, more resonating sound. The transition period involved in this change causes a squeaky quality to boys' voices.

Androgens A group of naturally occurring steroid hormones produced by both men and women

By the end of puberty, the body has reached a stage of reproductive readiness with two major components: mature reproductive anatomy and hormonally influenced sexual desire. The sex organs are fully developed and capable of procreating as well as recreating. Not only are parts such as the penis and vagina fully mature and capable of responding to sexual desire, but ovaries and testes are also fully able to produce viable ova and sperm, respectively. This is often the time when a young girl discovers that her clitoris is capable of providing sexual pleasure.

Testosterone The most notable androgen, recognized for fueling sexual desire and aggressiveness in males

In nature's eyes, humans are able and ready to propagate the species. Nature gives a boost in that our **gonads** (testes and ovaries), which have long been silent, now begin to produce hormones that stimulate sexual desire. **Androgens,** primarily **testosterone,** stimulate sexual receptor centers in the brain, which trigger feelings of

Shaving is an exciting rite of passage for teens.

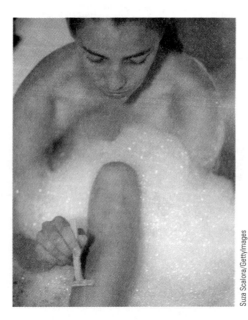

sexual desire. All of the cold showers in the world will not quell this sexual desire because, to a certain extent, it is fueled by hormones circulating in the bloodstream.

Most books and support materials for parents, preadolescents, and adolescents will reinforce the concept that maturation proceeds at its own unique pace, and barring evidence of medical problems, children will indeed grow into healthy adults. Pediatricians, many of whom have expanded their practices to address the health care needs of infants, children, and adolescents, need to be sensitive to physical growth along with the other aspects of sexual development. Family practitioners, nurse practitioners, physician's assistants, nurses, and other professionals as well need to be educated and comfortable with the realities of teen health to best meet the health needs of their patients. Ideally, information about the physical body should be able to be discussed along with concerns about sexual orientation, sexual decision making, protection from infection and unintended pregnancy, and so forth. To facilitate such conversations, however, the provider must be comfortable with such topics and able to create a safe space to talk with the teen patient.

In the physical realm, the Sexual Maturity Rating scale, sometimes referred to as the Tanner Scale (American Nurses Association, 1999), can be used to measure levels of physical maturity. The scale, as represented in Table 5.1, has five stages that allow for charting growth of pubic hair, breast development, and

Table 5.1 Sexual Maturity Rating Scale for Girls and Boys

Female		SMR	Male		
Breast	**Pubic Hair**		**Testes and Scrotum**	**Penis**	**Pubic Hair**
No development	No pubic hair	1	Testicular volume: <1.5 ml	Childlike	None
Breast bud, areola widens	Long, slightly pigmented, straight hair along labia	2	Testicular volume: 1.6–6 ml; scrotum: reddened, thinner, larger	No change	Light, downy hair laterally
Breast larger, more elevation. Extends beyond areolar parameter.	Increased in quantity, darker, more curly and coarser; present in typical female triangle	3	Testicular volume: 6–12 ml; scrotum: great enlargement	Increased length	Extended across pubis
Breast larger and more elevation. Areola and papilla form a mound projecting from the breast contour.	Hair more dense, curled, and adult in distribution but in a smaller quantity	4	Testicular volume: 12–20 ml; scrotum: further enlargement and darkening	Increased length and circumference	More abundant with curling
Breast adult appearance. Areola and breast in same plane, with papilla projecting above areola.	Abundant, adult-type pattern; hair extends to medial aspect of thigh.	5	Testicular volume: >20 ml; scrotum: adult appearance	Adult appearance	Adult quantity and distribution with hair present on inner thighs

Source: American Nurses Association (1999).

size and color of the penis and scrotum. Because the scale has no ages connected to it, health practitioners cannot make assumptions based on age, sex, or racial and ethnic background. Furthermore, a thorough physical exam is required which may or may not occur; some teens resist the physical inspection needed.

Ironically, sexuality educators have shared anecdotal reports with us of teens and young adults increasingly shaving their pubic hair. The motivation for such shaving has been explained, especially for young females, as a response to the trend for small underwear. Just as females would shave so that pubic hair would not show when wearing a bathing suit, shaving is seen as necessary when wearing bikini and thong underwear. Another explanation for both male and female shaving is connected to attitudes toward oral sex, with the presence of pubic hair thought to be "dirty." Consequently, examining teens relative to pubic hair growth may become less important for assessing their maturation.

Adolescence has a profound impact on sexuality for the rest of our lives. Often our body image and initial impressions about our masculinity and femininity that were formed at this time color how we view ourselves for the rest of our lives. Old labels and images such as "I'm not a good dancer" or "I'm shy" or "I'm not very good-looking" influence our self-concept and stay with us for years to come.

Body Image Issues

Both boys and girls at some point during the preteen and teen years become obsessed with physical appearance. So many changes are happening to the body, and peer comparisons become constant. Standing out for being "too fat" or "too short" or "too pimply" can leave children feeling self-conscious and sometimes the brunt of other's teasing.

Research has indicated that teens are becoming increasingly overweight, partly due to lack of exercise as well as increased consumption of high-calorie foods. Although states mandate that students have regular physical education classes, other programs often interfere with regular, daily exercise. There are barriers to participation in organized sports such as costs, lack of transportation, competing time commitments, competitive pressures, and lack of facilities (American Psychological Association, 2002). Early in 2003, a family in New York City attempted to sue McDonald's for contributing to the gross obesity of their children. The case was thrown out of court, but public articles began to appear in newspapers and pieces on television about the amounts of "junk" and fast food consumed by adolescents. The federal government in 2003 convened professionals to address the rise in obesity overall, with plans to address childhood and adolescent diet and exercise patterns. And the food industry, in response, has increased its efforts to improve the nutritional quality of its foods, which will entail reducing the fat, sugar, and salt content.

Another public health concern has been the growing numbers of teens who get depressed because of their appearance. The depression with looks can result in disordered eating, with an unrealistic expectation of normal body weight. The majority of teens with eating disorders are female, although boys are becoming vulnerable to body pressures as well (American Psychological Association, 2002).

Adolescent Sexual Behavior

What has improved significantly in recent years has been the recognition that asking teens "what behaviors they engage in" is necessary to understanding their needs and how to provide for better health. Close examination of various survey instruments will highlight a range of questions, some more specific than others.

For example, the National Survey of Adolescent Males surveyed males about the variety of genital experiences they had with females beyond sexual intercourse (Gates & Sonenstein, 2000). The importance of using clear language was evident in the phrasing of questions. For example, males were asked to answer yes or no to whether "a female touched your penis until you ejaculated or 'came.'" The Youth Risk Behavior Survey, in contrast, asks participants only about sexual intercourse (CDC, 2003). The questions focus on partner frequency, use of condoms and other forms of birth control, and alcohol and drug use, yet they cannot provide the depth of information needed to understand youth sexual behavior. The Henry J. Kaiser Family Foundation (Henry J. Kaiser Family Foundation, Hoff, Greene, & Davis, 2003) issued a report on teen sexual activity that focused on sexual intercourse, partners and relationships, abstinence, contraceptive use, pregnancy and sexually transmitted diseases, sex and substance abuse, and sexual pressure and dating violence.

Overall, different groups have studied selected samples of adolescents and various aspects of their adolescent sexual behavior. A full understanding is often limited by access to a broad group of subjects, along with limitations on what types of questions get asked. The government will more often fund studies related to teen pregnancy and sexually transmitted diseases. Data on masturbation, oral sexual behaviors, and anal sexual behaviors are more limited; some types of questions are deemed too sensitive to ask youth (A. Levine, personal communication, October 2003).

Masturbation   Conscious, erotic self-stimulation is thought to be among the most common expressions of adolescent sexual behavior, particularly for males. Kinsey and his associates discovered that the rate of masturbation was different for boys and girls (Kinsey, Pomeroy, & Martin, 1948). Among boys in that early study, the level of masturbation increased from 21 percent of 12-year-old boys to 82 percent of 15-year-old boys. Among girls, the level of masturbation increased from 12 percent of 12-year-old girls to 20 percent of 15-year-old girls. By the end of adolescence, more than 90 percent of the boys and about 35 percent of the girls had masturbated.

Other studies since Kinsey have shown that the level of masturbation for boys across adolescence is relatively unchanged, but the rate among girls has risen. By the time they reach the end of adolescence, approximately 75 percent of all girls reported having masturbated (Sorenson, 1983; Sarrel & Sarrel, 1984). The gender differences have been supported in later research, with 33 percent of girls by age 15 reporting that they had masturbated, compared to 58 percent of boys at that age (Baldwin & Baldwin, 1997).

Sexual Intercourse   Despite public health messages and the goals of the "abstinence until marriage" education efforts, adolescents do engage in sexual intercourse. National headlines were made, however, when the Henry J. Kaiser Foundation released its report in 2003 showing a decline in the rates of high school students grades 9 through 12 who had had intercourse over the past decade. In 1991, the rate was 54 percent compared to 46 percent in 2001 (Kaiser Family Foundation et al., 2003). Of concern to health providers and educators was the accompanying finding that for those who reported being sexually active, there was an increase in the use of condoms; substantial numbers of teen girls still became pregnant, with an estimated 4 million teens getting a sexually transmitted infection each year nonetheless.

As Laumann, Gagnon, Michael, and Michaels (1994) point out from the National Social Health and Life Survey (NSHLS), first sexual intercourse, especially for women, has traditionally been a symbol for loss of innocence, transition to adulthood, and assumption of responsibility for procreation for the next genera-

What Is Right for You?

It is easy to avoid openly examining our beliefs and values concerning sexual activity. Often our sexual behavior is dictated by the moment, not by our values and rational decisions. The goal of this activity is to help you clarify the sexual behavior that is comfortable and acceptable for you and to identify a plan for making sure you can stick to your sexual values.

Take a few minutes to really examine what you believe and respond to the following questions honestly and openly. You do not need to share this with anyone; however, you might enjoy discussing it with a close friend.

What would be some good reasons or advantages for you to choose to have premarital sex? (If you are married, substitute *extramarital* for *premarital* in each question.) *Example:* "It's fun."

What would be some good reasons or disadvantages for you to choose not to have premarital sex? *Example:* "I could get hurt."

What are some guidelines you need to follow if you choose to have premarital sex? *Example:* "Be honest with my partner about my motives for having sex."

What are some guidelines you need to follow if you choose not to have premarital sex? *Example:* "Don't drink too much."

List the reasons you might choose to have premarital sex in two columns, reasons that would make you feel guilty versus guilt-free reasons.

How can you tell when a premarital sexual relationship becomes unhealthy or harmful to yourself?

tion. The popular belief about the widespread level of premarital sexual intercourse is that this is a fairly recent phenomenon that is linked to social decay, a decrease in family values and the like. As Laumann et al. demonstrated, the drop in average age of first intercourse, and the increased level of adolescent sexual intercourse, has been at a fairly steady level for decades. Various studies have shown a general trend related to a decline in the average age of first intercourse and an increase in the number of sexual partners of adolescents.

By age 19, 20 percent of the girls and 45 percent of the boys in the Kinsey study had had intercourse. Thirty years later, Sorenson (1983) reported a 25 percent increase (from 20 to 45 percent) in the percentage of female adolescents having intercourse and a 14 percent increase (45 to 59 percent) among males. Using data from 1971 and 1976, Zelnick, Kanter, and Ford (1981) confirmed Sorenson's findings and added that the increases for whites was two times greater than for blacks.

Nearly another 10 years later, Forrest and Singh (1990) and Sonenstein, Pleck, and Hu (1989) reported another increase in the level of adolescent intercourse. Citing data from the National Study of Family Growth, Forrest and Singh demonstrated that the proportion of 15- to 19-year-old females having intercourse rose steadily in the 1970s and 1980s. In 1970, 28 percent of white and 45 percent of nonwhite girls were nonvirgins. By 1988, 52 percent of white and 65 percent of nonwhite girls had experienced sexual intercourse. By 1988, 25 percent of all 15-year-olds and 75 percent of all 19-year-old girls had experienced intercourse (Forrest & Singh, 1990).

The National Survey of Adolescent Males (NSAM) reported that approximately 30 percent of its 15-year-old subjects had experienced intercourse. By age 19, 86 percent of all the subjects had lost their virginity (Laumann et al., 1994).

The Youth Risk Behavior Survey. The Youth Risk Behavior Survey (YRBS) has yielded a large database for studying adolescent behavior. Federal funding and support have been instrumental to this research effort; the typical sexuality researcher seldom can get access to so many diverse students across the United States. Although the latest survey was administered in 2003, the analysis of data has not been published.

The survey instrument examines sexual activity comparing results by sex, race, age, and ethnicity. The data become invaluable to those determining policy to promote the sexual health of adolescents. Unfortunately, the section of the survey related to sexual behavior is limited to eight questions related to sexual intercourse (CDC, 2003). Discussion of oral and anal behaviors, along with greater sensitivity to the behaviors, and gay, lesbian, and bisexual youth are missing. The findings are further limited in that only students who attend high schools are surveyed.

The findings reported for 2001 showed that 46 percent of high school students had experienced sexual intercourse, 14 percent had had four or more sex partners, and 42 percent of sexually active high school students had not used a condom at the time of their last intercourse (CDC, 2003).

Analysis of 10 years of YRBS data, as presented in Table 5.2, reveals patterns among the youth surveyed. The prevalence of sexual experience, as defined by having had sexual intercourse, decreased 16 percent among high school students. The prevalence of multiple sex partners decreased 24 percent, yet the overall prevalence of current sexual activity did not change. Furthermore, the prevalence of alcohol or drug use before the last act of sexual intercourse among those defining themselves as sexually active increased 18 percent (CDC, 2003).

Number of Partners The information gathered from the NSHLS provided three interesting findings related to the number of sex partners adolescents have by age 18:

- As the average age for the onset of intercourse drops, the average number of teenage partners increases.
- Females from the oldest age cohorts had fewer partners before age 18 than women from the youngest cohorts.
- Females are catching up to males.

Concerning the first point, as teens are beginning to have sex at a younger age, they also are experiencing more partners. This finding is in contrast with teens over 50 years ago. At that time, teens who experienced first intercourse early (before 18 years of age) had fewer partners because they tended to marry their first sex partner. Often their first teenage encounter was as man and wife. Teens today rarely have first intercourse on their wedding night. Most of them have already had intercourse prior to this event (Laumann et al., 1994).

Laumann and colleagues also found differences among the age cohorts regarding the number of partners before age 18. The females from earlier generations (born between 1933 and 1942) were much less likely to have had five or more partners by age 18 than the youngest cohort (born between 1963 and 1967). This relates to the last finding—that females are catching up to males in terms of overall number of sexual partners. The number of sex partners for males and females by age 18 is less variable for the youngest cohorts than for the oldest.

The Youth Risk Behavior Survey data for 2001 found that 11.4 percent of females and 17.2 percent of males had had more than four sex partners during their lifetime. When grade in school is factored in, 9th graders reported 9.6 percent compared to 12th graders reporting 21.6 percent of students having had more than four partners. Over the 10-year period during which YRSB data have been reported, the percentage of students having more than four partners has gone down from 18.7 to 14.2 percent, a "trend" viewed positively by public health officials (CDC, 2000).

Table 5.2 Percentage of High School Students Who Reported Sexual Risk Behaviors, by Sex, Grade, Race/Ethnicity, and Survey Year

Characteristic	Ever Had Sexual Intercourse		≥4 Sex Partners During Lifetime		Currently Sexually Active†		Condom Use During Last Sexual Intercourse§		Alcohol Drug Use Before Last Sexual Intercourse§	
	%	(95% CI*)	%	(95% CI)	%	(95% CI)	%	(95% CI)	%	(95% CI)
Sex										
Female										
1991	50.8	(±4.0)	13.8	(±1.8)	38.2	(±3.4)	38.0	(±4.3)	16.8	(±3.2)
1993	50.2	(±2.5)	15.0	(±1.9)	37.5	(±1.8)	46.0	(±2.8)	16.6	(±2.2)
1995	52.1	(±5.0)	14.4	(±3.5)	40.4	(±4.2)	48.6	(±5.2)	16.8	(±3.0)
1997	47.7	(±3.7)	14.1	(±2.0)	36.5	(±2.7)	50.8	(±3.0)	18.5	(±3.0)
1999	47.7	(±4.1)	13.1	(±2.2)	36.3	(±4.1)	50.7	(±5.8)	18.6	(±3.4)
2001	42.9	(±2.8)¶	11.4	(±1.5)	33.4	(±2.5)	51.3	(±3.4)¶**	20.7	(±2.7)
Male										
1991	57.4	(±4.1)	23.4	(±3.0)	36.8	(±3.4)	54.5	(±3.8)	26.3	(±3.3)
1993	55.6	(±3.5)	22.3	(±2.7)	37.5	(±3.0)	59.2	(±3.8)	25.7	(±3.0)
1995	54.0	(±4.7)	20.9	(±2.6)	35.5	(±3.5)	60.5	(±4.3)	32.8	(±4.1)
1997	48.8	(±3.4)	17.6	(±1.5)	33.4	(±2.6)	62.5	(±2.8)	30.5	(±2.8)
1999	52.2	(±4.0)	19.3	(±3.6)	36.2	(±3.9)	65.5	(±4.3)	31.2	(±4.0)
2001	48.5	(±2.7)¶	17.2	(±1.6)¶	33.4	(±2.3)	65.1	(±2.7)¶	30.9	(±2.9)¶
Grade										
9										
1991	39.0	(±5.0)	12.5	(±2.9)	22.4	(±3.9)	53.3	(±6.2)	20.9	(±6.9)
1993	37.7	(±4.2)	10.9	(±2.0)	24.8	(±3.2)	61.6	(±5.7)	22.4	(±3.9)
1995	36.9	(±5.9)	12.9	(±3.0)	23.6	(±4.0)	62.9	(±5.5)	29.7	(±5.7)
1997	38.0	(±3.8)	12.2	(±2.5)	24.2	(±3.3)	58.8	(±5.6)	33.2	(±8.3)
1999	38.6	(±6.1)	11.8	(±2.3)	26.6	(±5.7)	66.6	(±7.8)	25.6	(±5.2)
2001	34.4	(±3.6)	9.6	(±1.6)	22.7	(±3.1)	67.5	(±3.3)¶	24.0	(±4.4)**
10										
1991	48.2	(±5.7)	15.1	(±2.8)	33.2	(±4.6)	46.3	(±4.7)	22.3	(±4.9)
1993	46.1	(±3.6)	15.9	(±2.0)	30.1	(±3.0)	54.7	(±4.5)	24.2	(±4.2)
1995	48.0	(±5.1)	15.6	(±2.0)	33.7	(±3.1)	59.7	(±4.6)	28.6	(±5.9)
1997	42.5	(±4.3)	13.8	(±2.7)	29.2	(±2.9)	58.9	(±3.6)	22.9	(±3.3)
1999	46.8	(±5.6)	15.6	(±5.0)	33.0	(±5.2)	62.6	(±6.1)	23.1	(±4.2)
2001	40.8	(±3.0)¶	12.6	(±1.8)	29.7	(±2.9)	60.1	(±4.5)¶**	27.7	(±3.1)
11										
1991	62.4	(±3.2)	22.1	(±3.6)	43.3	(±3.6)	48.7	(±5.8)	22.2	(±3.5)
1993	57.5	(±3.5)	19.9	(±3.1)	40.0	(±3.6)	55.3	(±3.0)	22.0	(±2.6)
1995	58.6	(±5.0)	19.0	(±3.7)	42.4	(±4.4)	52.3	(±6.2)	24.3	(±3.1)
1997	49.7	(±5.2)	16.7	(±2.9)	37.8	(±4.8)	60.1	(±5.2)	23.1	(±4.1)
1999	52.5	(±3.8)	17.3	(±4.1)	37.5	(±3.4)	59.2	(±4.8)	28.6	(±5.8)
2001	51.9	(±2.9)¶**	15.2	(±1.5)¶	38.1	(±2.6)	58.9	(±4.0)¶	24.7	(±2.9)¶
12										
1991	66.7	(±4.4)	25.0	(±4.0)	50.6	(±4.5)	41.4	(±3.6)	20.8	(±3.7)
1993	68.3	(±4.6)	27.0	(±3.6)	53.0	(±3.9)	46.5	(±4.0)	19.1	(±3.3)
1995	66.4	(±4.0)	22.9	(±3.5)	49.7	(±3.9)	49.5	(±4.4)	20.3	(±3.6)
1997	60.9	(±6.5)	20.6	(±3.5)	46.0	(±5.0)	52.4	(±3.5)	23.3	(±1.8)
1999	64.9	(±4.9)	20.6	(±2.8)	50.6	(±5.1)	47.9	(±5.7)	22.0	(±3.8)
2001	60.5	(±4.0)¶	21.6	(±2.4)¶	47.9	(±4.0)	49.3	(±3.1)¶**	25.4	(±2.6)¶

Table 5.2 *(continued)*

Characteristic	Ever Had Sexual Intercourse		≥4 Sex Partners During Lifetime		Currently Sexually Active†		Condom Use During Last Sexual Intercourse§		Alcohol Drug Use Before Last Sexual Intercourse§	
	%	(95% CI*)	%	(95% CI)	%	(95% CI)	%	(95% CI)	%	(95% CI)
Race/Ethnicity††										
Black										
1991	81.4	(±3.2)	43.1	(±3.5)	59.3	(±3.8)	48.0	(±3.8)	13.7	(±2.9)
1993	79.7	(±3.2)	42.7	(±3.8)	59.1	(±4.4)	56.5	(±3.8)	12.2	(±3.5)
1995	73.4	(±4.5)	35.6	(±4.4)	54.2	(±4.7)	66.1	(±4.8)	19.2	(±4.6)
1997	72.6	(±2.8)	38.5	(±3.6)	53.6	(±3.2)	64.0	(±2.8)	18.1	(±3.1)
1999	71.2	(±8.2)	34.4	(±10.3)	53.0	(±8.9)	70.0	(±5.4)	18.1	(±7.9)
2001	60.8	(±6.6)¶	26.6	(±3.7)¶	45.6	(±5.4)¶	67.1	(±3.5)¶**	17.8	(±2.6)¶
Hispanic										
1991	53.1	(±3.5)	16.8	(±2.6)	37.0	(±3.6)	37.4	(±6.2)	17.8	(±4.2)
1993	56.0	(±4.1)	18.6	(±3.1)	39.4	(±3.7)	46.1	(±4.4)	18.2	(±4.8)
1995	57.6	(±8.6)	17.6	(±3.7)	39.3	(±7.1)	44.4	(±11.1)	24.9	(±5.2)
1997	52.2	(±3.6)	15.5	(±2.4)	35.4	(±3.9)	48.3	(±5.6)	25.3	(±5.3)
1999	54.1	(±4.8)	16.6	(±3.6)	36.3	(±4.0)	55.2	(±6.8)	22.5	(±4.0)
2001	48.4	(±4.5)	14.9	(±1.7)	35.9	(±3.2)	53.5	(±5.1)	24.1	(±2.8)¶
White										
1991	50.0	(±3.2)	14.7	(±1.8)	33.9	(±2.8)	46.5	(±4.6)	25.3	(±3.7)
1993	48.4	(±2.8)	14.3	(±2.1)	34.0	(±2.1)	52.3	(±3.9)	24.4	(±2.7)
1995	48.9	(±5.0)	14.2	(±2.4)	34.8	(±3.9)	52.5	(±4.0)	26.6	(±3.1)
1997	43.6	(±4.2)	11.6	(±1.5)	32.0	(±3.1)	55.8	(±2.0)	26.0	(±2.5)
1999	45.1	(±3.9)	12.4	(±2.1)	33.0	(±3.3)	55.0	(±5.1)	27.4	(±4.8)
2001	43.2	(±2.5)¶	12.0	(±1.4)¶	31.3	(±2.2)	56.8	(±3.0)¶	27.8	(±2.2)
Total										
1991	**54.1**	**(±3.5)**	**18.7**	**(±2.1)**	**37.4**	**(±3.1)**	**46.2**	**(±3.3)**	**21.6**	**(±2.9)**
1993	**53.0**	**(±2.7)**	**18.7**	**(±2.0)**	**37.5**	**(±2.1)**	**52.8**	**(±2.7)**	**21.3**	**(±2.0)**
1995	**53.1**	**(±4.5)**	**17.8**	**(±2.6)**	**37.9**	**(±3.4)**	**54.4**	**(±3.5)**	**24.8**	**(±2.8)**
1997	**48.4**	**(±3.1)**	**16.0**	**(±1.4)**	**34.8**	**(±2.2)**	**56.8**	**(±1.6)**	**24.7**	**(±1.8)**
1999	**49.9**	**(±3.7)**	**16.2**	**(±2.6)**	**36.3**	**(±3.5)**	**58.0**	**(±4.2)**	**24.8**	**(±3.0)**
2001	**45.6**	**(±2.3)¶**	**14.2**	**(±1.2)**	**33.4**	**(±2.0)**	**57.9**	**(±2.2)¶****	**25.6**	**(±1.7)¶**

* Confidence interval

† Sexual intercourse during the 3 months preceding the survey

§ Among students who are currently sexually active

¶ Significant linear effect ($p < .05$)

** Significant quadratic effect ($p < .05$)

†† Numbers of students in racial/ethnic groups other than white, black, or Hispanic were too small for meaningful analysis.

Source: Centers for Disease Control [Online]. Available: www.cdc.gov/mmwr/preview/mmwrhtml/mm5138a2.htm.

Laumann et al. examined what motivated men and women to initiate first intercourse. Table 5.3 summarizes the reasons for first intercourse by sex. For those who wanted to engage in sexual intercourse, affection for one's partner was ranked first among women and second among men, while curiosity and readiness for sex were ranked first for men and second for women. For those who had not wanted to engage in sexual intercourse but were not forced, affection for one's partner was ranked first for women followed closely by peer pressure and curiosity/readiness for sex. Males reported their reasons as curiosity/readiness for sex first, followed by peer pressure. Contrary to popular belief, only a small percentage of males and females (4 percent and 3 percent, respectively) reported peer pressure as the underlying motivation for first intercourse.

Table 5.3 Reasons for Having First Intercourse by Sex

Attributed reasons	Wanted First Intercourse (%)		Not Wanted but Not Forced (%)	
	Men	Women	Men	Women
Affection for partner	24.9	47.5	9.9	38.5
Peer pressure	4.2	3.3	28.6	24.6
Curiosity/readiness for sex	50.6	24.3	50.5	24.9
Pregnancy	0.5	0.6	0.0	0.0
Physical pleasure	12.2	2.8	6.6	2.1
Under the influence of alcohol or drugs	0.7	0.3	3.3	7.2
Wedding night	6.9	21.1	1.1	2.7

Source: E. O. Laumann et al., *The Social Organization of Sexuality: Sexual Practices in the United States,* © 1994, University of Chicago Press. Reprinted with permission.

Data from the National Survey for Family Growth (NSFG), an ongoing study of women's and family health, reported a higher incidence of involuntary first intercourse. According to the study, approximately 8 percent of the 53,793 females ages 15 to 44 reported that their first intercourse was forced (categorized as either "rape" or "not voluntary") (Abma, Chandra, Mosher, Peterson, & Puccini, 1997).

First Sex Among Lesbian/Gay Youth Sexual behavior patterns in gay and lesbian youth are more complex because of the added dimension of coming to terms with a sexual identity that is different from their heterosexual peers. Despite increased attention to gay and lesbian issues in the media, widespread acceptance still seems problematic for mainstream America. Sexual behavior seems to be the fourth step in a five-step coming-out process that involves these stages:

1. Fear and suspicion that one's sexual desires and attraction are different (although still not clearly defined)
2. Labeling of those feelings as homoerotic (sexual feelings for someone of the same sex)
3. Defining oneself as gay or lesbian
4. Having one's first gay love affair
5. Becoming involved in the gay or lesbian subculture (Herdt & Boxer, 1992; Troiden, 1988)

Having sexual feelings for someone of the same sex (homoerotic feelings) almost always precedes sexual activity by several years among gay and lesbian people. Gay and lesbian youth today recognize feelings for same-sex partners and act on them earlier than their peers of 20 years ago (Savin-Williams & Rodriguez, 1993).

Oral Sex The popular media created quite a stir in 2002 when reports started circulating that teenagers were engaging in oral sex with a very casual attitude. During the Monica Lewinsky scandal, President Bill Clinton testified before a congressional committee, "I did not have sex with that woman." He did admit, however, to having experienced oral sex. It is not known just how influential that statement became, yet increasingly reports surface of boys in particular getting "blow jobs" from girls with whom they're not particularly involved. The Henry J.

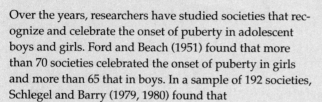

Other Cultures, Other Ways

Over the years, researchers have studied societies that recognize and celebrate the onset of puberty in adolescent boys and girls. Ford and Beach (1951) found that more than 70 societies celebrated the onset of puberty in girls and more than 65 that in boys. In a sample of 192 societies, Schlegel and Barry (1979, 1980) found that

80 had no rites of passage,
17 had ceremonies for boys only,
39 had rites for girls only, and
46 had ceremonies for both sexes.

Larger societies, with intensive agricultural and manufacturing bases, and those with more complex forms of social organizations, tended not to have initiation rites.

Of the societies celebrating puberty in girls, these celebrations usually coincide with the onset of first menses and are directly related to the sexual significance of menstruation. Schlegel and Barry found that first menses signified fertility and the tribe's continued existence.

These ceremonies often included seclusion of the young women, prohibiting any contact with men. In many instances, the ceremonies included instruction from older women in matters pertaining to sex and marriage. In some cultures, the young women were "deflowered" or subjected to piercing, tattooing, or genital adornment or mutilation. Frequently, the occasion was also marked by a feast or celebration.

Schlegel and Barry found that segregation from males at this time is usually based on avoiding contact with menstrual flow, which is feared because of its supposed ability to weaken a hunter's abilities or contaminate the tribe's meat sources.

For boys, unlike with girls' first menses, no clear demarcation indicates that puberty has begun. Generally, boys are given the rites when evidence is sufficient (usually secondary sex characteristics) that they have reached puberty. Boys' ceremonies are similar to girls' in that they

usually include some form of seclusion, instruction, and ritualistic physical sacrifice (often circumcision).

The Sexual Culture of Mangaia

In the 1950s, anthropologist Donald Marshall studied the sexual attitudes and activities of the people of Mangaia, the southernmost island in the Polynesian Cook chain. There, he found, the people were exposed to sexuality from early childhood. They listened to folk stories that included detailed accounts of sex acts and sexual anatomy, and they watched sensual ritual dances.

As adolescents, males underwent *superincision*, a surgical procedure in which the tissue at the end of the penis was cut and folded back, which exposed the glans. They were taught how to stimulate a woman's genitals and breasts with the mouth, how to bring female partners to orgasm, and how to control the timing of ejaculation. Mangaian girls were taught to be responsive and to participate actively during sexual activity.

In a practice called "night-crawling," a young male would sneak into the home of a young woman with the intent to have sexual intercourse. Because most homes had a single sleeping area, this act tended to be more public than private, though the other family members feigned sleep. The parents approved of night-crawling and listened for their daughter's laughter—a sign that she was happy with her partner. The parents encouraged their children to have more than one sexual partner before marriage, to find the most sexually compatible mate.

After marriage, couples in Mangaia continued to engage in sex more often than most Western countries. The emphasis, though, shifted from the number of orgasms during a single session to a goal of copulation every night. Throughout life, the emphasis for males and females alike was on pleasing the partner (Marshall, 1971).

Kaiser Family Foundation (2003), along with *Seventeen* magazine, reports that 23 percent of students in grades 7 through 12 have had oral sex. By 11th and 12th grades, that number increased to 42 percent (Billhartz, 2003). Anecdotally, teachers and counselors who talk with teens are learning that oral sex is "not sex." Probing further, the reports of casual oral sex seem more commonly to involve girls performing fellatio than boys performing cunnilingus.

Patterns in oral sexual behavior among adolescents have mimicked the changes of adults in the United States. In general, changes in cultural acceptance of nongenital sexual behavior have led to increasing levels of all forms of oral sex among adults (Wilson & Medora, 1999). This pattern holds true for adolescents. Between 40 and 50 percent of all teenagers have engaged in oral sex by the time they finish puberty (Young, 1986; Newman & Udry, 1988).

Cultural Attitudes About Adolescent Sexuality

How does U.S. society view adolescent sexuality? It seems to view adolescent sexual behavior in general, and intercourse in particular, as a "problem" that will lead to negative outcomes (such as unintended pregnancy, sexually transmitted diseases including HIV, and sexual abuse, among others). A surprising finding of the NHSLS study was that, even though increasing numbers of study subjects reported engaging in intercourse by age 18 and having more partners, almost 80 percent of the respondents still think that teen sex is always or almost always wrong. These views are inconsistent with their own behavior. No wonder adolescents get mixed messages about sex!

Many other cultures view this matter entirely differently and celebrate this time in a young person's sexual life. Indeed, in some Pacific Island cultures, adolescent sexual behavior is encouraged, not merely tolerated. This is not to say that these cultures advocate promiscuity. Most have rules pertaining to adolescent sex.

The United States has a conservative sexual history. American culture evolved from devoutly religious, puritanical ancestors who escaped persecution for their views in Europe by coming to this country. The American patriarchal culture emphasized the family and historically has viewed sex as something that occurs within the context of a marriage, with the primary function being procreation. A strong history, institutionalized formally in law and enforced informally through cultural taboos and parenting styles, perpetuated this view. The United States is still a country where sex education is not universally taught in every school. Even when it is, it is mostly a course in reproductive anatomy (Forrest & Silverman, 1989). In some states, nonprocreative sexual acts, including oral sex and anal intercourse between consenting adults (whether heterosexual or homosexual), is considered sodomy and is illegal.

Besides having a moral tradition that prohibits adolescent sexual education and experimentation, U.S. culture, like that of many industrialized societies, prolongs adolescent and young adult dependency. To succeed, adolescents, in most cases, need to further their education. For most of them, this means remaining indebted to their parents and pursuing additional training and education while either living at home or remaining financially obligated to their parents. In a sense, what this does is delay the transition from childhood to adulthood, and delaying with it adult privileges such as sexual experimentation. In many other cultures, adolescents are encouraged to begin to separate from their parents earlier, and this separation is often institutionalized in a formal rite of passage.

Education and Sexual Development

It has been argued that adolescents in the United States experience "retarded sexual development" (Martinson, 1982). Although statistics can be cited regarding specific sexual behaviors and such consequences as unintended pregnancies and rates of sexually transmitted disease, the knowledge base ranks poorly compared to other developed nations. They know significantly less about sexuality and place less value on issues such as consistent use of contraceptives and prevention of pregnancy than adolescents from other developed countries.

In a multinational study of teenage pregnancy and sexuality, U.S. youth scored the lowest of five similar industrialized nations (Canada, Sweden, France, England, and the Netherlands) on tests of knowledge and attitudes concerning sexuality

Paul and Rich: Tumultuous Adolescence

Rich and Paul, both 42, are white.

Paul and Rich met as adults and compared their experiences of going through puberty and adolescence. Even though Paul is gay and Rich is heterosexual, their adolescent years had many similarities, and both had a tremendous amount of curiosity and guilt about their sexual desires.

Rich's adolescence was a fairly typical experience for a straight, lower-middle-class young man growing up in urban America. His parents were high school graduates who worked in factories as piecework tailors. Although both were loving and attentive parents, neither was skilled at communicating openly with Rich about the issues he would face as an adolescent. Neither knew about the key developmental components of puberty and adolescence and weren't comfortable talking with Rich about these issues. Consequently, Rich's adolescence was a hit-or-miss, trial-and-error experience for which he was totally unprepared.

Rich remembers experiencing things such as wet dreams, his first "true love," masturbation, his first ejaculation, and how puzzled he was trying to figure out how male and female genitalia come together during sexual intercourse. He remembers agonizing about his first ejaculation, feeling as if perhaps he had injured himself or something had gone wrong because all of a sudden this liquid was coming out of the end of his penis. Rich had to be content with asking his friends or older brother about some of these things. Based on the responses he received, he knew that some of the answers were not the "right" ones. It took Rich several years to get over much of the guilt and shame he had about his sexual feelings and behavior during adolescence. He spent the better part of his 20s looking for the answers to unresolved questions and issues from his adolescence.

The major difference between Paul and Rich is in sexual orientation. Paul just never felt any sexual desire toward females. He played along when his friends talked about "getting laid" and carrying on with girls in general. Inside, however, Paul was troubled because he felt attracted to some of the boys in his class. In addition, Paul's church had a stated position against masturbation, which created much confusion and guilt in Paul whenever he engaged in that activity. He did not dare to discuss his sexual feelings with anyone connected with his church. Furthermore, as the only son of immigrant parents who did not discuss things of a sexual nature with him, he began to feel isolated. All through his adolescence, Paul agonized over who or what he was. He tried dating girls but found it unsatisfactory. He suspected he was gay but didn't want to admit it and believed he had no one in whom he could confide or trust while exploring this facet of himself.

Paul coped with adolescence by suppressing most of his sexual feelings. He denied that they existed and spent most of his time immersed in studying. Not until he entered college as a pre-med student did he finally give in to his urges to explore this part of himself. Later, in medical school and a steady relationship with another male student, Paul was able to work through some of the pain and confusion that had marred his adolescence.

Critical Thinking

If Rich and Paul were adolescents today, how might their stories be different?

Use your Virtual Workbook to explore your answer to this question at **http://health.wadsworth.com/blonna1.**

and conception (Dryfoos, 1985). Lack of basic information concerning sexual anatomy and physiology, contraception, and pregnancy were cited among other findings as indicators of what international experts would consider arrested sexual development.

As discussed in Chapter 1, the Sexuality Information and Education Council of the U.S. (SIECUS) has developed guidelines for comprehensive sexuality education.

sex in society 5.2

Access to the Truth

For 20 years, the Network for Family Life Education, based at the Rutgers University Center for Applied Psychology, has provided resources, advocacy, training, and technical assistance in support of age-appropriate, balanced comprehensive sexuality education in New Jersey and now nationwide. In 1994, the network asked young people if they would read a newsletter about sexuality and health written by teens, for teens. The response was an immediate and electric "*Yes!*" The National Teen-to-Teen Sexuality Education Program was thus established, and today it has five thriving components:

- *SEX, ETC.*, the award-winning newsletter written by teens, for teens, a free resource produced three times each year by a multiethnic board of New Jersey high school students (circulation began with 30,000 copies in 1994 and in 2003 has risen to 2.1 million copies)
- Discussion Guides designed to help adults spark lively discussions about vital health topics in each issue of *SEX, ETC.*, including a newly published teaching manual
- *The Roadmap: A Teen Guide to Changing Your School's Sex Ed*, a book to teach teens to become advocates for effective sexuality education
- Youth Media Outlets such as a monthly column on MTV.com and feature articles in *Teen People* magazine
- A Web site—www.sexetc.org—launched in 1999, that offers teens more than 300 articles written by their peers, weekly feature stories, reader polls, quizzes, opportunities to get involved, and honest and expert answers to frequently asked questions through the Ask the Experts feature

The Ask the Experts section of the Web site takes in questions from teens all over the world, and a panel of 12 experts, including health educators, physicians, social workers, psychologists, and other professionals, responds to over 350 questions a week. Each question is given a private, confidential, and individual response that is edited carefully by the experts and returned to the teen in about 3 to 5 days. The Web site averages 350,000 teen users each month, and in 2002, it individually answered more than 18,000 teen questions.

The average age for teens writing to the site is about 15 years old, but it ranges from 13 to 21. The kinds of questions teens send to the SEX, ETC. Web site reflect their general ignorance and naiveté about most sexuality issues. The site receives a substantial percentage of questions about body image, penis size, breast size, and whether or not to shave pubic hair. In addition, the majority of questions are about what behaviors are risky for pregnancy, how to make sex more pleasurable and less painful, and how to access birth control, gynecological care, and STI testing.

The site's experts always offer honest and completely straightforward answers to all questions sent in. They also provide information about negotiating and communicating with partners, reducing risk, delaying sexual involvement, and finding alternatives to high-risk behaviors. It is clear that teens are not getting the vital health information they need at home or at school.

The popularity of Web sites that offer information about sexuality shows how greatly teens (and adults) need honest and accurate information that they can access when they need it. Many Web sites feature FAQs and Ask the Experts sections, including www.teenwire.com, www.gurl.com, and www.puberty.org. Most teens are not comfortable asking parents their most intimate questions (although the SEX, ETC. Web site encourages them to try), and most teachers in schools are ill equipped or forbidden to respond to questions about contraception, abortion, sexual response, body image, growth and puberty, safer sex, and many other topics.

Having a place where teens can find information, resources, and answers to their most pressing questions is a service that has been needed for a long time. Although the Internet can have all kinds of negative and potentially dangerous possibilities, being a source of honest, accurate information about health and sexuality is one of its best uses, especially for teens.

Source: Elizabeth Casparian, New Jersey Network for Family Life Education (2003).

At the same time, the U.S. government continues to fund abstinence-based curricula that do not cover such topics as birth control methods, sexual orientation concerns, and sexual decision-making skill development, to name a few.

Education Online

Government leaders, state and local departments of education, not-for profit agencies devoted to health, educators, and parents have debated just what children and teens need to know about sexuality for over 100 years (Moran, 2000). Unintended pregnancies and sexual infections, whether syphilis concerns from the early 1900s or HIV/AIDS concerns in the late 1900s and early parts of this century, remain the driving forces behind the debate. Unfortunately, what has often won out are moralistic policies focused on heterosexual marriage as a solution, rather than health policies that focus on the health and welfare of children.

As the Internet becomes increasingly available, children and youth are connecting with good sources to answer their myriad questions. Sex in Society 5.2 highlights the work of one such source that provides reliable information to teens.

Consequences of Teen Risk-Taking Behaviors

Of the estimated 11 million unmarried adolescent females who are having intercourse, reports indicate that between 900,000 and 1 million become pregnant each year. The majority of these pregnancies are unplanned, with one-fourth of unintended pregnancies ending in abortion (CDC, 2000) and one-tenth in stillbirth or spontaneous abortion/miscarriage (McGrew & Shore, 1991).

The teens who maintain their pregnancies are more likely to have pregnancy-related problems than women who delay childbearing until they are in their 20s. Adolescents are more likely to suffer from toxemia, hemorrhaging, and miscarriages than women who delay pregnancy. In addition, teen mothers are more likely to drop out of school, need public assistance, receive poor prenatal care, have low-birthweight babies, and a higher infant mortality rate (CDC, 2000). These unmarried, teenage mothers face a harder future than their peers who delay bearing children until they are older and married. Although keeping pregnant teens out of public school is illegal, most (approximately 80 percent) wind up dropping out and do not return (White & DeBlassie, 1992). Because of the twin burdens of the lack of a high school degree and the need for child care, these teens earn less, have less schooling, work in blue-collar professions and in general have a lower standard of living than their peers who delay marriage and childbirth.

Most of the negative health outcomes associated with teenage pregnancy are believed to be caused by **biological immaturity,** women having children before their bodies are physiologically ready for them. Some evidence suggests that teenagers, given adequate prenatal care and proper nutrition, may have as good or better pregnancy outcomes than women who are older (Trussel, 1988).

Unfortunately, obtaining adequate prenatal health care is the exception rather than the norm for most teens who get pregnant. Many are not under the care of a physician, midwife, or other health care provider for all three trimesters of pregnancy. As a result, routine testing and screening is delayed or is not done. When routine trimester examinations are not done, close monitoring of the size, weight, positioning, and vital signs of the fetus is not possible. In addition, these visits provide an opportunity for the health care provider to assess the health of the pregnant teen and talk about critical issues such as nutrition, substance use, and plans for delaying future pregnancies and adequately caring for their child if the pregnancy is going to be carried to full term.

Biological immaturity The incomplete anatomical and physiological development associated with early adolescence or preadolescence

Approximately 95 percent of unmarried teenage mothers keep their babies (Steven-Simon & White, 1991). Most of them continue to live at home and rear their babies with the help of their parents or grandparents while they try to cope with the realities of parenthood.

Other teens who become pregnant decide they aren't ready to become mothers and decide to use foster care or place their babies for adoption. Foster care is designed to provide temporary help for mothers or parents who feel they can't take care of their child now but will be able to do it in the near future. Under foster care, mothers still have legal rights to their children, have formal visitation privileges, and are actively involved with their children. Women who place their children for adoption permanently give over their rights as parents to another person or family.

Foster care and adoption offer viable options for teen mothers who are unable to cope with the demands of being a parent. Regardless of which of these options for coping with an unintended pregnancy is chosen, carrying the pregnancy to term and following through with giving up the baby can be extremely stressful. Many pregnant teens choose to terminate their pregnancies rather than be forced to choose between keeping their children, putting them in foster care, or placing them for adoption. Increasingly, however, states are mandating that minors not be able to secure abortions without parental consent. Parental consent laws remain another area of controversy among politicians, health care providers, and reproductive rights activists.

Good communication between teens and their parents, along with growing up in a supportive family, is clearly a healthy ideal. Nonetheless, many teens cannot share their pregnancies with their parents and get the guidance and help they need to manage their situations. The news too frequently reports cases where babies have been abandoned and killed.

Other negative health consequences are associated with adolescent sexual activity. Adolescents have higher rates than all other age groups of syphilis, gonorrhea, and pelvic inflammatory disease (PID). Adolescents also engage in sexual behavior that has high risk for HIV/AIDS (Jemmott, Jemmott, & Fong, 1992). Although the number of 13- to 19-year-olds reporting being infected with HIV is small (3,130 from 1981 through June 1998), many more young people are thought to be infected with HIV (CDC, 1998). In addition, since one in five of all people diagnosed with AIDS is between 20 and 29 years of age (101,368 cases from 1981 through June 1998), and the incubation period for AIDS can last several years, many, if not most, of these people became infected when they were teenagers.

Dealing with Adolescent Sexuality

Some people believe that the best way to deal with adolescent sexuality is to be honest with young people. If parents think their adolescent children would be better off to delay sexual intercourse or other forms of sexual activities with a partner, the best way for them to deal with it is to tell their children this and explain why. The healthy way to do this is to admit honestly to young people that sex is a powerful force in their lives and that, as parents, you would prefer them to redirect that sexual energy from sexual intercourse into other, less risky sexual outlets, such as hugging, kissing, and masturbation. To deny the power of adolescent sexual urges or, worse, not mention it and hope the subject will never come up is unhealthy and dishonest.

Trivializing adolescent sexual desire with simplistic advice such as "When you feel horny, take a cold shower" contributes to the mixed messages adolescents are already receiving about their sexuality. These mixed messages can be a real source of stress. On the one hand, their bodies are telling them, "Yes, yes, yes," and on the other hand, adult society is telling them, "No, no, no." Media—music stars, television, movies—that target adolescents are telling them it is OK and a normal part of teenage rebelliousness to give into, even glorify, their sexual urges, yet parents tell them to take a cold shower and the urges will disappear.

To further complicate matters, federally funded abstinence-only sex education curricula purport to reduce the incidence of unintended pregnancy and sexual intercourse. Parents can help their children by learning about and supporting comprehensive sexuality education programs in their local school districts.

Gay adolescents face an even tougher problem. Not only do they have to deal with the mixed messages and pressures associated with this part of their lives, but they also face a wall of silence concerning their own emerging preferences. Gay adolescents usually learn early on that discussing their attraction to same-gender partners is taboo. Few social supports and people are available to turn to for these adolescents whose school guidance counselors and other community helpers are often either misinformed about how to help these young people or homophobic and a threat to the very youth they are being paid to care for. Many school districts forbid teaching that homosexuality is an acceptable lifestyle. Local chapters of Parents and Friends of Lesbians and Gays (PFLAG) and other gay and lesbian organizations are excellent places to find help and information about resources.

The murder of Matthew Shephard brought the issues of violence against LGBT teens and young adults to the public consciousness. Helping teens and adolescents learn to accept themselves and develop tolerance and respect for the sexuality of others remains an ongoing challenge to schools and agencies working with youth.

Color Day Production/GettyImages

Parents can be a great source of support and information.

Healthier Teens

One of the national health objectives for Healthy People 2010, a federal government plan to improve the health of Americans, is to improve the health of youth by sustaining the decrease in their rates of pregnancy, birth, and gonorrhea and reducing rates of HIV and other STD infections. The U.S. teen birthrate remains one of the highest among developed nations along with rates of STD infection. Child Trends, a nonprofit, nonpartisan research center that studies children and families, reviewed more than 150 research studies to identify the factors that contribute to improving adolescent reproductive health. Sound public policy and programming require that a holistic approach be taken, looking at the adolescent, the adolescent's family, the role of peers, the teenager's partners, the school context, and the neighborhood and community context (Manlove, Terry-Humen, Papillo, Franzetta, Williams, & Ryan, 2002). Some of the key summary findings are as follows:

1. Males are more likely than females to initiate sexual activity at an earlier age, yet for both sexes, earlier onset of puberty and an older appearance are associated with teens becoming involved in sexual activity. Adolescents who are engaged in positive activities such as sports and school and who are confident in their ability to delay activity are more likely to do so.
2. Adolescents with close family ties and good communication engage in more positive reproductive behaviors, whereas those whose mothers were teens at the time of their birth and have sexually active teen siblings are more likely to engage in risky behaviors.

3. Teens are influenced by their friends, and when their peer group engages in risky behaviors, they are more likely to do so themselves.
4. Adolescents who have experienced coercive sex and those who have much older sexual partners appear to be at greater risk for multiple partners, lack of contraception, and pregnancy.
5. There is variability in the types of sexuality programs offered in schools, with some programs associated with reduced sexual activity and increased contraceptive use and other programs associated with delayed sexual activity. It is difficult, however, to separate the school from the community context.
6. Higher rates of sexual activity, pregnancy, and birth are associated with higher rates of poverty.

Overall, Manlove et al.'s (2002) analysis shows that the best programs focus on early childhood development, combine sexuality education for older children with community service activities, and send nurses to visit with teenage mothers.

Beginning with the Adolescent Family Life Act in 1981, the federal government funded programs designed to prevent teen pregnancy through the promotion of chastity and self-discipline. An attachment to the Welfare Reform Act in 1996 provided $50 million annually to state programs that would teach "abstinence-only until marriage"; those states that accept federal funds were required to match the federal grants with state funds (three state dollars to every four federal dollars). The Special Projects of Regional and National Significance—Community Based Abstinence Education (SPRANS-CBAE) in 2001 provided funding for subsequent years to continue the educational efforts for abstinence-only-until-marriage programs (Kreinin, 2003).

Despite research findings on effective educational programs, statistical data on teen sexual activity, reports of dating violence and harassment related to sexuality, undesirable outcomes of unwanted pregnancy and infection, realities of teen parenting, and other pertinent issues, controversy still persists in the United States surrounding the design and implementation of comprehensive programs to meet the sexual health needs of adolescents.

Your responses to the Personal Assessment, Thought Questions, and Test Yourself! quiz questions can be logged online in your Virtual Workbook at **http://health.wadsworth.com/blonna1.**

Personal Assessment

5.1 Rites of Passage

U.S. culture has been criticized for lacking traditional rites of passage that help adolescents make a smoother transition from childhood to adulthood. The purpose of this assessment is to help you explore rites of passage in our culture and others by reflecting on your own experiences. This assessment will enable you to understand why adolescence is often troubling for youth in the United States.

1. Read Sex in Society 5.1, "Other Cultures, Other Ways," in this chapter.

2. Describe, in writing, your own thoughts and feelings about this reading.

3. How do you think these rites of passage would be accepted in the United States?

4. List and describe any cultural rituals that you have experienced while growing up that could be considered rites of passage, and explain how they differ from the examples in the reading.

Thought Questions

1. Describe the different psychological theories and their contributions to the understanding of healthy sexual development.

2. How do bonding, nudity, and toilet training practices affect the development of healthy sexuality?

3. What are the effects of masturbation on childhood and later adult health?

4. What are some of the key developmental issues that young adolescents confront?

5. What are the pros and cons of sexual activity during adolescence?

Test Yourself!

1. Maslow identified characteristics of those who achieve self-actualization through "transcendence." Someone who is a transcender would most likely
   a. focus on the financial rewards of work.
   b. embrace change and creativity.
   c. prefer what is familiar, tried, and true.
   d. be judgmental of others.

2. Modern personality theorists
   a. widely support the Freudian perspective that libidinal energy is the basis for sexuality.
   b. agree that biology is the primary influence on sexual development.
   c. increasingly examine social and environmental influences that help frame ideas of what is normal and expected.
   d. reject all earlier theories of development as being antiquated and irrelevant.

3. Masturbation in young children
   a. is statistically rare.
   b. should be encouraged by parents and teachers.
   c. is normal and usually self-limiting.
   d. can lead to other forms of interpersonal sexual activity.

4. A primary developmental task of adolescence is
   a. to form a sense of identity.
   b. to create close, intimate relationships with members of the opposite sex.
   c. to achieve positive self-esteem through experimentation.
   d. to separate from parents and live independently.

5. All but which of the following are considered secondary sex characteristics in males?
   a. Increased muscle development
   b. Pubic hair
   c. Facial hair
   d. Higher voice

6. The term used to describe the biological transition from childhood to adulthood is
   a. *puberty.*
   b. *transcendence.*
   c. *adolescence.*
   d. *maturation.*

7. Most research on adolescent sexual behavior has revealed
   a. little interpersonal sexual activity until the last years of high school.
   b. drastic differences in the experiences of boys and girls.
   c. increasing rates of sexual experimentation as teens age.
   d. greater experimentation among gay and lesbian students than heterosexual students.

8. Today, teens who want detailed answers to their questions about sexuality
   a. can go online to Internet sites and receive quality information.
   b. will find that the majority of school programs talk about sexuality issues in an honest, comprehensive manner.
   c. will initiate conversations with their parents
   d. complain that no resources are available to them.

9. Which statement about nudity is most accurate?
   a. All cultures react to public nudity in the same way, expecting adults to be dressed.
   b. Families are encouraged to be nude as much as possible in order to teach positive messages about the body.
   c. Young children seem to enjoy nudity and develop a sense of personal modesty as they age.
   d. Most children get upset seeing their parents naked.

10. Becoming an "askable parent" for your child's sexuality questions requires
    a. always being serious when discussing sexuality.
    b. not discussing anything that makes you uncomfortable.
    c. being careful not to make mistakes with information.
    d. letting your child know your values on a subject.

Media Menu

You can link to the following online tools by visiting
http://health.wadsworth.com/blonna1.

Film

Perceiving Gender Roles
Teen Slang for Having Sex
Adolescent Body Image
Adolescent Sexual Risk Taking

 InfoTrac Activity

Shelby, L. (2003, February–March). Youth first: An integrated sexuality education program for pre-adolescents. *SIECUS Reports*, 31 (3), 31.

 Web Resources

Here are sites where teens can write and get honest answers to their sexual health questions:

www.teenwire.com
www.sexetc.org
www.goaskalice.columbia.edu
www.gurl.com
www.puberty.org

The following resources are of additional value to adolescents and adults:

Advocates for Youth

www.advocatesforyouth.org

Creates programs and promotes policies that help young people make informed and responsible decisions about their sexual and reproductive health with the purpose of preventing pregnancy and sexually transmitted diseases, including HIV. Large selection of links as well as links to minority youth sites. One section, which changes monthly, addresses contemporary issues that affect society and the way in which we live.

Coalition for Positive Sexuality

www.positive.org

A grassroots volunteer group started in 1992 to respond to the health crisis among Chicago teenagers. Teens receive information needed to make healthy decisions about sex, condom availability, and sex education. This site has FAQs with links to answers, national Web links, and information on sexuality, health issues, and birth control.

References

Abma, J. C., Chandra, A., Mosher, W. D., Peterson, L., & Puccini, L. (1977). Fertility, family planning, and women's health: New data from the National Survey of Family Growth. *National Center for Health Statistics, Vital Health Statistics, 23*, 19.

American Nurses Association. (1999). Sexual maturity rating scale [Online]. Available: www.nursingworld.org/mods/archive/mod4/ceah2.htm.

American Psychological Association. (2002). *Developing adolescents: Reference for professionals.* Washington, DC: National and Child Health Bureau, Health Resources and Services Administration, and the U.S. Department of Health and Human Services.

Baldwin, J. D., & Baldwin, J. I. (1997). Gender differences in sexual interest. *Archives of Sexual Behavior, 26*(2), 181–210.

Billhartz, C. (2003, February 25). Teens don't realize risk of their oral sex practices. *CDC News Updates.*

Butler, J. (1999). *Gender trouble: Feminism and the subversion of identity.* New York: Routledge.

Carrera, M. (2003, October). *The Children's Aid Society— Carrera Adolescent Sexuality and Pregnancy Prevention Program.* Paper presented at the Network for Family Life Education's 20th Anniversary Conference, "20 Years of Great Sex(Ed): Lessons from the Past, Plans for the Future."

Centers for Disease Control and Prevention. (1998, June 2). AIDS information [Online]. Available: www.cdc.gov/nchstp/hiv_aids/stats/cumulati.htm.

Centers for Disease Control and Prevention. (2002, September 27). Trends in sexual risk behaviors among high school students—U.S., 1991–2001. *Morbidity and Mortality Weekly Report, 51*(38), 856–859.

Centers for Disease Control and Prevention. (2003, July). *Why is an awareness of sexual behavior important?* [Online]. National Center for Chronic Disease Prevention and Health Promotion. Available: www.cdc.gov/nccdphp/dash/sexualbehaviors/index.htm.

Centers for Disease Control, U.S. Department of Health and Human Services. (2000, July). *Health, United States, 2000.* DHHS Publication No. 00-1232. Washington, DC: U.S. Government Printing Office.

Dryfoos, J. (1985). What the United States can learn about prevention of teenage pregnancy from other countries. *SIECUS Report, 14*(2), 1–7.

Erikson, E. (1978). *Childhood and society* (2nd ed.). New York: Norton.

Ferber, S. G., Laudon, M., Kuint, J., Weller, A., & Zisapel, N. (2002, December). Massage therapy by mothers enhances the adjustment of circadian rhythms to the nocturnal period in full-term infants. *Journal of Developmental & Behavioral Pediatrics, 23*(6), 410.

Ford, C. S., & Beach, F. A. (1951). *Patterns of sexual behavior.* New York: Harper.

Forrest, J. D., & Silverman, J. (1989). What public school teachers teach about preventing pregnancy, AIDS, and sexually transmitted diseases. *Family Planning Perspectives, 21*, 65–72.

Forrest, J. D., & Singh, S. (1990). The sexual and reproductive behavior of American women 1982–1988. *Family Planning Perspectives, 22*, 206–214.

Gates, G. J., & Sonenstein, F. L. (2000, November/December). Heterosexual genital sexual activity among adolescent males: 1988 and 1995. *Family Planning Perspectives, 32*(6).

Globus, S. K. (2002, Spring). Touch me, I'm yours: The benefits of infant massage. *Special Delivery, 25*(1), 8.

Gordon, S., & Gordon, J. (1983). *Raising a child conservatively in a sexually permissive world.* New York: Simon & Schuster.

Gurian, M. (1996). *The wonder of boys.* New York: Putnam.

Hall, C. S. (1954). *A primer of Freudian psychotherapy.* New York: Mentor.

Hatcher, J. L., & Scarpa, J. (2002, July). *Encouraging teens to adopt a safe, healthy lifestyle: A foundation for improving adult behaviors.* Child Trends Research Brief. Washington, DC: Child Trends.

Hedgepeth, E., & Lemich, J. (1996). *Teaching about sexuality and HIV.* New York: New York University Press.

Henry J. Kaiser Family Foundation. (2003). *Teen sexual health fact sheet* [Online]. Available: www.kff.org.

Henry J. Kaiser Family Foundation, Hoff, T., Greene, L., & Davis, J. (2003). *National Survey of Adolescents and Young Adults: Sexual health, knowledge, attitudes, and experiences* [Online]. Publication No. 3218. Available: www.kfg.org.

Herdt, T. G., & Boxer, A. (1992). Introduction: Culture, history, and life course of gay men. In G. Herdt (Ed.), *Gay culture in America: Essays from the field.* Boston: Beacon.

Jemmott, J. B., Jemmott, L., & Fong, G. T. (1992). Reductions in HIV risk-associated sexual behaviors among black male adolescents: Effects of an AIDS prevention intervention. *American Journal of Public Health, 82*(3), 372–377.

Kaplan, H. S. (1974). *The new sex therapy.* New York: Brunner/Mazel.

Kinsey, A. C., Pomeroy, W. B., & Martin, C.E . (1948). *Sexual behavior in the human male.* Philadelphia: Saunders.

Kreinin, T. (2003, May). Letter from the president of the Sexuality Information and Education Council of the U.S. to SIECUS membership.

Laumann, E. O., Gagnon, J. H., Michael, R. T., & Michaels, S. (1994). *The social organization of sexuality: Sexual practices in the United States.* Chicago: University of Chicago Press.

Levine, J. (2002). *Harmful to minors: The perils of protecting children from Sex.* Minneapolis: University of Minnesota Press.

Lopiano, C. (2001). *Equity in women's sports: A health and fairness perspective* [Online]. Available: www.womenssportsfoundation.org.

Lorber, J. (2001). The social construction of gender. In P. S. Rothenberg (Ed.), *Race, class, gender in the United States* (pp. 47–56). New York: Freeman.

Manlove, J., Terry-Humen, E., Papillo, A., Franzetta, K., Williams, S., & Ryan, S. (2002, May). *Preventing teenage pregnancy, childbearing, and sexually transmitted diseases: What the research shows.* Child Trends Research Brief. Washington, DC: Child Trends.

Marshall, D. (1971). Sexual behavior on Mangaia. In D. Marshall & R. Suggs (Eds.), *Human sexual behavior: Variations in the ethnographic spectrum.* Englewood Cliffs, NJ: Prentice Hall.

Martinson, F. M. (1982). Against sexual retardation. *SIECUS Report, 10*(3), 3.41.

Maslow, A. (1970). *Motivation and personality* (2nd ed.). New York: Harper & Row.

McGrew, M., & Shore, W. (1991). The problem of teenage pregnancy. *Journal of Family Practice, 31,* 17–25.

Montague A. (1986). *Touching* (3rd ed.). New York: Columbia University Press.

Moran, J. (2000). *Teaching sex: The shaping of adolescents in the 20th century.* Cambridge, MA: Harvard University Press.

Newman, S., & Udry, J. (1988). Oral sex in adolescent populations. *Archives of Sexual Behavior, 14,* 41–16.

Reports of child sexual abuse. (2001, January). *Juvenile Justice Bulletin.*

Sarrel, L., & Sarrel, P. (1984). *Sexual turning points: The seven signs of adult sexuality.* New York: Macmillan.

Savin-Williams, R., & Rodriguez, R.G. (1993). A developmental, clinical perspective on lesbian, gay male, and bisexual youth. In T. P. Gullets et al. (Eds.), *Adolescent sexuality.* Newbury Park, CA: Sage.

Schlegel, A., & Barry, H. (1979). Adolescent initiation ceremonies: Cross-cultural codes. *Ethnology, 18,* 199–210.

Schlegel, A., & Barry, H. (1980). The evolutionary significance of adolescent initiation ceremonies. *American Ethnologist, 7,* 696–715.

Sonenstein, F. L., Pleck, J. H., & Hu, L. C. (1989). Sexual activity, condom use, and AIDS awareness among adolescent males. *Family Planning Perspectives, 2*(14), 152–158.

Sorenson, R. (1983). *Adolescent sexuality in contemporary America.* New York: World, 1983.

Steven-Simon, C., & White, M. (1991). Adolescent pregnancy. *Pediatric Annals, 20,* 322–331.

Troiden, R. (1988). *Gay and lesbian identity: A sociological analysis.* New York: General Hall.

Trussel, J. (1988). Teenage pregnancy in the United States. *Family Planning Perspectives, 20,* 262–272.

Watson, J. *Behaviorism* (1970). New York: Norton.

White, S., & DeBlassie, R. (1992). Adolescent sexual behavior. *Adolescence, 27,* 183–191.

Wilson, S. M., & Medora, N. P. (1999). Gender comparisons of college students: Attitudes towards sexual behavior. *Adolescence, 25,* 615–627.

Young, S. M. (1986). Attitudes and behavior of college students to oral-genital sexuality. *Archives of Sexual Behavior, 9,* 61–67.

Zelnick, M., Kanter, J., & Ford, K. (1981). *Sex and pregnancy in adolescence.* Beverly Hills, CA: Sage.

chapter *six*

Adult Sexuality

Student Learning Objectives

After reading this chapter, students will be able to

- Describe the typical developmental tasks associated with young adulthood through older adulthood.

- Relate the findings of a variety of studies concerning the sexual behavior of college students and young adults.

- Assess a variety of living arrangements of the college years and young adulthood.

- Examine the major developmental tasks associated with adulthood.

- Assess a variety of sexual lifestyles in adulthood.

- Explain the impact of aging on sexual response and behavior.

- Describe the developmental course of long-term straight, gay, and bisexual relationships.

- Identify the major areas of discord and stress in marital and long-term intimate relationships.

- Discuss the effects of divorce and widowhood on adult sexuality.

Test your understanding of these objectives by taking the end-of-chapter quiz, available online at **http://health.wadsworth.com/blonna1.**

activity teaser: *What do you really need to have a successful relationship? Find out with the Personal Exploration Activity on page 177.*

case study 6.1

Maria, aka Supermom

Maria, 35, identifies as white, Italian American.

Maria has been married for 15 years and has three children, ages 12, 10, and 7. Married as soon as she finished at the local community college with an associate's degree, she worked full-time for a year at an accounting office. As soon as she started having her kids, however, the idea of continuing to work and pay for day care made no financial sense. She and her husband decided she should stay home with the kids, and she could bring in some money doing child care in her home.

Once the kids were in school all day, Maria realized that she wanted to finish her own education and earn her bachelor's degree in accounting. All along she's taken primary responsibility for the child rearing, cooking, cleaning, and chauffeuring the kids to appointments, activities, and play dates. She was an officer with the PTA, den mother for the Cub Scouts, Sunday school teacher, and all-around busy stay-at-home mom. The change of going back to school has markedly increased her stress but, in an odd way, also energized her.

Maria is finding that her relationships with her kids and husband are changing. She seems to have less time to give each the attention they want. Maria heads off for her own classes as soon as the kids are on their way. She carries a cell phone for emergencies and has been lucky that the kids have stayed well and she hasn't been beeped in the middle of her classes. Dinners aren't quite as nutritious as they had been, with more drive-through pickup meals than she'd like. She likes to get up at 5:30 A.M to enjoy the quiet of the morning before all the chaos sets in. That has been a good time for her to study while running the wash.

She and her husband find that they have to schedule "dates" now in order to be together as a couple. At the end of the week, it takes purposeful planning to keep the romance alive. It hasn't been easy, juggling the demands of motherhood, housework, and school, but everyone is adjusting. Maria feels she's making a successful passage into another phase of her life.

Critical Thinking

Can you identify some strategies Maria and her family could develop to reduce her workload and stress levels?

Use your Virtual Workbook to explore your answer to this question at **http://health.wadsworth.com/blonna1.**

Intimacy A gradual process of sharing one's innermost feelings with another

The primary task we face as young adults, according to Erik Erikson (1978), is the development of **intimacy**—forming committed, intimate, loving relationships. We begin to move away from the adolescent focus on ourselves toward exploring mutually satisfying relationships. This stage emphasizes commitment, both in intimate relationships and in work.

This is an exciting time of life. We meet new friends, explore intimate, loving relationships, and test the waters for work and career possibilities. This is the first time many college students are living apart from their parents. It is a time of unparalleled freedom. Students who have mastered the developmental tasks of adolescence and childhood enter this period in their lives ready and eager to sample all that life has to offer. Maria's life, as described in Case Study 6.1, highlights the many demands of adulthood, some of which compete for time and attention.

Forming Friendships

New adult friendships form the basis of intimate relationships for many college students. Intimacy grows out of friendships as we become more trusting and comfortable with each other. In his book *Friendship*, Joel Block (1980) contends that humans are "wired" with a basic desire for contact with others. Our friend-

Friendships fill a special place in our lives.

ships, Block believes, are what make us whole. He says that friends enrich our existence and bond with us to form a conspiracy against the world. We like one another, understand each other, share interests, and have similar lifestyles or problems in life.

Although college literally throws people together (dorm pairings, class scheduling, and so on), what is it that draws friends together? Many friendships grow out of meeting people who share similar interests and experiences. We meet fellow students who have the same major, take the same classes, and join the same organizations. These similarities provide the initial attraction. If the attraction is strong enough, it provides the basis for spending more time together. As the friendship progresses, the friends share more time and experiences, reinforcing their commonality, deepening their bonds, and enriching their lives. Many people form their deepest friendships in college during young adulthood.

Friendship is a unique bond. Although it is fraught with entanglements that also characterize romantic relationships—competition, jealousy, and betrayal—it offers what Block calls "psychological space." Friendships are more open-ended than relationships with family, mates, or lovers. Unlike these other, more intimate relationships, our friendships provide separate lives that allow time off and away from entanglements. Consequently, friends develop a greater tolerance for growth and change. We are most truly ourselves with our friends.

Dating and Intimate Relationships

Whereas friendships may be casual, intimacy by definition is deeply personal and trusting. Intimate relationships are characterized by sharing deep personal information. Intimacy grows out of friendship and usually is nurtured through dating. We'll cover intimacy in detail in Chapter 10, "Intimate Relationships."

Every society has some rituals or norms for pairing and courtship. Although the "rules" for dating and courtship vary from culture (and subculture) to cul-

Dating provides an opportunity to get to know each other.

ture, every society has traditions that it passes along from one generation to the next. Adults who came of age in the late 1960s and early 1970s in the United States vividly remember the differences between the rigid rules of the 1950s and the more liberated late 1960s and early 1970s. Prior to the cultural revolution of the 1960s, a young woman would not even consider asking a man out for a date. Men were expected to ask women out, pay for the evening's activities, and be responsible for picking up and dropping off their dates. Women were expected to wait for men to call them, even if a woman was interested and wanted to initiate contact. The popular media played out these and other traditional dating scenarios, and mothers and fathers passed them on to their daughters and sons. Everyone was assumed to be heterosexual, and sex was not a part of the evening's activities.

The face of dating today looks dramatically different. As will be discussed in this chapter, it may be more comfortable for students to use the terms *hooking up* and *seeing someone* rather than *date* (Crawford & Popp, 2003). Regardless of the term used, the behavior involved reflects greater role flexibility. A woman can initiate a date, pick up her date, and pay for herself. Straight, gay, and bisexual men and women have their own clubs, organizations, and dating services that make finding a partner easier and safer. In the past, bars and clubs for gay and lesbian women were disguised and subject to harassment from bullies and the police. Today they are more accepted and open, with directories available identifying various facilities, particularly in urban areas.

Although the rituals and rules of dating change over time, the purpose of dating hasn't changed much. Dating is a mechanism for developing intimate relationships. Intimate relationships, in turn, influence both sexual behavior and living patterns.

Emotional and Social Wellness

The emotional dimension of wellness requires that we acknowledge the full range of emotions associated with our changing roles and responsibilities. Most of the major developmental tasks associated with the adult stages of our lives are part of social wellness: forming intimate relationships, committing ourselves to others and to our work, being productive—in relationships, work, and so on. Understanding our emotional responses and developing interpersonal social skills become critical as we navigate the challenges associated with adulthood.

The social legacy we develop and leave behind can be one of a caring child, loving partner, and/or devoted parent. We can move through the stages of our relationships eagerly anticipating the changes and tasks that await us. We can also move through life and relationships with a self-centeredness that obscures all propensities for caring, sharing, and nurturing. Adulthood and old age may be viewed as opportunities for continued growth, reflection, and self-acceptance; for some, this stage of life may be marked by bitterness and regret. Overall health is enhanced by positive attitudes and a willingness to remain socially engaged.

College Sexual Standards

Many people equate intimacy with sexual activity and love, yet they are three separate entities. A person can be intimate and sexual with another person but not love that person. One can be in love, but with limited sexual involvement. And a person can be sexual with another but neither love nor be intimate with that person. In a survey of more than 10,000 adults, most respondents agreed that the best possible combination of all three would be to be sexual with someone toward whom you feel both intimate and loving (Blumstein & Schwartz, 1983).

Research on college sexual mores has often focused on students' attitudes toward "premarital sex," defined as premarital intercourse, and "double standards" for males and females, specifically looking at how males and females engage in the same behaviors but are judged differently. Sexual standards may have been prefaced with such adjectives as *permissive* or *traditional*. Primary concern was when behaviors took place relative to marriage or a commitment to marry.

In our discussions with students about acceptable dating behaviors, invariably the word *slut* will enter the conversation. Males anecdotally report not being interested in a woman who has had too many partners; females express their concern that they wouldn't want to be considered a slut by having engaged in sex too quickly or with too many males. At the same time, there is an expressed view that promiscuity by either sex is less than desirable.

A review of the research confirms that sexual attitudes may have become more egalitarian in recent years, yet there are still differences for males and females. Females may be judged for having had sex at an early age, having had many partners in the past, and for having sex outside a committed relationship. Males may also judge behaviors differently when seeking dating partners as opposed to long-term partners (Crawford & Popp, 2003).

Because of sampling issues, it is more difficult to assess lesbian, bisexual, and gay student mores. The process of "coming out," finding a partner, and being free to date openly is of paramount concern to the gay, lesbian, and bisexual community of students. Although working toward committed relationships may be a goal, judging behaviors as "premarital" obviously doesn't work. Like their heterosexual peers, however, gay, lesbian, and bisexual individuals may judge a potential partner's past sexual history.

All students, irrespective of sexual orientation, however, need to assess their personal levels of interest, sexual involvement, and commitment as they form pairs with others. Engaging in behavior that is consistent with one's personal values and feeling comfortable in sexual situations continue as challenges during college years.

Hooking Up

The term **hooking up** has increasingly been used to describe a variety of sexual interactions that take place on a casual basis, often with alcohol part of the picture. Students may refer to having "hooked up" with someone over a weekend, yet the specifics of that interaction may be unclear. Two individuals may have met at a party or bar and engaged in some form of sexual behavior without the need for commitment (Lambert, Kahn, & Apple, 2003). *Hooking up* may be defined as "a sexual encounter between two people who may or may not know each other well, but who usually are *not* seriously dating" (Lambert et al., 2003, p. 129). When asked about experiences with hooking up, researchers found college students citing the occurrence of petting below the waist, oral sex, and sexual intercourse as part of the behaviors included in the definition (Paul, McManus, & Hayes, 2000).

Hooking up A sexual encounter between two people who may or may not know each other well and are not seriously dating

In addition to the term not being specific, males and females who hook up may have differing expectations of what sexual behaviors they want to engage in. Alcohol further complicates the situation, which may lead to participation in sexual behaviors that are not desired. Students may have "bad hooking-up experiences," where the next day they regret the behavior and do not care to even talk with the sexual partner. At the most negative would be cases where the interaction involved force and qualified as sexual assault. One study found that college students thought their peers were more comfortable with hooking up than they themselves were. Men were more comfortable with hooking-up behaviors than women, yet men were less comfortable than women believed them to be, and women were less comfortable than men believed them to be. Overall, although it may appear that hooking up is the norm for college campuses, peer pressure and misperceptions of comfort may be part of the picture (Lambert et al., 2003).

Students have also described having "friends with benefits." In those situations, a comfortable friendship exists with consensual sexual activity. There is no apparent expectation that the two will see themselves or be viewed by others as a couple.

Research on Adult Behavior

The National Health and Social Life Survey (NHSLS) conducted by Laumann, Gagnon, Michael, and Michaels (1994) remains a critical source of data for understanding adult sexual behavior. Their research relied on random sampling, well-constructed survey instruments, and interviews. Controversy about the "need" to study adult sexual behavior—even for its public health value—led to congressional opponents effectively stopping National Institute of Health funding for the initial survey designed in the late 1980s (Laumann & Michael, 2001). The researchers were able, however, to secure funding from seven foundations: The Robert Wood Johnson Foundation, the Henry J. Kaiser Family Foundation, the Rockefeller Foundation, the Andrew Mellon Foundation, the New York Community Trust, the John D. and Catherine T. MacArthur Foundation, and the American Foundation for AIDS Research. Although it would be exciting and valuable to have periodic, government-sponsored, comprehensive studies of adult sexual behavior, such efforts have not been widely funded.

Nonetheless, various efforts have been made to provide more information about adult sexual behavior since Kinsey's detailed work in the mid–20th century. Students may find great personal value in reading qualitative research, where issues are explored in greater depth. Carol Ellison and Bernie Zilbergeld have each discussed female and male sexuality in depth from their experiences as clinical practitioners and psychologists. Both *Women's Sexualities* (Ellison, 2000) and *The New Male Sexuality* (Zilbergeld, 1999) provide students the opportunity to understand that their own personal behaviors and needs are "normal" and part of the spectrum of human sexual behavior.

Laumann and colleagues (1994) reported in *The Social Organization of Sexuality* that the sexual behavior of most American adults was rather conventional. Although popular culture would lead to the opposite conclusion, the actual data collected point to most reporting a limited number of sexual partners with a somewhat limited repertoire of sexual activities. A significant finding was that the critical factors that frame our sexual lives are gender, age, and marital status, with only modest differences in behavior when such characteristics as race/ethnicity, educational level, or religious affiliation are taken into account (Laumann & Michael, 2001).

Sexual Partners

Laumann and colleagues studied the number of sexual partners their subjects had, providing comparisons by gender, age, marital status, education, religion, and race/ethnicity. Table 6.1 shows the number of sexual partners during the past 12 months and since age 18.

The researchers discovered that most people interviewed reported a modest number of partners over the course of their lifetime. Married and cohabiting couples reported being faithful to their partners. Those who reported having had more than one partner during the past 12 months were not married or living with anyone, and they were mostly young and male. The researchers did discover that the more educated people were, the more partners they had had over their lifetime. An important explanation for that finding was that many who pursue a college education delay marriage; sexual relationships develop, yet individuals are more likely to be somewhat older before committing to one partner (Michael, Gagnon, Laumann, & Kolata, 1994, p. 104).

Looking at those between ages 18 and 24, 57 percent of subjects reported having had only one partner in the past 12 months, compared to 9 percent who had had five or more partners during that time. Another study specific to college students found that the total number of sex partners for both the previous year and total lifetime had increased for college men and women (Reinisch, 1992). The average number of total sexual partners for college women was 5.6 compared to 11.2 partners reported by males.

Sexual Behavior Among College Students

The trends we discussed in Chapter 5 regarding adolescent sexual behavior seem to continue into the college years. Specifically, evidence suggests increasing levels of sexual activity among college students over the past two decades, and women seem to be catching up to men in terms of the number of partners, level of sexual activity, and activities engaged in. Data concerning the sexual behavior of college students are difficult to extract from large-scale studies. Often, data on college students are reported in studies of adolescent or teenage sexual behavior because the teen years extend into the first year or two of college. College students are also merged into studies of adult sexual behavior.

In one study, similar percentages of male and female college students were found for the following behaviors: vaginal intercourse (68 percent for men and women), masturbation (men 78 percent, women 71 percent), performing oral sex (60 percent men, 68 percent women), receiving oral sex (64 percent men, 71 percent women), anal intercourse (6 percent men, 10 percent women), and using pornography (58 percent men, 37 percent women) (Person, 1989).

The frequency of sexual activity for men and women aged 18 to 29 is compared within Table 6.2. From these data, women aged 18 to 29 seem to enjoy a slightly higher level of sexual activity. Table 6.2 illustrates the percentages of men and women engaging in various levels of sexual activity over a 12-month period.

Other interesting findings from Laumann et al. regarding the sexual behavior of 18- to 29-year-olds were related to masturbation and oral sex. Those behaviors are presented in Tables 6.3, 6.4, and 6.5 later in this chapter.

Approximately 41 percent of the men and 64 percent of the women reported that they currently did not masturbate. Of those who masturbated, approximately 30 percent of the men and only 10 percent of the women did so at least once a week.

Men and women in the 18- to 24-year-old age group were similar in their levels of both active and receptive oral sex. Approximately 72 percent of the men and 70

Table 6.1 Number of Sex Partners in Past 12 Months and Since Age 18

	Sex Partners Past 12 Months				Sex Partners Since Age 18					
	0	1	2–4	5+	0	1	2–4	5–10	10–20	21+
Total	12%	71%	14%	3%	3%	26%	30%	22%	11%	
Gender:										
Men	10	67	18	5	3	20	21	23	16	
Women	14	75	10	2	3	31	36	20	6	
Age:										
18–24	11	57	24	9	8	32	34	15	8	
25–29	6	72	17	6	2	25	31	22	10	
30–34	9	73	16	2	3	21	29	25	11	
35–39	10	77	11	2	2	19	30	25	14	
40–44	11	75	13	1	1	22	28	24	14	
45–49	15	75	9	1	2	26	24	25	10	
50–54	15	79	5	0	2	34	28	18	9	
55–59	32	65	4	0	1	40	28	15	8	
Marital status:										
Never married, noncohabiting	25	38	28	9	12	15	29	21	12	
Never married, cohabiting	1	75	20	5	0	25	37	16	10	
Married	2	94	4	1	0	37	28	19	9	
Divorced, separated, widowed, noncohabiting	31	41	26	3	0	11	33	29	15	
Divorced, separated, widowed, cohabiting	1	80	15	3	0	0	32	44	12	
Education:										
Less than high school	16	67	15	3	4	27	36	19	9	
High school graduate or equivalent	11	74	13	3	3	30	29	20	10	
Some college/vocational	11	71	14	4	2	24	29	23	12	
Finished college	12	69	15	4	2	24	26	24	11	13
Master's/advanced degree	13	74	10	3	4	25	26	23	10	13
Current religion:										
None	11	68	13	7	3	16	29	20	16	16
Mainline Protestant	11	73	13	2	2	23	31	23	12	8
Conservative Protestant	13	70	14	3	3	30	30	20	10	7
Catholic	12	71	13	3	4	27	29	23	8	9
Jewish	3	75	18	3	0	24	13	30	17	17
Other religion	15	70	12	3	3	42	20	16	8	13
Race/ethnicity:										
White	12	73	12	3	3	26	29	22	11	9
Black	13	60	21	6	2	18	34	24	11	11
Hispanic	11	69	17	2	4	35	27	17	8	9
Asian	15	77	8	0	6	46	25	14	6	3
Native American	12	76	10	2	5	28	35	23	5	5

Note: Row percentages total 100 percent.

Source: From *Sex in America* by Robert Michael, et al. Copyright © 1994 by CSG Enterprises, Inc., Edward O. Laumann, Robert T. Michael, and Gina Kolata. By permission of Little, Brown, and Company, Inc.

Table 6.2 Frequency of Sexual Intercourse During Past 12 Months and Since Age 18

Master Status Variables	Not at All	Frequency of Sex in the Past Year (%)			
		A Few Times per Year	A Few Times per Month	Two to Three Times a Week	Four or More Times a Week
Men					
Total population	9.8	17.6	35.5	29.5	7.7
Age:					
18–29	21.4	35.9	54.9	64.2	23.8
30–44	23.2	46.2	119.1	93.2	18.3
45–59	36.2	64.1	120.0	67.2	12.3
Marital status:					
Never married, not cohabiting	22.0	26.2	25.4	18.8	7.6
Never married, cohabiting	0.0	8.5	35.6	37.3	18.6
Married	1.3	12.8	42.5	36.1	7.3
Divorced/separated/ widow, not cohabiting	23.8	22.5	28.5	20.5	4.6
Divorced/separated/ widow, cohabiting	0.0	8.3	36.1	44.4	11.1
Education:					
HS graduate equivalent	10.1	15.1	34.4	31.7	8.7
Finished college	9.0	15.8	43.9	25.8	5.4
Women					
Total population	13.6	16.1	37.2	26.3	6.7
Age:					
18–29	15.7	26.4	69.6	65.6	22.7
30–44	33.5	47.8	118.5	82.3	17.8
45–59	76.2	59.2	110.6	46.2	7.7
Marital status:					
Never married, not cohabiting	30.2	23.5	26.0	13.3	7.0
Never married, cohabiting	1.4	6.9	31.9	43.1	16.7
Married	3.0	11.9	46.5	31.9	6.6
Divorced/separated/ widow, not cohabiting	34.3	23.2	21.9	16.8	3.7
Divorced/separated/ widow, cohabiting	0.0	9.4	39.6	39.6	11.3
Education:					
HS graduate equivalent	10.8	15.9	37.7	29.6	6.0
Finished college	12.5	18.3	33.5	29.7	6.1

Source: The Social Organization of Sexuality: Sexual Practices in the United States, by E. Laumann et al. (Chicago: University of Chicago Press, 1994). Used with permission.

percent of the women reported ever performing oral sex on their partners. Of this group, 28 percent of the men and 19 percent of the women reported performing oral sex during their last sexual encounter with their partners. Similar percentages for men (75 percent ever and 29 percent last encounter) and women (75 percent ever and 24 percent last encounter) were reported for receiving oral sex.

Living Arrangements of College Students

Living arrangements of college students vary, determined by personal finances, whether they are commuting or living on campus, whether living with a friend or romantic partner, and so forth. At some universities, the majority of undergraduates live in either dormitories or apartments. Other institutions have minimal housing for full-time students, are more accommodating to the commuting student, and have sizeable populations who attend school part-time. Whereas the married undergraduate student used to be the exception years ago, today many students are both married and older, some with young children. Consequently, more colleges are finding the need to include day care facilities on campus. The National Coalition for Campus Childcare has surveyed campuses to determine the availability of child care for their students and employees. At the majority of institutions, students participate in the centers in a variety of ways from student teachers, paid work/study students, unpaid student observers, researchers, and other roles. As more nontraditional students are drawn to undergraduate and graduate education, the need for such facilities grows (Thomas, 2000).

Single

Many college students are single and live off-campus, either at home with their parents or in shared living environments. In 1991, the overwhelming majority of young adults lived at home. Decades ago, the majority of men and women in this age group were married and out of their parents' houses. The current pattern where young adults remain living with parents has been tied to trends in delaying marriage, increasing percentage of never-marrieds, high cost of housing, and the need for more people to continue education.

The U.S. Bureau of the Census (2002) reports that there is a substantial increase in the proportion of "young, never-married" adults. For example, in the past three decades, the proportion of women who have never married doubled for those ages 20 to 24 and more than tripled for women ages 30 to 34 (Fields, 2001). Additionally, the median age of marriage has been pushed back to 25 years for women and 27 for men (U.S. Bureau of the Census, 2002). It must be noted, however, that the census bureau does not ask how many of the "never-marrieds" have that status due to being gay or lesbian and therefore are unable to marry.

Cohabiting

According to the U.S. Bureau of the Census (2002), about 6.3 million people in the United States cohabited in 1998. Of those, approximately half were under 25 years of age. No accurate numbers have been forthcoming regarding the actual number of college students who cohabit. **Cohabitation** is distinguished from having roommates of the opposite gender by the nature of the sexual interaction between cohabiters. *Cohabiters* are lovers who live together but are not married. They initially describe their relationship as intimate and affectionate but not necessarily as leading to marriage.

Cohabitation Living together without being married

Relationship Contract: How Much Am I Willing to Compromise?

The goal of this activity is to help you decide what you really need to have a healthy, happy, and supportive long-term relationship.

The following questions could be made into a relationship contract by which you and your future long-term partner agree to abide. Answer the questions as if you could have your ideal in the relationship. If you are in a relationship now, ask your partner to do the same and then compare your answers. This should cause a lively debate.

Freedom
Will we still maintain our outside friendships? Do we have the freedom to make new friends? Are we free to spend time with our same and opposite-sex friends without our partner? In what types of activities can we participate? Will we participate in sexual relationships outside this one?

Money
How will we make sure money is not a problem for our relationship? Will we have a budget, and, if so, what do we do if one does not follow the budget? Will we keep our own money or have a joint bank account? What will be our financial priorities?

Chores
How will we divide our responsibilities so that neither of us feels overwhelmed or taken advantage of?
Who will do the laundry, pay the bills, clean the house, take care of the yard, shop for groceries, cook, buy gifts for our families, run the errands?

Free Time
Will we spend all of our free time together? What types of activities will we do to keep the relationship from becoming boring? Will we spend most of our free time with friends, family, or alone?

Children
Will we have children? How many? What lengths are we willing to go to if one of us is infertile?

Married

For comparison, students may want to interview parents and grandparents who attended college about attitudes toward being a married student during their time in school. Generations ago, to be married was often thought incompatible with formal education, particularly for women. Some institutions of higher learning in the early to mid–20th century either strongly discouraged or outright forbid undergraduates to be married.

Today, most undergraduates who plan on marriage wait until they finish school. Data show that for undergraduate students surveyed during 1999–2000, 21.6 percent were married, with 76.8 percent reporting "not married." Within the unmarried group, however, can be individuals committed to a partner and possibly living with that partner (National Center for Education Statistics, 2000).

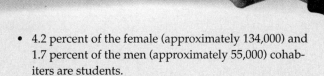

sex in society 6.1

Cohabitation Facts

- An estimated 6.3 million Americans were in cohabitation relationships as of March 1998. That is up from about 5.3 million as recently as 1995.
- The age breakdown is as follows:

  15.5 percent of men and 22.1 percent of women under 15 to 24;
  38.7 percent of men and 37.2 percent of women 25 to 35;
  21.8 percent of men and 23.1 percent of women 35 to 44;
  23.9 percent of men and 17.5 percent of women over 45

- 4.2 percent of the female (approximately 134,000) and 1.7 percent of the men (approximately 55,000) cohabiters are students.
- 37 percent of college-educated women had lived in a cohabitating relationship, and that number is rising.
- Most cohabitations are short-lived, and the couple either separates or marries.

Source: U.S. Bureau of the Census, "Current Population Survey," Center for Demography and Ecology (University of Wisconsin, Madison, 1998).

Adult Sexual Behavior

We will extend the discussion of sexuality during the college and young adult years into adulthood and old age. The phrase "use it or lose it" is often bantered about to express the idea that overall sexual health and activity connect to ongoing patterns established in life. The data from the NHSLS study continue to provide a portrait of adult behavior.

Laumann and Youm (2001) developed a model to explain the factors that influence a person's mode of sexual expression. Figure 6.1 shows the determinants of sexual expression.

There are three areas where individual attributes are key. First, *individual preferences* for specific sexual activities and level of sexual interest must be considered. Great variability exists from person to person as to what they want to do and how strong their drive is to engage in a specific activity. Those preferences may be different when a college student has moved from one partner to another, changed after a negative experience, and so forth. Second, *physical health* becomes important; a person may or may not be able to participate in activities due to impaired physical and/or mental health. Depression and erectile dysfunction, for example,

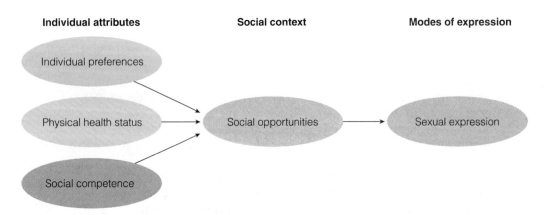

Figure 6.1 *Model of Determinants of Sexual Expression*

Source: E. O. Laumann and Y. Youm, "Sexual Expression in America," in Laumann and Michael, *Sex, Love, and Health in America* (2001), p. 111.

are two conditions that are known to interfere with sexual activity. *Social competence* as a third factor refers to the skills and resources needed to initiate and maintain social relationships. Individuals have to be able to communicate with a partner as well as be able to compete effectively for the attention of a potential partner. Social competence would seem to be a learned set of behaviors yet certainly can be influenced by how one is feeling about her- or himself at a set period of time.

Finally, the model posits that the three individual attributes jointly affect the *social opportunities* individuals confront when attempting to establish sexual relationships: who do you meet, where do you go, what are your social networks, how does geographic context affect socializing, and so on. All together, the four factors then affect what modes of sexual expression will result (Laumann & Youm, 2001).

In 2003, books, magazine articles, and popular television programs began to highlight what were being termed "sexless or no-sex marriages." Within relationships in which time was consumed by dual careers, children, and fatigue, the frequency of sexual activity was reported to be diminished. Therapists were providing advice, couples were going public with their concerns, and issues once thought private were making their way into popular discourse. As in many areas of sexuality, the power of the media can obscure and/or highlight what may or may not be going on in the privacy of the bedroom.

Physical and Intellectual Wellness

As we move through adulthood, we continue to be responsible for maintaining and enhancing our physical well-being. The experiences we've had earlier on may "catch up," making physical health no longer something to be taken for granted. The choices we made, behaviors we adopted, and lifestyles we lived will either enhance or undermine our sexuality. Abusing our bodies and letting our physical well-being decline will have a negative impact on our sexuality. Everything from body image to sexual response to overall energy level may decline. This will impact negatively on our social relationships with lovers, spouses, employers, and others. Better body image, sexual response, and energy level will help us meet the demands of our ever-changing sexuality. This state of wellness will not only enhance our personal functioning but also positively influence our relationships.

The ability to gather information, critically analyze it, and make good decisions are hallmarks of high-level mental functioning. Rational thinking and logical reasoning can help us understand the nature of our ever-changing sexuality as we pass through young adulthood into adulthood and old age. Having reasonable expectations about our sexuality, based on solid information, can guide us in decision making. It also can help us avoid unrealistic expectations about relationships and sexuality that are likely to lead to personal unhappiness and dissatisfaction with partners. It is important to determine the personal value of the information to which we're exposed—what relates to us, what can constructively impact our sexual health.

Masturbation in Adulthood

Adult masturbation is often viewed as a second-class sexual experience and is inversely related to the availability of a steady partner (Laumann et al., 1994). The common belief is that masturbation is primarily motivated by the relief of sexual tension. This belief grows out of a Western cultural viewpoint that masturbation is juvenile sexual behavior, almost preintercourse in its development. We join Laumann et al. in taking issue with this notion. In Chapter 7, we provide a detailed overview of masturbation throughout the life cycle.

Laumann et al. have examined masturbation in light of its relational context. They believe that masturbation, like all forms of sexual expression, is driven by a variety of social and biological factors throughout the life cycle and can have complementary, supplementary, or independent status with reference to partnered sex. This means that masturbation can enhance partnered sexual activity. It also can be an additional source of sexual expression within the context of the relationship, and last, it can serve as a solitary source of sexual pleasure independent of partnered sex.

Table 6.3 illustrates the frequency of masturbatory behavior by age and other selected demographic variables. Results shown here are not segregated by sexual orientation. Laumann et al. emphasize one of the key findings of the table: The level of masturbation is not related to relationship status. Although the table does show a decline in the level of masturbatory behavior among married people, it does not show a similar pattern among those who are single but cohabit. This group tended to be younger overall than the married sample.

Rather than reinforce the stereotype that masturbation is a substitute for partnered sex, this finding shows that this isn't necessarily so. The frequency of individual masturbation is as likely to be a function of social factors and a

Table 6.3 Frequency of Masturbation

| | Frequency (%) | | | |
| | Not at All | | Once a Week | |
Master Status	Men	Women	Men	Women
Total population	36.7	58.3	26.7	7.6
Age:				
18–24	41.2	64.4	29.2	9.4
25–29	28.9	58.3	32.7	9.9
30–34	27.6	51.1	34.6	8.6
35–39	38.5	52.3	20.8	6.6
40–44	34.5	49.8	28.7	8.7
45–49	35.2	55.6	27.2	8.6
50–54	52.5	71.8	13.9	2.3
55–59	51.7	77.6	10.3	2.4
Marital status:				
Never married, not cohabiting	31.8	51.8	41.3	12.3
Never married, cohabiting	15.8	54.9	36.8	12.7
Married	42.6	62.9	16.5	4.7
Divorced/separated/widow, not cohabiting	30.2	52.7	34.9	9.6
Divorced/separated/widow, cohabiting	41.2	50.9	17.6	12.7
Education:				
HS graduate equivalent	45.1	68.4	20.0	5.6
Finished college	24.2	47.7	33.2	10.2
Master's/advanced degree	18.6	41.2	33.6	13.7

Source: The Social Organization of Sexuality: Sexual Practices in the United States, by E. Laumann et al. (Chicago: University of Chicago Press, 1994). Used with permission.

variety of reasons as it is the availability of alternative outlets. Table 6.4 gives some of the reasons for masturbation, cited by gender.

Sexual Intercourse Among Adults

Table 6.2, presented earlier, shows the frequency of sexual intercourse in the past year. Laumann et al. summarize the three main levels of sexual activities for adults: About 35 percent have sex with a partner two or more times per week, about 35 percent have partnered sex one to a few times per month, and the remaining 30 percent have partnered sex only a few times a year. These rates were fairly consistent across all racial, ethnic, and religious groups. About 7 to 8 percent of the respondents had partnered sex four or more times a week, and about 10 percent reported having had no sex at all during the previous year. This response, the researchers point out, paints quite a different picture of adult sexual behavior than the one portrayed in the popular media. The sexual activity of most Americans is much more modest than the frequency and expectations created by the media.

An additional finding concerning partnered sexual activity related to the number of sex partners during the past year. As Table 6.1 points out, the number of different sex partners in the past year declines with age. In general, the largest percentage of respondents in each age cohort reported only one sex partner during the past year. Two moderating factors seem to be marital and cohabiting status. Young, single, noncohabiting men and women were much more likely than all other groups to report two or more different partners during the previous year.

Adult Oral Sex Activity

Table 6.5 illustrates the frequency of oral sexual activity among adults. The table does not segregate by sexual orientation. Straight and gay men and lesbian and heterosexual women are lumped together. The proportion of men reporting having had oral sex performed on them during their lives was similar to that of women reporting ever having had cunnilingus performed on them—roughly 75 percent. This percentage drops dramatically, however (about 50 percent), when oral sexual behavior is reported as latest sexual experience. Laumann et al. interpret this response as meaning that, although the majority of American men and women have experienced oral sex, it isn't as much a staple in their sexual repertoire as vaginal intercourse and kissing.

Laumann et al. view the increased frequency of oral sex as one of the basic changes in U.S. sexual behavior during the past century. They reported that the current incidence is probably an outgrowth of a trend that began in the 1920s. Kinsey and his colleagues publicized oral sex in the late 1940s, and it has continued to work its way into the fabric of American sexual behavior. The impeachment proceedings of President Clinton in the late 1990s provided daily grist for a discussion of oral sex—was oral sex really "sex"? In 2003, the U.S. Supreme Court ruled that oral and anal sexual behavior were not criminal. Specifically, the high court struck down Texas's Homosexual Conduct law that made oral and anal sex between homosexuals criminal activity (Lambda Legal Defense Fund, 2003). The

Table 6.4 Reasons for Masturbation

Reasons for Masturbation	Gender of Respondent (%)	
	Men	Women
To relax	26	32
To relieve sex tension	73	63
Partner unavailable	32	32
Partner doesn't want sex	16	6
Boredom	11	5
Physical pleasure	40	42
Go to sleep	16	12
Fear of AIDS/STD	7	5
Other	5	5

Source: The Social Organization of Sexuality: Sexual Practices in the United States, by E. Laumann et al. (Chicago: University of Chicago Press, 1994). Used with permission.

Table 6.5 Frequency of Oral Sex

	Men	Women	Occurrence of Active Oral Receptive Sex (%)				Occurrence of Oral Sex (%)			
			Men		Women		Men		Women	
Master Status Variables	Mean Frequency of Sex per Month		Life	Last Event	Life	Last Event	Life	Last Event	Life	Last Event
Total population	6.5	6.3	76.6	26.8	67.7	18.8	78.7	27.5	73.1	19.9
Age:										
18–24	7.2	7.4	72.4	27.7	69.1	19.1	74.2	28.9	74.7	24.2
25–29	7.6	7.5	84.8	32.0	76.2	23.8	84.8	33.7	79.8	24.3
30–34	6.7	6.8	78.9	29.6	76.6	19.1	78.9	32.2	83.1	22.3
35–39	6.6	6.1	82.3	30.4	71.3	21.0	87.5	29.8	73.7	23.3
40–44	5.9	5.5	84.0	31.2	72.7	16.9	85.7	28.9	76.8	12.6
45–49	6.2	5.5	73.4	21.2	65.2	21.6	77.4	22.1	72.7	18.3
50–54	5.5	4.6	60.0	16.1	48.5	11.7	66.0	13.8	59.4	12.6
55–59	4.4	3.5	58.4	9.9	38.9	5.5	58.0	14.1	44.3	6.9
Marital status:										
Never married, not cohabiting	5.6	5.3	66.7	28.9	59.4	21.0	70.3	32.8	67.7	26.8
Never married, cohabiting	8.6	8.8	85.7	30.2	72.2	21.5	89.3	34.0	76.4	22.7
Married	6.9	6.5	79.9	25.2	70.7	16.9	80.4	23.0	73.9	16.9
Divorced/separated/ widow, not cohabiting	5.4	5.1	81.5	30.1	64.1	25.4	88.1	34.5	73.1	24.2
Divorced/separated/ widow, cohabiting	8.0	7.6	80.0	29.7	79.6	16.3	80.0	37.8	85.2	20.4
Education:										
Less than high school	6.5	6.3	59.2	16.4	41.1	10.1	60.7	16.4	49.6	13.2
High school graduate or equivalent	6.9	6.3	75.3	30.1	59.6	16.4	76.6	25.3	67.1	18.5
Some college/ vocation	6.6	6.3	80.0	31.1	78.2	20.7	84.0	31.0	81.6	22.2
Finished college	6.0	6.4	83.7	23.7	78.9	22.9	84.6	31.1	83.1	20.7
Master's/advanced degree	6.1	5.1	80.5	20.6	79.0	28.8	81.4	30.4	81.9	27.0

Source: The Social Organization of Sexuality: Sexual Practices in the United States, by E. Laumann et al. (Chicago: University of Chicago Press, 1994). Used with permission.

ruling was seen as a great victory for the gay and lesbian community, where members could have been punished for engaging in the same behaviors practiced by heterosexuals.

Adult Anal Sexual Activity

Unlike oral sex, anal sex has yet to make a serious entry into the basic fabric of American sexual behavior. The overall level of heterosexual anal intercourse in the past year was around 9 percent. Only 2 percent of those ever having anal intercourse reported engaging in this activity at their last sexual encounter. As with other forms of sexual activity reported in the NHSLS, anal intercourse seems to be reported across all categories of respondents and is not limited to certain racial, ethnic, or religious groups.

Some evidence indicates that a small segment of adolescent and college women view heterosexual anal intercourse as an acceptable alternative to vaginal penetration. We, too, have received similar anecdotal reports from students engaged in internships in family planning agencies and from other health care providers serving young women.

Adult Relationships

One of the major developmental tasks of adulthood is the continuation and deepening of the commitment to relationships that began in young adulthood. For most Americans, this means a commitment to marriage and a family. For many, the commitment to someone else does not involve marriage but, instead, cohabitation. This is also a period frequently marked by divorce or the death of a spouse. In the remaining part of this chapter, we'll examine the changing nature of adult relationships.

Singlehood

A significant percentage of Americans are choosing to remain single for life. Reasons for remaining single include changes in sexual standards, greater financial independence for women, changing economic times, and shifting conceptions of marriage. Sometimes, postponing marriage results in an inadvertent slide into permanent singlehood (Cavanaugh, 1993). As people postpone marriage, they often realize that they can live satisfying lives being single. There is less urgency to marry, especially if they feel no desire to have children.

Regardless of the reasons, most people who chose to remain single for life in one study reported that they were quite happy. Contrary to popular beliefs, most singles are not lonely, and they develop alternative social patterns based on friendships and nonmarital love relationships. The satisfaction that singles derive from these relationships and their careers is more than adequate for their happiness (Phillis & Stein, 1983).

Dating and Single Adults   The two most stressful issues for single people are how to handle dating and others' expectations that they should marry (Cavanaugh, 1993). The United States is a "couples-oriented" society that puts a premium on adults interacting socially as part of a heterosexual couple. The prevailing assumption is that everyone expects to get married someday. This view puts inordinate pressure on single people, especially when friends and associates are continually trying to "fix them up." Singles typically find themselves having to defend their position. Old friendships also tend to disappear when a friend marries and starts a family.

Gay single people find themselves in a double-bind. People are continually trying to fix them up with members of the opposite sex so they can "find someone" and settle down. When gay singles finally do "find someone," they may not feel comfortable sharing their relationship with their straight friends.

Cohabitation   Unmarried adult couples who live together are not much different from married couples. They share, argue, quarrel, make decisions about money, sex, household labor, and so on. The reasons for adults living together but not marrying are many and varied. Generally speaking, three forms of cohabitation are casual or temporary involvement, preparation or testing for marriage, and a substitute for or alternative to marriage.

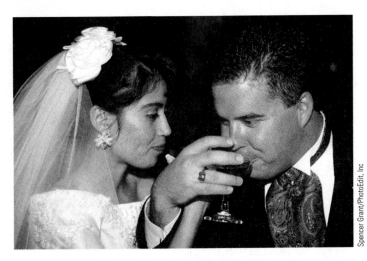

Weddings are important rituals that symbolize hope and lifelong commitment.

Monogamy Married to only one person at a time

Marriage

The vast majority of Americans want to marry, although they are postponing it longer than in the past. The median age at first marriage has been rising for the past three decades. Even though it is an integral part of most cultures, marriage takes many forms and assumes many different purposes throughout the world. In the United States, most people take the following issues for granted concerning marriage: a legal bond, having children, permanence, heterosexuality, sexual exclusivity, emotional exclusivity, and **monogamy** (Berry & Williams, 1987).

U.S. culture also expects more from marriage than many other cultures do. Historically, marriages were intended to provide a stable economic unit in which to rear children. Today, people expect marriage to fulfill their social, emotional, financial, and sexual needs. When people marry, they find that many of these expectations are unrealistic and cannot be fully realized. This discovery can lead to frustration, disillusionment, separation, and divorce. They also find that marriage is hard work. Even under the best of circumstances and with a good match in a partner, successful marriage requires continual assessment, communication, commitment, and willingness to change.

The Developmental Course of Marriage   Berry and Williams (1987) propose a developmental model of marriage across adulthood, shown in Figure 6.2. In the early, honeymoon phase, marriage is at its most intense. The two spend considerable time together, talking, sharing interests and leisure, establishing their roles within the relationship, arguing, and making up. As the honeymoon phase begins to wind down and the couple settles into a routine, the intensity of the honeymoon phase diminishes and, along with it, marital satisfaction. A big reason for

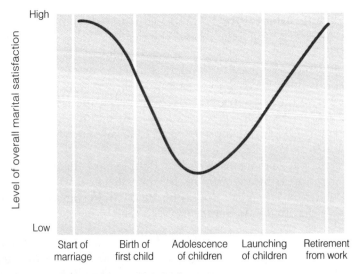

Figure 6.2 *Berry and Williams Model of Marriage*

Source: "Assessing the Relationship Between Quality of Life and Marital and Income Satisfaction: A Path Analytic Approach," by R. E. Berry and E. Williams, *Journal of Marriage and the Family, 47*(1987), 107–116. Copyrighted 1987 by the National Council on Family Relations, 3989 Central Avenue NE, Suite 550, Minneapolis, MN 55421. Reprinted with permission.

sex in society 6.2

Learning by Laughing at the Movies

Laughter is one human behavior that is shared by people all over the world. It represents a positive emotion, with the power to reduce stress, relieve pain, and encourage healing. Laughter stimulates the heart, alters the rhythms of breathing, and positively impacts the immune system (Hales, 2003). We can laugh at a joke. We can laugh at a situation watched on television or on the big screen. The power of creating laughter, along with making people feel good, is that wonderful lessons about life can be transmitted in a nonthreatening manner.

Many movies have been made with central themes on the institution of marriage. Some of the recent selections listed here illustrate how film can tackle various crises and sexual themes with humor, reality, and diversity.

La Cage aux Folles (1978) is a French-made film, later turned into a Broadway musical, that humorously deals with a gay couple whose son, much to their chagrin, is planning a marriage to a woman. The woman is the daughter of a conservative minister of morality for the government. Through the meeting of the parents and ensuing charades, humor is used to illustrate basic parental concern for children's happiness. Students may be more familiar with the American version of the film entitled *The Birdcage*, starring Robin Williams.

The Wedding Banquet (1997) shows the culture clash and secrecy involved when the parents of a rich Taiwanese family visit their son in New York City, not knowing he is gay and living with his partner. To help a female tenant who is an immigrant in need of a green card, a fictitious marriage is arranged. The film uses humor to address issues of love, marriage, homosexuality, and cultural traditions.

Meet the Parents (2000) focuses on the introduction of the male character to his fiancée's somewhat unwelcoming parents. The father, in particular, is very uncomfortable that his possible future son-in-law is a male nurse. The macho father views the female-identified profession negatively, not to mention the overall clumsiness of the man.

Monsoon Wedding (2001) looks at the marriage rituals among upper-middle-class Indians. Although the culture subscribes to arranged marriages, the influences of Western culture on the values of family members add to the culture clash.

Far from Heaven (2002) is not a comedy but rather an intense look at the breakup of an upper-class family as the wife learns of her husband's homosexuality. Although a "period piece," it teaches how oppressive and secretive being gay yet trying to live the heterosexual life was in the 1950s.

My Big Fat Greek Wedding (2002) depicts culture clash at its finest. A Greek American woman, hoping to break free from her overbearing family, falls in love with an upper-class non-Greek male. The differences in the families are extreme, from the Greeks being joyous and involved in every aspect of each other's lives, to the stereotypical WASP family, being overwhelmed by the outgoing, involved way of the soon-to-be in-laws.

Overall, this sampling of films highlights the cultural variations around weddings. What is as important, however, is that the themes of love, family, and working through conflict are underscored. Whether the couples live "happily ever after" is a question better left to fairy tales.

---

this outcome is the birth of children. Children result in less time available for the mate and the relationship.

Marital happiness reaches its lowest point during the midlife phase of the relationship, which also coincides with adolescence of the couple's children. A myriad of problems—ranging from financial issues to coping with teenagers to changing roles for husband and wife—contribute to the unrest.

Happiness begins to rebound when the children leave home as adults. This frees up time and money, and the couple has rediscovered privacy to reestablish the things in their relationship that provide pleasure, as well as investigate new things together.

Marital happiness continues to rise in the later adult years and carries over into retirement. Depending on a number of factors ranging from health to retirement income, the couple continues to enjoy their freedom and in some cases relationships with their children's families and their grandchildren.

Rob & Sas/CORBIS

More than half of all married couples report being extremely sexually satisfied with their sexual relationship.

Obviously, not all couples fit the Berry and Williams model. Other variables, such as physical illness, children living at home into their 30s, and loss of jobs, can strain the relationship. In some cases, children growing up and leaving the nest magnify problems in the relationship that lead to divorce. Not all relationships flourish in retirement. Sometimes work serves as a buffer between a couple and their problems.

Sexual Satisfaction and Happiness   Sexual satisfaction and happiness in marital and other partnered relationships have two dimensions: physical satisfaction and emotional happiness (Laumann et al., 1994). The relationship between the two is complex. Highly satisfying physical relationships usually bring with them high emotional happiness. High levels of emotional satisfaction, however, don't necessarily indicate high levels of physical satisfaction.

Overall, a fairly high proportion of men (47 percent) and women (41 percent) described their partnership as extremely physically pleasurable. Satisfaction seems to vary with age. Among men, the level of physical satisfaction was high to begin with and increased with age. Among women however, high levels of physical satisfaction dropped significantly after age 55. Findings are similar regarding emotional satisfaction. Laumann et al. account for this by explaining that men in their 50s and older are more likely than similar-aged women to acquire new sex partners after divorce.

Sources of Marital Problems   The potential sources of trouble over the life span of a marriage range from loss of initial sexual passion to economic instability in retirement. Many relationships are doomed from the

healthy sex hints 6.1

Lessons from Happy Marriages

In a happy marriage:

1. The partners find their prime source of joy in each other but maintain separate identities.
2. They are generous and giving out of love, not because they expect repayment or are keeping score.
3. The partners enjoy a healthy and vigorous sexual relationship.
4. The partners "fight" in a constructive way, airing feelings and frustrations without attacking or blaming the other.
5. The partners communicate with each other openly and honestly.
6. The partners trust each other.

7. Both talk about their future together. They have mutual goals.
8. The best marriages tend to be ones in which the partners are similar in these ways:
   - ethnicity
   - locality (geography; urban or rural)
   - maturity (emotional and social)
   - goals and ideals
   - intelligence levels
   - amount of education
   - economic level and financial resources
   - social strata
   - value system
   - religious beliefs

sex in society 6.3

Midlife Crisis or Middle-Age Myth?

You have heard the story before. A happy, successful 45-year-old businessman quits his job, leaves his wife and kids, and runs off to Tahiti with his 25-year-old secretary. Or, perhaps it is the 40-year-old mother of two facing the "empty nest" who jumps into her convertible BMW with her 25-year-old tennis instructor and heads west into the sunset in a torrid blaze of passionate sex.

These and other "midlife crises" that have been popularized by the print and film media make interesting stories and pose a romantic solution to many of the difficult issues that appear during middle age. In real life, however, relatively few people experience such catastrophic, radical changes. New information fueled by long-term research on aging is showing that middle age is the very best time of life. It is a developmental stage unlike most others, because it is not tied particularly to changes in the body, such as early childhood, adolescence, and old age. Midlife is characterized more by psychological adaptations and is reality based.

By midlife, many of the stressful questions that faced us as young adults are answered, such as, Will anyone ever love me? Will this marriage work out? Will I ever find a job? What kind of lifestyle can I afford to lead? By midlife, most people have found love. If they are married, they are more likely to stay married (the overwhelming majority of divorces occur within the first 6 to 8 years of marriage). They have settled into a job and have a pretty good idea of where they are headed (most professionals who are going to "make it" have made it by this time). They have a good sense of their earning capacity and therefore can gauge the kind of lifestyle they can expect.

Although the myth of midlife is that this period is characterized by unrest, discomfort, dissatisfaction, and upheaval, the reality is that it is a comfortable, satisfying time. It is a time to enjoy the rewards of 10 to 20 years of scuffling. It is a time to push a little easier at work, to get off a little early to watch your kid's Little League game. It is a time to focus on vacations and social gatherings, to take a class to learn how to paint or improve your backhand. It is a time to lighten up a little.

Midlife is a period of gradual adjustment, not tumultuous change. It gradually unfolds and is based on several adjustments to reality. For most people it is based in reality, not fantasy. Those most likely to experience a true crisis (about 5 percent) are people who generally have experienced similar crises in all developmental stages of their lives. Their lives are based on unrealistic (therefore unrealized) notions and expectations. One of the major criticisms of earlier studies of midlife is that they were based on small numbers of case studies of atypical populations (mostly affluent, professional, and white). In the recent cross-sectional studies of more representative samples of Americans, researchers found that the average person's midlife adjustment is based on reality. People gradually adjust their expectations to fit the reality of their lives. By the time they settle into midlife, they have learned to make the best of what they have and are not constantly longing for things that are beyond their reach.

Source: R. Blonna, *Coping with Stress in a Changing World* (3rd ed.) (Dubuque, IA: McGraw-Hill, forthcoming), p. 537.

start because they are based on an ideal that never can be fulfilled. Many expectations are unrealistic as a result of immature or romantic perceptions. The continuing intensity and bliss of romantic love cannot be expected to continue throughout marriage. Bliss turns to boredom and aggravation, passion to comfort, and happiness to times of sadness. This does not mean that love is dead. Romantic love should be expected to transform into mature love.

Furthermore, communication problems can sabotage a relationship. These problems may be rooted in a lack of assertiveness in which one or both members of the couple are unable to stand up for themselves. Communication problems also can arise when the partners are unable to express positive and constructive thoughts and feelings. Many people grow up in an environment where communication revolves around problems and the expression of negative emotions. Relationships can wither from a lack of expressions of recognition, caring, tenderness, and compassion.

Communication problems can be summarized as stemming from a lack of communication skills, the lack of desire to communicate, or both. The easier problem to remedy is the skill-based one. If one or both members of the relationship do not know how to communicate clearly and effectively or don't know how to fight fairly, they can learn—assuming they have the desire. If either or both don't have the desire to work things out, no amount of skill will improve the situation.

Loss of desire to talk and work things out is a warning sign of a deteriorating relationship. Sometimes a vicious cycle begins in which a lack of skill in communicating leads to a deteriorating relationship, which feeds a loss of desire. Low levels of desire keep the cycle going by not having the interest in talking about problems in the relationship. In the last case, one or both members may want to try to communicate in general but think the problem is too difficult to talk about. Or they may want to try to communicate more effectively but lack the energy and commitment necessary to work out their problems.

Couples who want to resolve their problems but don't know where to start can benefit tremendously from couple's counseling. Sometimes, problems that seemed insurmountable before counseling seem workable after seeing a therapist.

Another factor, money—or, more precisely, what money means to each partner—is a major source of stress in long-term relationships. If the two differ in their perceptions and values surrounding money, this difference could create problems within the relationship. For instance, one partner may view money as relatively unimportant, only a means to obtain the things necessary for survival. The other, however, perceives money as important—a ticket to a better life, higher status, more luxuries, and so on. This couple is in trouble because their core values concerning money are the opposite. Often this variance is reflected in how much they spend and what they buy. If one partner perceives that the other is spending too much and making unnecessary purchases, it is bound to lead to problems. As described in Case Study 6.2, couples can develop a plan to override their differences.

Or one person may view credit as a fundamental economic necessity and have no problem with outstanding balances on credit cards, loans, and home equity lines. Meanwhile, the other may not be comfortable even with a mortgage or a car loan, preferring to delay all purchases until they can be paid for in cash. The problem is compounded by today's easy access to credit and aggressive marketing.

healthy sex hints 6.2

Fighting Fairly

- Use *I* rather than *you*. Instead of saying, "You're insensitive," say, "I feel hurt when you ignore me."
- Don't argue without good reason. Think before you speak.
- Don't fight in front of other people, including your children. The issue involves only the two of you.
- Don't make personal attacks—name-calling, put-downs—that you will regret later.
- Be specific. Don't generalize.

- Focus on only the issue that precipitated the argument.
- Learn to use active listening skills so your partner will know he or she is being heard.
- If you cannot agree after a "fair fight," agree to disagree or to renew the discussion later.
- Take responsibility for your own behavior. Avoid blaming.
- Obviously, do not resort to physical attacks or any form of violence.

case study 6.2

Tom and Suzanne: Dealing with Finances

Tom and Suzanne, both age 30, are white.

Tom and Suzanne have an interesting way of dealing with family finances. They met at age 27 in graduate business school, where they were pursuing their MBAs. Both had lived by themselves for a few years and had several years of work experience behind them. Each had savings and checking accounts.

In discussing marriage, both were concerned about financial independence and protecting their savings, income, and spending patterns. Tom was a saver. He had banked well over $20,000 in savings before he met Suzanne, and he wanted to preserve this money. He was disciplined and always paid cash, even for his personal automobiles.

Suzanne was a spender. She believed in buying with credit cards, and catalog shopping was a favorite pastime. Saving was something people did once they turned 50 and began to think about retirement. For as long as she could remember, she had outstanding balances on her credit accounts yet eventually would pay them off.

Being so different concerning money but so alike in a number of other ways, Tom and Suzanne decided that after they were married, they would have three separate accounts: his, hers, and ours. The "ours" account would be used for all joint bills (rent, food, joint vacations, and child rearing (if it came up). Suzanne had wanted other expenses covered from this account, such as car purchases and retirement savings, but Tom, knowing she was a spender and he'd wind up contributing more than she, did not accept this arrangement. After reviewing salaries and projected earnings, they decided that each would contribute two weeks take-home salary to the joint account, with the other two weeks kept separately. With basic expenses covered, each could then spend and/or save without guilt or explanation.

Despite some stress, things have worked out okay for Tom and Suzanne. He's still a saver and has over $20,000 in his bank account. She's still a spender and has a $15,000 car loan and credit card debts exceeding $3,000. Tom considered helping her out with some payments but decided against it, as he thought she'd never learn if he were to bail her out. Some of their friends think they're a little eccentric and that their marriage seems more like a business than a loving partnership. In any case, for the time being it seems to work for them.

Critical Thinking

Some would argue that married couples who maintain separate checking accounts demonstrate a lack of trust in their relationships. Others might argue that it is wise for two people with different approaches to managing money to keep some of their finances separate. What is your view on money management within a marriage?

Use your Virtual Workbook to explore your answer to this question at **http://health.wadsworth.com/blonna1.**

The perception of money affects everything from long-term planning to daily quality of life. It also involves the perception of gender roles as couples decide if one or both partners will work, whose job is more important, if one of them is to leave a career to take care of the children, and so forth. If one partner has a traditional gender role concerning money and the other doesn't, this could be a major source of marital discord. Couples need to discuss these issues and develop creative approaches to deal with their own money and the "couple's" money.

Unrealistic expectations about sex within the marriage also can lead to dissatisfaction. The partners might have differing expectations about the frequency of sex, use of protection, level of desire, and a host of other variables. These differing and unrealistic expectations about sex can be a sign of sexual incompatibility. Often, couples who cohabit in preparation for marriage do so in an effort to gauge sexual compatibility before they enter into a marital relationship. Unfortunately no evidence is available to suggest that couples who do this are more likely to stay together and have marital satisfaction than noncohabiters (Masters, Johnson, & Kolodny, 1992).

Once people leave the single life and pair off in either cohabiting or marital relationships, sex changes. It no longer is as frantic or as segmented from the rest of one's life as it was when the couple lived separately. Although sexual pleasure is not sacrificed, sex becomes integrated into the ebb and flow of the couple's life. It is balanced with other needs and responsibilities—an important developmental task in this stage of the relationship. If a partner is unable or unwilling to communicate about sexual concerns and problems, the problems can worsen and become a source of stress within the relationship. Partners who cannot adjust become sexually dissatisfied and may turn to extramarital sex or divorce.

As we've reported, the frequency of sexual intercourse declines as relationships age. Sexual activity peaks within the first year of marriage and then begins to drop off. The frequency of sexual relations is highly correlated with marital satisfaction. In one study, 9 of 10 married couples who were having sex three or more times a week reported satisfaction with their relationships (Blumstein & Schwartz, 1983). Conversely, only half of couples having sex one to four times a month were satisfied with their relationships. A more recent study found a similar relationship between the frequency of marital sex and level of satisfaction with the relationship (Laumann et al., 1994).

Many factors affect the level of sexual activity within a relationship. Work and other responsibilities affect the level of energy people have. Sexual desire may change in response to stress. Sometimes people have common sexual dysfunctions (such as situational erectile dysfunction in men) that lessen sexual frequency and pleasure.

Parenting and Relational Satisfaction   Children can be a major source of stress within a committed adult relationship. Whether married or cohabiting, straight or gay, children change a couple's established patterns of interaction. As we've seen from the Berry and Williams analysis of marital happiness and adult developmental phases, satisfaction within a marriage reaches its lowest point about the time the children reach adolescence. Even though this seems to indicate that adolescents are responsible for their parents' stress, the demands of parenting pose formidable stressors at all stages of child development.

Parenting requires a tremendous amount of time and effort. The specific demands change with the child's stage of development, but the responsibility remains. Newborns require constant supervision. Even when they are sleeping, parents learn to sleep lightly, ready to react to their children's cries for help in the night. Young children need help with everything from getting washed and dressed to cutting the food on their plates. Older children need parents to spend time helping them with everything from doing their homework to getting them safely to and from friends' houses. Parents of young adolescents spend countless hours carpooling their kids all over the place, and parents of older teens stay up all hours of the night waiting for the safe return of their teenager and the family car.

Children decrease up to half the amount of time parents have to share activities with each other (Cavanaugh, 1993). This can disrupt everything from a couple's sexual relationship to the time they spend pursuing hobbies or other activities. In addition to the stress associated with the sheer time demands of children, children's needs are unpredictable. From early-morning feedings of babies, to car-pooling, to waiting for an adolescent to return home from a date, children pose unpredictable demands on the time, temperament, financial resources, and parents' sexual desire.

Divorce   Not all marriages progress completely through the Berry and Williams phases described earlier in the chapter. More than half of all first marriages end in divorce. Raw numbers are misleading when interpreting divorce statistics. The divorce *rate*, which examines numbers of divorces in relation to numbers of marriages, rose steadily for 20 years, reaching a high of 5.3 divorces per 1,000 Americans in 1981, then began declining. In 2000, there were a reported 4.7 divorces for every 1,000 people (Hughes, 2003).

Most people marry with the hope that the relationship will last forever. Divorce, therefore, often represents a loss of this hope. This often is accompanied by the loss of economic status (particularly for low- and middle-income women), lifestyle, security of familiarity, friends, and sometimes children. The psychological effects of divorce can be compared with those of the grieving process associated with death of a loved one. First, shock sets in ("Is this really happening to me?"), followed by disorganization ("Everything feels topsy-turvy"). Volatile emotions, then guilt ("It's my fault") usually follow. Loneliness, too, often accompanies divorce. Finally, after several months to a year, these feelings are replaced by a sense of relief and acceptance.

The grieving process leads to healing, a cleansing of wounds, that allows divorced people to move on with their lives. If, after a year or so, the divorced person hasn't gotten over the divorce and begun to accept what has happened, counseling and psychotherapy may be helpful.

Approximately three in four divorced persons remarry, most within 3 years after their divorce. Although most remarried people report that their second marriage is better than their first, the likelihood that this marriage also will end in divorce is greater than that among first marriages. No one knows why this is so for sure, but some of the reasons given are less willingness to stay in the second marriage when they are embittered, closer scrutiny of the second marriage, financial problems (such as alimony and child support), and the trauma of divorce being less threatening after having experienced it once.

Long-Term Gay, Lesbian, and Bisexual Relationships

Most research regarding relationships has related to married heterosexuals, with far less written regarding long-term gay, lesbian, and bisexual relationships. In fact, the prevailing stereotype has been that such relationships were unlikely to even exist. In practice, gay and lesbian couples have increasingly had commitment ceremonies, where vows are shared, friends and family may be present, and some of the rituals of traditional marriages are repeated. In August 2002, the *New York Times* decided to begin publishing reports of commitment ceremonies in its Sunday Styles section. What had been the "Wedding" section became the "Weddings/Celebrations" section, with the backgrounds of gay and lesbian couples written up in the same manner as those of heterosexual couples. The newspaper required that couples celebrate their commitment in a public ceremony and/or enter into a legally recognized civil union (which at that time was in Vermont) or register their **domestic partnership** in those places allowing registration (*New York Times*, 2002). The significance of that editorial decision is reflected in the fact that the *New York Times* has national distribution, is considered a mainstream newspaper, and is a powerful force in public opinion. At the same time, the biographies of any couples reported tend to reflect high-level positions of employment, education at highly ranked universities, and be the children of parents who also wield levels of power and influence in their respective lives.

Domestic partnerships Registered relationships between gay and lesbian couples

On a national level, gay and lesbian activists have been working to change legislation that would enable them to marry. When Hawaii changed its laws to allow for gay and lesbian marriage, federal legislation in the form of the Defense of Marriage Act was initiated. That law passed in 1996 ensuring that if a same-sex couple married in one state, their marriage did not have to be recognized in any other. It also defined marriage as being between a man and a woman. In 2003, Massachusetts legalized gay and lesbian marriage, furthering the national controversy.

The politics surrounding marriage for lesbian and gay couples relate on one level to principles of fairness, constitutional protections, and recognition of loving, committed relationships. On another level, the politics are rooted in the economic protections of legal marriage. Health insurance, pensions, inheritance, and the like, are "rights" that come within marriage and affect daily living. As of 2003, 10 states and the District of Columbia provide benefits for domestic partners of public employees. Hawaii, California, and New Jersey have the broadest domestic partnership laws, with Vermont endorsing civil unions (Cahill & Slater, 2003, p. 6).

Religious conservatives maintain that marriage must be seen as a union between a man and a woman. Nonetheless, the Netherlands in 2000 became the first nation to make same-sex marriage legal, followed by Belgium in 2003 and the provinces of Ontario and British Columbia in Canada in 2003. Other countries have provisions for gay and lesbian couples to varying degrees (Cahill & Slater, 2003, p. 7).

Because of the controversies related to marriage, legislation has been more successful thus far in the area of registered domestic partnerships and civil unions. Urban governments, some universities, and some corporations have extended health and pension benefits to the partners of their employees.

A prospective study of 65 gay and 47 lesbian long-term relationships found that the duration of the relationship was a predictor of satisfaction (Kurdek, 1989). Gay and lesbian subjects in relationships of longer than an 8-year duration reported greater satisfaction than relationships of shorter duration. Furthermore, lesbian couples reported higher levels of relationship satisfaction than gay men (Kurdek, 1989).

Another study found that as homosexuals aged, those in close, committed relationships were the happiest (Lipman, 1986). Variables related to happiness in relationships, such as commitment, companionship, intimacy, and fulfillment of needs, were the same for homosexual and heterosexual couples.

The stereotypical picture of old age for gay men and women is one of unhappiness and loneliness. In actuality, it is quite the opposite. As a rule, homosexual men and women may be better prepared for the demands and challenges of old age than many traditional heterosexual couples. Because of stereotypical male and female gender roles, traditional heterosexual marriages are more likely to be built on dependency. In traditional heterosexual relationships, husbands rely on wives for certain activities, and wives are more dependent on husbands for other activities.

In the absence of social norms for gay male or female relationship roles, gay and lesbian relationships are, of necessity, more egalitarian. Each partner has been socialized to be self-reliant. The lack of hard-and-fast gender role stereotypes forces homosexual men and women to communicate more effectively and to be more flexible and creative in meeting relationship needs. Gay men and women are more willing to communicate, experiment, and be more attentive to detail in their sexual behavior (Kurdek, 1993).

Research on long-term relationships for those identifying as bisexual has, by definition, needed to examine adult relationship patterns along with assumptions held about sexual orientation. If a bisexual woman, for example, has a long-term committed relationship with another woman, has she moved to a lesbian identity, or does she maintain her identification within that relationship, choosing to be monogamous and not be involved with men?

Weinberg, Williams, and Pryor (2001) have conducted longitudinal research with a group of adults from the San Francisco area. Beginning in 1983, surveying again in 1988 and then in 1996, the researchers were able to collect data that describe how changing life commitments such as marriage and parenthood affect sexuality. They also analyzed how age-linked social roles changed commitments and how individuals have been affected by various sexual identity movements such as queer politics. As individuals got older, changes were found in sexual involvement, the direction of sexual behavior, ties to the bisexual community, and the stability of sexual identity. Specifically, as people got older, their levels of sexual activity declined, citing reasons such as reduced energy levels, menopause-related concerns, fear of AIDS, and partner availability.

Weinberg and colleagues also found that there was a move toward monogamy with a sexual drift in the direction of heterosexuality. Part of that drift was explained by some participants as owing to having moved away from San Francisco, where people were more likely to be "out" and available. Fear of AIDS sometimes led people to choose heterosexual monogamy, thinking that option left them safe from infection. At the same time, more than one-fifth of the study group had become exclusively homosexual in their sexual behavior, feeling sex and relationships were easier with same-sex partners.

In contrast to lesbian and gay older adults, aging bisexuals do not have the same social networks and political groups for affirmation. Generational differences and newer political approaches have not created a bisexual community, whereas gay and lesbian communities are more visible. Nonetheless, participants were very clear about their identities as bisexual, able to look at their sexual history and sustained dual attraction (Weinberg et al., 2001).

Stages in Homosexual Relationships   In one of the most extensive, long-term prospective studies of male homosexuals to date, McWhirter and Mattison (1984) followed 156 gay couples for more than 20 years. The subjects were gay couples who had been together approximately 9 years before enrolling in the study. The researchers found that gay relationships, like those of their heterosexual counterparts, went through a series of stages.

Stage 1: Blending. This stage characterizes the first year of the relationship. As with heterosexual couples, this year has the highest levels of sexual activity, strong love and passion, and a merging of personal interests.

Stage 2: Nesting. Nesting takes place during years 2 to 3, emphasizing relationship building and starting a home together. Ambivalence, problems, and doubts about the relationship are most likely to begin to surface at this stage.

Stage 3: Maintaining. The third stage is characterized by a decline in passion and frequency of sexual activity, with an emphasis on conflict resolution and reassertion of some of the individuality subverted during the initial stages of the relationship.

Stage 4: Building. The building stage occupies years 6 through 10 and is marked by increased personal productivity and independence but also enhanced collaboration and developing sense of trust and dependability between the partners.

Stage 5: Releasing. From years 11 to 20, this stage is characterized by merging of money and other assets and beginning to take each other for granted. Sexual activity drops off noticeably in this stage.

Stage 6: Renewing. The last stage extends beyond 20 years together and is marked by personal security and a restored sense of partnership based on remembering shared experiences and good times together.

Because of better planning throughout their relationship, homosexual men and women may be better prepared for dealing with losses such as the death of their partner and retirement. Many homosexuals have planned for their own financial support and have consciously developed supportive social networks. They also may be better prepared to cope with hardship, having lived a life of adversity as a member of a stigmatized group. This combination of attitude, social and financial resources, and self-reliance may help gay men and women cope with the demands of aging.

Sexuality in Older Adults

In Erik Erikson's (1978) final stage, old age, our major developmental task is to maintain integrity in the face of death. This last stage begins in older adulthood with the growing awareness of the nearness of death. This is a time for facing our mortality and accepting the worth and uniqueness of our lives.

Maintaining integrity entails evaluating our lives and accomplishments. In a sense, we are verifying our existence and seeking its meaning. We do this by looking back at where we've been, what we've accomplished, whom we have touched (Erikson, 1978). This process often involves reminiscing with family, friends, and others.

One problem with discussing "old age" is the need to define it. College students may think old begins in the 60s and 70s, whereas 70-year-olds may view those in their 80s and 90s as being "old." When widows and widowers reenter the social scene, they need to acclimate to what may seem to be new dating rules. In particular, at what point should couples be sexual with each other? Will dating lead to love, commitment, and possible remarriage? How does one's family react to the new partner?

Particular attention and educational programs have been developed for older adults who must learn to practice safer sex. HIV/AIDS rates among older adults are not uncommon (D. Joslin, February 2003, personal interview), yet many are not prepared to integrate condom use, for example, into their social and sexual lives ("The Elderly and HIV" Conference, 2000).

Sexual Response and Aging

Sex doesn't necessarily get better or worse as we age; it just gets different. Many myths have arisen in regard to sexual response and aging. The following three are common ones that usually surface during classroom discussions in our classes:

Once you start to get old (over age 50), you lose interest in sex.
Older people aren't sexually attracted to each other.
Older people can't perform sexually or have orgasms.

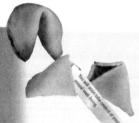

healthy sex hints 6.4

Changes in Sexual Response Associated with Aging

Women

The following changes are associated with sexual response in women who have gone through menopause:

1. The vagina is less elastic and not able to expand as much.
2. Physiological responses to sexual stimuli take more time.
3. Vaginal lubrication takes longer and may be less effective in reducing vaginal irritation.
4. The clitoris is smaller but not less responsive.
5. The intensity of orgasmic contractions diminishes slightly.
6. The ability to have multiple orgasms does not change.

Men

The following physiological changes have been observed in men older than age 55:

1. Arousal takes longer and may require manual stimulation of the penis.
2. Erections tend to be less firm.
3. Less semen is ejaculated.
4. There is less need to ejaculate to enjoy sexual activity.
5. The intensity of orgasmic contractions is slightly diminished.
6. More time is necessary to get another erection.

case study 6.3

Happy Harry

Harry, 78, is white.

Harry is living in an apartment at a newly developed senior residence. The residence is private and costs approximately $5,000 a month. Harry doesn't mind the cost because his meals are free, the staff takes care of most of his needs, and his pension, fortunately, provided nicely for his retirement. Harry's children no longer need his financial support, so he's enjoying life without worrying about taking care of anyone else.

Harry had been happily married to June, but when she passed away 5 years earlier, he decided he could no longer live in their house by himself. Little did he know how much in demand he would be once he arrived at the residence! The ratio of ladies to gentlemen is 4:1, and Harry is very popular. He knows he's not the best-looking guy, but he is agile and loves to dance, go out to movies, and generally have a good time. He's decided not to commit to any one woman, although he's had plenty of offers. At this point, being a free man with a lot of attention is just fine.

As for sex . . . well, he does have one or two special ladies with whom he spends the night. He feels a bit like a teenager again, sneaking around the residence hoping that one doesn't see him enter the room of the other.

> ### Critical Thinking
> The ratio of men to women in many adult residences is such that "partner sharing" may become necessary for heterosexual individuals. How do you think you would react to such an arrangement? Would sharing a partner be acceptable if the alternative meant being unattached?
>
> Use your Virtual Workbook to explore your answers to these questions at **http://health.wadsworth.com/blonna1.**

Physiologically, most men and women change very little during their 30s and early 40s. The most noticeable changes in sexual response in women are associated with menopause. They begin to experience a syndrome called the **female climacteric** between 45 and 55 years of age, as a result of a drop in levels of estrogen production associated with menopause. Common symptoms are hot flashes, irritability, inability to concentrate, and declines in sexual desire. The climacteric ends with menopause, which is the cessation of ovulation and loss of fertility. About one-fourth of women experience menopause before age 45, half from 45 to 50, and the remaining fourth after the age of 50 (Kart, 1994).

The changes in sexual physiology among most men in their 40s and 50s are less noticeable. Although sperm production slows down after age 40, it continues into the 80s and 90s. Similarly, though male sexual hormone levels decline gradually after age 55, most men have no noticeable drop-off in sexual desire. About 5 percent of men older than 60 experience the **male climacteric,** which produces symptoms similar to those of menopause. Men, however, do not lose their fertility as a result of the climacteric as women do when they experience menopause.

These physiological changes, in men and women, which basically revolve around the sexual response slowing and the intensity of response lessening slightly, are more than offset by greater comfort about sexuality, no fear of pregnancy, familiarity with one's partner, and extending the sex act.

Female climacteric A syndrome experienced by women between about 45 and 55 years of age as a result of declining levels of estrogen production associated with menopause

Male climacteric A syndrome experienced by about 5 percent of men in their 40s and 50s, characterized by diminished interest in sex, loss of appetite, fatigue, and inability to concentrate

Changing Relationships

Older age is often affected by the changing nature of relationships and family life as the commitment to relationships that began in young adulthood continues and deepens. For many, this is a period marked by divorce or the death of a mate or

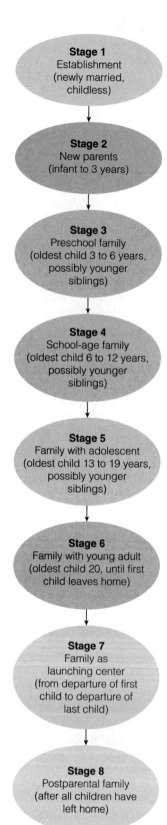

Stage 1
Establishment
(newly married,
childless)

Stage 2
New parents
(infant to 3 years)

Stage 3
Preschool family
(oldest child 3 to 6 years,
possibly younger
siblings)

Stage 4
School-age family
(oldest child 6 to 12 years,
possibly younger
siblings)

Stage 5
Family with adolescent
(oldest child 13 to 19 years,
possibly younger
siblings)

Stage 6
Family with young adult
(oldest child 20, until first
child leaves home)

Stage 7
Family as
launching center
(from departure of first
child to departure of
last child)

Stage 8
Postparental family
(after all children have
left home)

Figure 6.3 *Duvall's Family Life Cycle*

lover. The case study featuring Harry illustrates that loss of a partner need not mean loss of a social and sexual life.

Duvall (1977) developed an often-cited eight-stage theory of the family life cycle given in Figure 6.3. Stage 8, the postparental years, generally coincides with late adulthood and old age. Many events blend during this time: menopause and other physiological changes of aging, retirement, older children leaving the nest, and grandchildren, to name just a few. Although often characterized negatively as a time of loss and failed health, it also is a dynamic period in which newfound freedom, psychological and social stability, and wisdom can be a springboard to greater happiness for couples.

Duvall's model admittedly assumes that "family life" includes children. Obviously there are adults, coupled or single, who have never had children. Some older adults also have no contact with their children and extended family.

Most older couples today have grown old together. The average couple can expect at least 15 years of living together after the last child leaves. This is quite different from the turn of the century, when death affected half of all marriages before the last child left the house (Kart, 1994).

Studies have revealed mixed findings concerning marital satisfaction and happiness in the older years. In general, most of those who remain married report high levels of marital satisfaction in their older years, but divorce among older people has doubled since 1960 and is predicted to be more prevalent in future populations over age 65 (Kart, 1994).

Marital Satisfaction and Aging

As married couples reach midadulthood, happiness that was at an all-time low in their early 40s begins to rebound when the adult children leave home (Berry & Williams, 1987). Children's moving out frees up time and money. The couple finds they have the time, money, and privacy to reestablish the things in their relationship that provide pleasure, as well as investigate new things together.

Marital happiness continues to rise in the later adult years and carries over into retirement. Depending on a number of factors ranging from health to retirement income, the couple continue to enjoy their freedom and, in some cases, relationships with their children's families and grandchildren (Cavanaugh, 1993).

Most of us know couples who have celebrated their 50th, or golden, wedding anniversary. We marvel at their longevity and wonder about the secret to their success. Researchers have studied this issue, and the findings are inconsistent. Part of the problem lies with defining happiness. Older couples differ from younger ones in their standards for happiness. They share a history that includes memories of the Great Depression, world wars, and more traditional roles for marriage and marital satisfaction. Their marital happiness and contentment may be based on a different set of standards than those of younger married people.

A long-term study of 17 happily married couples found that the most significant factor related to marital satisfaction was their ability to adapt to change and "roll with the punches" (Weishaus & Field, 1988). These couples had the ability to adapt to changing circumstances that normally might be interpreted as stressful and potentially damaging to the relationship. They might view a serious illness, for instance, as an opportunity for caring and closeness rather than anger and alienation.

Divorce in Older Couples

In many cases, marital dissatisfaction in older adulthood is not related to any age-specific cause but, rather, resurfaces after years of being subordinated by issues related to child rearing. With the children grown and out of the house, old tensions and discontent surface and become a source of stress. Dependency is a key issue in the level of marital satisfaction in older couples. The extent of dependence of one mate on the other seems to be related to the strength of the relationship and its ability to last. When dependence is mutual and the level is relatively equal for both partners, relationships are strong and close. When dependence is not equal and one partner's needs are much greater than the other's, marital conflict is much more likely (Cavanaugh, 1993). When dependence is not equal or mutual, one partner may perceive normal developmental issues such as retirement and relocation as threatening, and, therefore, they become a source of resentment, discontent, and stress. Other issues that dampen marital happiness in old age include health problems, caring for sick parents and children, and financial problems.

Divorce is particularly distressing to older adults because of the long time invested in another's personal and practical life. In general, the longer the marriage, the greater is the trauma. In many cases, an elderly person's identity is closely wrapped up in being another person's husband or wife. Loss of this status often results in loss of economic status and lifestyle, friends (who often choose sides), and self-concept (Cavanaugh, 1993).

Divorce carries a much greater stigma for elderly people than for young people. Because of this, many elderly people underreport their status as divorced when filling out forms, applying for services, and the like (Kart, 1994). Divorce in an elderly person, particularly a woman, also may account for much greater loss than for a younger adult because of retirement, the empty nest, and relocation of family. Whereas younger divorced persons still have a job to report to, children to care for and interact with, and friends and family in the vicinity, elderly people often face the loss of these important connections.

Widowhood

Although a person can become widowed at any time during a marriage, it is much more likely later in life. **Widowhood** is more common for women; more than half of all women over age 65 are widows, whereas just 15 percent of men are widowers at that age. The two main reasons are that men have a shorter average life expectancy than women and women tend to marry men older than themselves. Consequently, most married women in the United States can expect to live between 10 and 12 years as a widow if they choose not to remarry (Cavanaugh, 1993).

Widowhood The period of time between loss of spouse and remarriage

Widowhood can be stressful in a number of ways besides ending a partnership. U.S. society does not have well-defined social roles for widowed people. Therefore, they often are left alone by family and friends who don't know how to respond to them. Widowed individuals also may feel awkward as single people trying to fit into their previously coupled world.

Men are generally older than women when they become widowed. Men are thought to be less able to cope with the death of their wife than women are by the loss of their husband. This outcome may be a result of the way men are reared; the wife's having been the husband's only close confidant; the lack of experience of most men in cooking, cleaning, doing the laundry, and so forth; and the tendency of men to be more socially isolated than women (Cavanaugh, 1993).

Women may be able to cope better because they have more extensive social networks and are better equipped to live alone, as most are able to maintain a household and take care of themselves. At the same time, women's widowhood behavior patterns seem to be more variable than men's.

Not all women find widowhood equally stressful or stressful at all. In studying more than 300 widows in Chicago, Lopata (1973) found six different behavior patterns in women after the deaths of their husbands:

1. "Liberated wives" were able to grieve the loss of their spouse and move on to live full productive lives.
2. "Merry widows" went on to live lives of fun, dating, and various forms of entertainment.
3. "Working widows" continued their career or took a new job.
4. "Widows' widows" continued to live alone, were independent, and enjoyed the company of primarily other widows.
5. "Traditional widows" moved in with their children and took an active role in the lives of their grandchildren.
6. "Grieving widows" were unable to work through their loss and willingly isolated themselves from others.

The death of a loved one can lead to feelings of helplessness, hopelessness, and a sense of emptiness that can precipitate a variety of physical and mental illnesses. Cohen and Syme (1985) studied 4,500 adults over age 45 who had lost a spouse to premature death. Their study became known as the "broken heart" study because they found that nearly 40 percent of the surviving spouses died of heart problems during the 6 months following the death of their spouse. The percentage of deaths dropped steadily after this time and returned to that of the control group after 5 years. Other studies have confirmed these findings and have indicated that one of the factors mediating a return to normal risk of death is remarriage of the surviving spouse (Hafen, Frandsen, Karren, & Hooker, 1992).

healthy sex hints 6.5
Dealing with Grief and Loss

The death of a loved one ranks at the top of life's most stressful events. The loss can impact all dimensions of our health—we may lose our appetite, feel depressed, experience a sense of emptiness in our home, not be able to concentrate, and so forth. How individuals grieve varies, with some able to cry openly while others bury themselves in tasks. Individual reactions to loss may also depend on whether a death was sudden or the culmination of a long and painful illness.

The loss of one's partner can be devastating. Individuals who have lived decades as part of a couple may struggle to understand how to find joy in life and live independently. Some may need to find a new partner quickly; others may feel that the lost love could never be replaced.

Grieving for a lost partner can be compounded by the relationship having been secret. It may be difficult to openly grieve and attend a funeral, for example, if your partner had never shared your existence with too many others. Long after the death of the famous aviator Charles Lindbergh, and shortly after the death of Senator Strom Thurmond, the facts of their secret "other" families came

to light. Those descendents who had long been recognized as family were suddenly confronted with learning that the father they had loved had a past with which they were unfamiliar.

Whatever the circumstances, however, individuals must work through their grief. The following guidelines may prove beneficial:

- Accept your feelings, and understand that such emotions as anger, guilt, and relief are normal.
- Accept help from others, who may bring food, provide emotional comfort, and listen to you talk about your loss.
- Although grief can be private, you don't have to pretend to be strong and hold in your feelings.
- Give yourself time—grieving can be a long process. There is no set timetable for working through grief. There may be good days and bad days.
- Seek professional help if you remain intensely distressed for more than 6 months.

Source: Adapted from Hales (2003, p. 615).

Grief and Loss in Nontraditional Long-Term Relationships

In a study of grief and loss among those in **nontraditional relationships** (extra-marital affairs, cohabitation, and homosexual relationships), the normal stages of grief were compounded by the nontraditional nature of the relationships studied (Doka, 1987). In homosexual and other relationships, conflicting needs compound the healing process of grief. A need to declare and demonstrate sorrow and affection for the loved one is tempered by a need to maintain secrecy and fear that the relationship will be disclosed. Some hospitals, for instance, restrict access to "husbands or wives" or "immediate family." The need for social support, and to grieve with the other mourners, is countered by a sense of social isolation and distancing. These compounding factors are minimized for homosexual couples who are not maintaining a secret relationship. Being active in the gay community has helped gay couples develop social support networks that enable them to cope more effectively with a variety of issues associated with aging (Quam & Whitford, 1992).

Nontraditional relationships Any relationships other than a monogamous, legal marriage between a man and a woman

Spiritual Wellness

Adulthood and old age are potentially a time of great spiritual awakening and renewal. For most people this is a time of developing intimate, loving relationships, making permanent (sacramental) commitments, having children, caring for sick and dying parents, and coming to terms with our own mortality. We are forced to examine these issues, all of which have a spiritual dimension. Understanding the meaning of these events, coping with them and their universality, help us develop a sense of connectedness with something other than ourselves. If we allow ourselves to look beyond the self and gain strength through connecting with others, we can enhance our spirituality, which can help us lead more satisfying and productive lives.

Your responses to the Personal Assessment, Thought Questions, and Test Yourself! quiz questions can be logged online in your Virtual Workbook at **http://health.wadsworth.com/blonna1.**

Personal Assessment

6.1 Relationship Contract

Relationships are fluid, yet many couples move toward commitment. Traditionally, heterosexual couples will marry. Until the institution of marriage is extended to gay and lesbian couples, commitment ceremonies remain an emerging ritual that parallels weddings. How couples structure their commitment varies tremendously, regardless of sexual orientation.

The purpose of this assessment is to help you examine the nature of your intimate relationships. A secondary purpose is to help you realize that you have the ability to structure your relationships any way you want.

Fill out the following relationship contract. There are no right or wrong answers. Just jot down your thoughts and feelings regarding the various categories. You may wish to ask your instructor for the opportunity to go over your contract with other students in a small group.

Name
Should the wife take on the husband's last name?
Should the husband take on the wife's last name?
If the partners are same sex, will either or both change last names?
Should both take on a hyphenated last name?
Should both take a new name?
Should both keep their own name?
What will the children's surname be if there are any?

Birth Control
What kind?
Whose responsibility?

Household Duties
Who does what?

Leisure Time
Should evenings and weekends be spent together?
Who decides what to do?
Should vacations be spent together? With children? Separately?

Living Arrangements
Where will the couple live?
What kind of privacy do you need?
Shared bedroom?
Do you want to live with others?
What will you and your partner do if you want to live in different places because of jobs or for any other reasons?

Money
Will both partners work?
If so, will you pool your money?
Or will each keep own salary?
Or will the cost of living expenses be shared equally and the rest kept for yourselves?

Sexual Rights
Commitment to monogamy?
Who initiates sex?
Is either partner free not to respond?

Children
How many?
When?
Adopt?
Who will take primary responsibility for rearing the children?
Will one partner have to quit a job?

Other Relationships
Are you and your partner free to make relationships with other people?
With those of the same sex?
With those of the opposite sex?
What is to be the extent of these relationships?
Do you include each other in these relationships?

Thought Questions

1. What are some of the major developmental tasks of college students? Compare these to the major developmental tasks associated with adolescence.

2. Compare and contrast sexual behavior during the college years with that of middle adulthood. What are the differences?

3. What is Berry and Williams's model of marital satisfaction? Identify the stages.

4. What are the similarities and differences between long-term heterosexual relationships and lesbian and gay unions of the same duration?

5. What factors contribute to satisfaction and happiness in long-term relationships?

6. What changes in sexual response are associated with aging?

Test Yourself!

1. A primary developmental task of young adults is to
   a. develop friendships with peers.
   b. form a committed, intimate relationship with a partner.
   c. learn to trust others.
   d. identify one's sexual orientation.

2. Which generalization about sexual behavior among college students is most accurate?
   a. Rates of sexual activity are similar between males and females.
   b. Fewer students participate in oral sex compared to earlier generations.
   c. There is no evidence of a double standard in values for male and female behavior.
   d. The majority of students cohabit prior to committing to marriage.

3. Couples who are happily married tend to do all but which of the following?
   a. Maintain some level of individual identity
   b. Share similar interests and values
   c. Fight effectively, laying blame where it belongs
   d. Communicate honestly

4. Berry and Williams have developed a model for the phases of adult marriage. When do couples report being the most satisfied with their marriage?
   a. At the time of the birth of their first child
   b. When their children are adolescents
   c. During the honeymoon phase, at the beginning
   d. Once children move out of the house

5. The concept of "fighting fairly" includes all but which of the following?
   a. Avoiding personal attacks
   b. Taking responsibility for your behavior
   c. Being able to discuss all the things that have been bothering you
   d. Not fighting in front of others

6. Changes in female sexual response associated with aging include
   a. loss of sex drive.
   b. less clitoral response.
   c. less vaginal lubrication.
   d. loss of orgasm.

7. Changes in male sexual response associated with aging include
   a. less firm erections.
   b. loss of sex drive.
   c. increase in semen production.
   d. loss of the ability to ejaculate.

8. Marriage is a form of relationship commitment
   a. between two consenting adults.
   b. open to gay, lesbian, and heterosexual couples.
   c. shown to endure for the majority of couples.
   d. that offers financial, personal, and health benefits.

9. Long-term gay and lesbian relationships
   a. are not possible in the oppressive culture of the United States.
   b. have been proven more stable than heterosexual relationships.
   c. go through stages similar to those in a marriage, yet with economic differences.
   d. require individuals to assume traditional roles within the relationship.

10. Which statement about widowhood among women is least accurate?
    a. Women are often better able to cope with the loss than men.
    b. Women quickly remarry after the loss of a spouse.
    c. Some women feel liberated and adopt lifestyle changes, such as traveling.
    d. Traditional widows move in with their children and become involved in raising their grandchildren.

Media Menu

You can link to the following online tools by visiting
http://health.wadsworth.com/blonna1.

 **InfoTrac Activity**

Ponnuru, R. (2003, July 28). Coming out ahead: Why gay marriage is on the way. *National Review, 55* (14).

Bradley, G. V. (2003, July 28). Stand and fight: Don't take gay marriage lying down. *National Review, 55* (14).

 **Web Resources**

College Sex Talk

www.CollegeSexTalk.com

A Web site operated by Dr. Sandra Caron, certified sexuality educator and professor, where students can write in questions and receive age-appropriate responses to their concerns about sexuality.

National Institutes of Health

www.nih.gov

Typing "sexuality" into the search box will link users to numerous articles examining sexuality and health.

Administration on Aging, Department of Health and Human Services

www.aoa.gov

A Web site with information on sexuality in later life, HIV/AIDS and older adults, and so forth.

National Association on HIV over 50

www.hivoverfifty.org

A site devoted to older adults infected with HIV and/or those in need of information for themselves or others.

Senior Site

www.seniorsite.com

Sexual health information for older adults.

References

Berry, R. E., & Williams, E. (1987). Assessing the relationship between quality of life and marital and income satisfaction: A path analytic approach. *Journal of Marriage and the Family, 49,* 107–116.

Block, B. (1980). *Friendship: How to give it, how to get it.* New York: Macmillan.

Blumstein, P., & Schwartz, P. (1983). *American couples.* New York: Morrow.

Cahill, S., & Slater, S. (2003). Marriage: Legal protection for families and children—A policy brief from the National Gay and Lesbian Task Force Policy Institute [Online]. Available: www.ngltf.org.

Cavanaugh, J. C. (1993). *Adult development and aging.* Belmont, CA: Wadsworth.

Cohen, S., & Syme, S. L. (1985). *Social support and health.* Orlando, FL: Academic Press.

Crawford, M., & Popp, D. (2003, February). Sexual double standards: A review and methodological critique of two decades of research. *Journal of Sex Research, 40*(1).

Doka, K. J. (1987). Silent sorrow: Grief and loss of significant others. *Death Studies, 11*(8), 455–469.

Duvall, E. M. (1977). *Family development.* Philadelphia: Lippincott.

The Elderly and HIV Conference. (2000, December). Wayne General Hospital and William Paterson University.

Ellison, C. (2000). *Women's sexualities.* California: New Harbinger.

Erikson, E. (1978). *Childhood and society* (2nd ed.). New York: Norton.

Fields, J. (2001, June 29). [Report.] *U.S. Department of Commerce News.* U.S. Census Public Information Office. Washington, DC: U.S. Government Printing Office.

Hafen, B. Q., Frandsen, K. J., Karren, K. J., & Hooker, K. R. (1992). *The health effects of attitudes, emotions, and relationships.* Provo, UT: EMS Associates.

Hales, D. (2003). *An invitation to health* (10th ed.). Belmont, CA: Wadsworth/Thomson Learning.

Hughes, R. (2003). The demographics of divorce: United States and Missouri [Online]. Available: www.missourifamilies.org.

Kart, C. (1994). *The realities of aging: An introduction to gerontology.* Boston: Allyn & Bacon.

Kurdek, L. (1989). Relationship quality of gay and lesbian cohabiting couples. *Journal of Homosexuality, 15*(3–4), 93–118.

Kurdek, L. (1993). The allocation of household labor in gay, lesbian, and heterosexual married couples. *Journal of Social Issues, 49*(3), 127–139.

Lambda Legal Defense Fund. (2003). Cases: *Lawrence and Garner v. Texas* [Online]. Available: www.cache.lambdalegal.org.

Lambert, T. A., Kahn, A. S., & Apple, K. J. (2003). Pluralistic ignorance and hooking up. *Journal of Sex Research, 40*(2), 129–133.

Laumann, E., Gagnon, J. H., Michael, R. T., & Michaels, S. (1994). *The social organization of sexuality: Sexual practices in the United States.* Chicago: University of Chicago Press.

Laumann, E. O., & Michael, R. T. (2001). *Sex, love, and health in America: Private choices and public policies.* Chicago: University of Chicago Press.

Laumann, E. O., & Youm, Y. (2001). Sexual expression in America. In E. O. Laumann & R. Michael (Eds.), *Sex, love and health in America.* Chicago: University of Chicago Press.

Lipman, A. (1986). Homosexual relationships. *Generations, 10*(4), 51–54.

Lopata, H. Z. (1973). *Widowhood in an American city.* Cambridge, MA: Schenkman.

Masters, W. H., Johnson, V. E., & Kolodny, R. C. (1992). *Human sexuality* (4th ed.). New York: HarperCollins.

McWhirter, D., & Mattison D. (1984). *The male couple.* Englewood Cliffs, NJ: Prentice Hall.

Michael, R. T., Gagnon, J. H., Laumann, E. O., & Kolata, G. (1994). *Sex in America: A definitive survey.* Boston: Little, Brown.

National Center for Education Statistics. (2000). *Percentage distribution of undergraduates by marital status: 1999–2000.* U.S. Department of Education, 1999–2000 National Postsecondary Student Aid Study (NPSAS:2000). Washington, DC: Author.

Paul, E. L., McManus, B., & Hayes, A. (2000). Hookups: Characteristics and correlates of college students' spontaneous and anonymous sexual experiences. *Journal of Sex Research, 37*(1), 76–88.

Person, E. S. (1989). *Women—Sex and sexuality.* Chicago: University of Chicago Press.

Phillis, D. E., & Stein, P. J. (1983). Sink or swing? The lifestyles of single adults. In E. R. Allegeir & N. B. McCormick (Eds.), *Changing boundaries: Gender roles and sexual behavior.* Palo Alto, CA: Mayfield.

Quam, J. K., & Whitford, G. S. (1992). Adaptation and age-related expectations of elder gay and lesbian adults. *Gerontologist, 32*(3), 367–374.

Reinisch, J. M. (1992). *The Kinsey Institute new report on sex.* New York: St. Martin's.

Thomas, J. A. (2000, October 10). Childcare and laboratory schools on campus: The national picture [Online]. National Coalition for Campus Children's Centers. Available: www.campuschildren.org.

Times will begin reporting gay couples' ceremonies. (2002, August 18). *New York Times*, National Section.

U.S. Bureau of the Census. (2002). *Median age at first marriage* [Online]. Available: www.census.gov.

Weinberg, M. S., Williams, C. J., & Pryor, D. W. (2001, April). Bisexuals at midlife: Commitment, salience, and identity. *Journal of Contemporary Ethnography, 30.*

Weishaus, S., & Field, D. (1988). A half century of marriage: Continuity or change? *Journal of Marriage and the Family, 50,* 763–774.

Zilbergeld, B. (1999). *The new male sexuality* (rev. ed.). New York: Bantam Doubleday Dell.

chapter *eight*

Sensuality *and* Sexual Behavior

Student Learning Objectives

After reading this chapter, students will be able to

- Compare and contrast sensuality and sexuality.
- Compare and contrast celibacy and abstinence.
- Describe a variety of nonpenetrative sexual behaviors.
- Know how to give a sensual massage.
- Evaluate the myths associated with masturbation.
- Compare and contrast a variety of positions for vaginal intercourse.
- Identify the factors associated with healthy anal sexual behavior.
- Describe a variety of oral sex behaviors.
- Explain the effects of spinal cord injury on sexual behavior.

*Test your understanding of these objectives by taking the end-of-chapter quiz,
available online at **http://health.wadsworth.com/blonna1**.*

activity teaser: *Is your arousal boost an arousal block to your partner? Find the answer in the Personal Exploration Activity on page 246.*

case study 8.1

Delores: Sex in Pregnancy

Delores, 26, identifies as African American.

Delores is a 26-year-old nontraditional sophomore. She is married and the mother of a 6-month-old son, Greg. Delores describes her sexual experiences during her pregnancy.

Before I got pregnant, I was very concerned about the effects it would have on my sex life with my husband, Joe. We were married for 3 years and had a very satisfying sex life. I was worried about that changing. I've always liked sex, and I've kept in shape through running and lifting weights. I was concerned about gaining weight and my body changing shape. But I decided that I wouldn't limit my weight gain and make the baby suffer.

During the first trimester, my sex drive dropped a lot. I wasn't as horny as I normally was, and I had terrible morning sickness. Actually, I had morning, afternoon, and evening sickness and could hardly keep any food down. Other than that, though, nothing much changed. The frequency of sex dropped in half, but the kinds of things we did—positions—didn't change.

During the second trimester, my morning sickness disappeared, and I felt much better. I had put on some weight, but it really didn't affect our intercourse. I was concerned about bouncing around too much and things like rolling off the bed, but for the most part we didn't change our behaviors. The good news was that my sex drive returned to normal.

During the third trimester, things changed again. I had put on over 20 pounds and had a big belly. I was really concerned about deep penetration. I worried that it might hurt the baby, but my doctor reassured me that everything would be OK. I didn't have much energy, so we made love less often. We couldn't use any man- or woman-on-top positions. I've always liked the woman-on-top position with me sitting on my husband's lap, and I had to give that up, too.

I found that the only position we could use was the spoon [side-by-side] position. That allowed us to have full-body contact without putting pressure on my belly. It also allowed my husband to massage my breasts and belly. I had no desire for him to perform oral sex on me, but sometimes I liked to satisfy him that way, particularly on those days when I didn't have much energy. Overall, I think our sex life survived my pregnancy very well.

Critical Thinking

Pregnancy definitely imposes some unique challenges to our sexual desire and response. If you have never been pregnant, how do you think being pregnant will influence your sexual desire and response? If you have been pregnant before, how did it influence your sexual response and desire? Would you do anything differently regarding these issues the next time you are pregnant?

Use your Virtual Workbook to explore your answers to these questions at **http://health.wadsworth.com/blonna1.**

As Delores has shown us, one's sensuality and sexual behavior manifest themselves in many ways. In this chapter, we'll examine sensuality and how it is related to sexual behavior. We'll consider the full range of sexual behaviors, starting with celibacy.

Sensuality

As we discussed in Chapter 7, sexual response originates in our brain and senses, but what *is* sensuality? What makes a person sensual? Is it the richness and texture of her features (thick, long hair; distinct, angular nose; high cheekbones; long, exotic nails; tantalizing perfume/cologne; self-assured body language)? Is it his attitude (a deep thinker, caring/loving personality, down-to-earth simplicity)? Could it be her appreciation of life (enjoys great food, appreciates music, likes nature, enjoys physical activities)? We will answer these questions and provide hints on how to enhance and develop one's sensuality since it is the basis for all sexual response and behavior.

Although they are intimately related, sexuality and sensuality are different. **Sensuality** is the quality of being sensual, of experiencing life fully through all of the senses. **Sexuality,** you will remember, is a broad term that refers to all aspects of being sexual, encompassing a variety of biological, psychological, and cultural

Sensuality Experiencing things through all five senses

Sexuality Broad term that refers to all aspects of being sexual

variables. Sensuality is a part of our sexuality. People who are very sensual have a heightened awareness of sight, sound, taste, touch, and smell. They use this increased awareness to experience life through all of these senses whenever possible. They approach each experience, every day, through this context or frame of reference. A walk in the woods or down a bustling city street is a symphony of sounds, colors, scents, tastes, and textures.

This increased sensitivity to and appreciation of all sensory stimuli carries over into their sexuality and lovemaking. The heightened awareness of all the senses enhances lovemaking. Sensual lovers delight in all aspects of their partners and their surroundings, making sex a feast for the senses. Sex isn't just a genital-driven quest for orgasm. It is a five-course gourmet meal that may include climax as the entree.

Developing Sensuality

William Burnham, a pioneering educational psychologist, believed that all humans are born as sensual creatures (Burnham, 1932). As newborns, we experience life through all of our senses. Burnham referred to this as being "fully integrated." Little separates our intellect and our senses.

A good example of this integration is how children play in the grass. Think about how toddlers play in the grass. They roll around in it, close their eyes, lie back in it, and listen to the sounds the wind makes as it blows through the high blades. They pull out handfuls of grass, throw them up in the air, and watch the blades fall to earth. They take a blade of grass and examine it carefully, rolling it around in their fingers, maybe even against their cheeks with their eyes closed. As they squeeze the grass between their fingers, they notice that oils are secreted. They smell this oil and taste it. Satiated with the grass, they move on to the next activity.

How many of us as adults take the time to get into the "grassiness" of life anymore? Have we lost our ability to revel in the "grassiness," or do we still have it but don't utilize it? We authors believe that we still have the ability to be fully integrated with the here and now of our lives but do not take advantage of it as often as we could. Along the course of our lives, most of us, for many reasons, stop experiencing life with all of our senses. We pay less and less attention to anything other than sight and sound (the primary senses we need to get through our work day). Of course we still occasionally remark about "how good something tastes" or how "nice something smells," but these observations are more often than not isolated and not part of our overall orientation to life.

What transforms the sensual child into a constrained adult? Why does this happen? Are we afraid of what others would think if they were to see us rolling in the grass at age 18 or 28 or 48 years? Or have we "been there, done that?" Are we too jaded to enjoy the simple, free, sensual delights that surround us?

We've asked our students these questions, and the results are very interesting. Often, students will just stare at us like we are crazy and then say, "Yeah, right, I can just see myself rolling around the grass like a baby, pulling up handfuls of grass." When pressed about what they would feel, they admit that such behavior would make them "feel weird" or "self-conscious." Many said, "What would other people think?" Many fear that such behavior could get them labeled by other people as "crazy" or at the very least "strange." Some even worry that a neighbor might think they are on drugs and call the police.

We asked them to think of other, less conspicuous scenarios such as sitting on the beach and playing with a handful of sand (chosen because of the diversity of the size, colors, and textures of things found within it), watching a sunset, making bread from scratch, giving someone a shampoo, and listening to the wind blow through the trees on a brisk autumn day. In most cases the opposition to these activities was the same, but two other major issues were time and familiarity. "Who has the time?" and "Been there, done that" were often their refrains.

Often, it's not until we make the connection between their sensuality and their sexual pleasure that they begin to take the topic seriously. Losing the ability to be sensual can greatly affect our ability to experience sexual pleasure and experience eroticism through all of the senses. In many cases it can lead to dysfunction (in Chapter 12 we describe "sensate focus," a technique used by sex therapists to help dysfunctional people relearn how to be sensual). Our advice is to *make the time* now to enhance your sexuality and prevent dysfunction. By slowing down and integrating all of your senses into your daily experiences, you are setting the stage for doing the same thing in the boudoir.

healthy sex hints 8.1
Becoming a More Sensuous Person

Becoming more sensual starts with acknowledging the need to and giving yourself permission to *indulge* your senses. For some people this will involve unlearning some of the prohibitions and inhibitions you were raised with. It's OK to pamper yourself.

Sight: Enhance Visual Sensations

Most of us take our sight for granted and don't look at visual detail as something we can develop and expand. If something beautiful passes through our lives, we acknowledge it and move on. Try the following tips to develop and enhance the sights in your life.

1. Discover *flowers;* keep flowers on your desk, in your kitchen, and elsewhere in your home.
2. Immerse yourself in art (pictures, posters, photographs, drawings).
   - Paint/shoot/draw them yourself, buy art books, or cut works of art out of
   - Magazines.
   - Visit art galleries, museums, and online art sites (such as www.art.com).
   - Don't worry about what you don't know about art; focus on *what you like* and *surround yourself* with it (Marrone, 2002).
3. Take a good look at nature (sunsets, sunrises, natural beauty).
   - Star gaze.
   - Watch the sun rise and set.
   - Become an ardent cloud watcher.
   - Watch the waves crash, the tides move in and out, a local brook/stream tumble over rocks and cascade over cliffs (Eiseman, 1999).

4. Explore minienvironments.
   - Scoop a handful of sand where the water meets the shore, and spend 30 minutes examining it.
   - Take a close look at snowflakes, icicles, and frost on leaves.
   - Spend a half an hour exploring a tide pool (Eiseman, 1999).
5. Add color to your life.
   - Open your shades and let the sun shine in.
   - Drape colorful sun shades over your windows (pale orange will help trigger an endorphin release (Eiseman, 1999).

Touch: Enhance Tactile Stimulation

1. Try massage.
   - Take turns giving and receiving foot and hand massages.
   - Your feet contain over 7,000 nerve endings. Stimulating them sends pleasurable electrical impulses coursing throughout your body (Bender, 1999).
   - There are over 40,000 nerve endings in the palms waiting to be rubbed, scratched, and tickled (Kemp, 2000).
2. Knead dough.
   - Try making bread by hand and/or throwing pottery. Nothing beats these two nonsexual activities for developing an appreciation of touch.
   - Kneading dough or clay is one of life's most enjoyable tactile delights. It slows you down, stimulates the more than 40,000 nerve endings of the palms and hands, and is great practice for massage.

Types of Sexual Behavior

One way to present the many forms of sexual behavior is to place them on a continuum from celibacy to oral/anal sex. This presentation is useful in understanding safer sex options, as well as choices in fertility control.

Celibacy and Abstinence

Celibacy is defined as abstaining from sexual intercourse. Although the formal definition of celibacy refers specifically to abstaining from sexual intercourse and never marrying, many people assume that celibacy and abstinence mean total

Celibacy Abstaining from sexual intercourse

3. Give/receive shampoos.
   - There is nothing quite like having someone else wash your hair slowly and lovingly with warm water and lots of shampoo.
   - Practice on your pet. He or she will love you for it, and you will derive tactile joy from doing it.
   - Combine a long, gentle shampoo with a sensual bubble bath or shower. Take time to wash your partner with lots of soap, bubbles, and shampoo. Use a wash towel or sponge to add different textures to the experience.
4. Pet your pet.
   - Snuggling into the furry comfort of your pet's luxurious fur/hair is a sensual pleasure you both will enjoy.
   - Try to brush/comb your pet's coat at least once a week. It will slow you down and help you learn to relax and appreciate the luster of beautiful fur/hair.
5. Indulge yourself with different fabrics to wear.
   - Treat yourself to something that feels good: silk underwear; satin sheets; fleece scarves and mittens; a cashmere or angora sweater; a flannel nightshirt; leather pants, vest, or blazer. Soft, supple leather has always had a sexual appeal, as does soft, well-worn denim.
6. Be naked more.
   - Sleep naked, swim naked, run outside in the rain naked, sunbathe naked (of course, do this in places where you won't get arrested for indecency).
   - Start slowly. Sleep naked beneath clean satin, flannel, or Egyptian cotton sheets. Feel the sensations on your flesh.

Smell: Enhance Olfactory Delights

1. Use perfumes, colognes, soaps, and other scents.
   - Scientists have finally found the existence of pheromones in humans.
   - Perfumes, soaps, and other products that contain human pheromones switch on parts of the brain (hypothalamus) and increase feelings of well-being and self-confidence (Kraus, 2000; Brand, 2001).
   - Scents range from very light to heavy and from musky to fruity, to floral.
   - Goins (2001) suggests rubbing your partner's favorite scents on parts of your clothing, like your shirt collar, so he or she can smell it as you give him or her a good-bye/hello hug and kiss.
2. Light candles.
   - Use candles to set the mood (candles combine scents with color to heighten both visual and olfactory sensations).
   - Use candles in the bathroom when you take a bath.
   - Use them at night to serve as sensual night lights while you watch TV.
   - Use candles to add to the joys of a special meal.
   - Use seasonal candles to add the scents of the season to your day. For instance, pine candles have always been associated with the winter holidays (Bender, 1999).
3. Try sachet bags.
   - Use sachet bags of your favorite scent to liven your room, closet, office, or car.
   - Make your own sachet bags by using leftover pieces of cloth, cuttings from your favorite plants, pine needles, or flower petals.
4. Buy or pick flowers.
   - Flowers help develop and maintain your olfactory senses.
   - Flowers such as lilac can provide a gentle scent, while others, such as honeysuckle, can sometimes be too overpowering. Your local florist can help you identify flowers that meet your sensual demands.
5. Experience nature.
   - Walk or bicycle more. You'll be amazed at the different smells that surround you if you get out of that protective cocoon (your car).

avoidance of all forms of sexual release and the absence of sexual desire. Celibacy may or may not include masturbation and fantasy as forms of sexual release. Celibate people also have varying degrees of sexual desire. Not all celibate people lack sexual interest and desire, though; they merely choose to channel that energy and desire into different avenues of expression.

Celibacy is usually associated with a spiritual or religious sacrifice and is considered to be a lifelong commitment. Priests and nuns, for instance, declare a vow of celibacy so they may devote themselves fully to serving God and never marry. It is a conscious, willful diversion of sexual energy into nonsexual activity. Kathleen Norris (1996) uses the phrase "celibate passion" to describe how celibate monks are able to transform sexual energy into a sense of deep caring and love that she found to be unique among celibate people.

Not all people who choose celibacy, however, do so as part of a religious commitment. Actually, all of us choose to wait before we engage in intercourse. Many people choose celibacy because they are not ready to begin having intercourse, and they satisfy their sexual needs through other behaviors. We all develop at our own pace, and some of us are simply not ready as soon as others are.

We sometimes choose celibacy because we need time to recover or grieve from relationships that have ended. We need time to heal emotionally and are not interested in forming sexual relationships at the time. Others choose celibacy be-

healthy sex hints 8.1 (continued)

Taste: Sample Your World

1. Taste your partner.
   - Experience your partner with your mouth.
   - Experience all parts of his or her body.
   - Take a shower together and drink the water from his or her flesh. Lick the beaded water off your partner's nipples and body.
   - Experiment with oral sex.
   - Play with sensual eating.
   - Put together a sensual snack feast of fresh fruits, cheeses, and a bottle of wine.
   - Put it on a big platter with some crackers, and spend an hour eating it slowly in bed while you feed each other and toast your good fortune.
   - Some people like to play with things such as whipped cream or chocolate syrup in bed and lick these delights off each other (the authors have found this to create a sticky mess that can often put a damper on rather than heighten the sensual experience).
   - Try mixing tastes when you can. Moving from a tart to sweet or mild to potent taste sensation can awaken your taste buds.
   - Slow down and take smaller bites. Savor rather than devour your food, and enjoy the process of eating as well as the outcome.

Sound: Listen to the Environment

1. Make music a part of your day.
   - Music can relax you, help you forget your problems, reduce stress, recharge your batteries, and even turn you on.
   - Certain rhythms and beats mimic your body's natural tempo during sex.
   - Matching music (such as Caribbean or Latin) to the movements of your lovemaking can enhance the response (Goins, 2001).
2. Listen to nature.
   - Listen to the wind blow through the trees, the waves crash on the shore, the steam trickle through the rocks.
   - Walk in the woods; listen to the birds.
3. Become comfortable with silence.
   - Build "quiet time" into each day.
   - Allow your mind to unclutter by shutting out auditory stimuli for 20 minutes each day.
   - Listen to your partner's breathing (holding your partner or being united in intercourse and listening to his or her breathing can be both a sensual delight and a sexual turn-on).

In general, try to *slow down* and *pay attention* to the interplay of your five senses in whatever you are doing whenever you can. This will increase your awareness of how the senses work together and reinforce the importance of becoming more sensual.

case study 8.2

Susan: Choosing to Be Celibate

Susan, 31, divorced, identifies as bisexual.

I've been celibate for the past year and a half. I'm 31 years old, have a 5-year-old daughter, work full-time, and go to school full-time. Things just never worked out with my daughter's father, and ever since I've been back to school, I haven't had the energy to even think about sex. My schedule is crazy, and I don't have much free time. When I have time off, I prefer to spend it with my daughter. I don't have the time to spend on cultivating a relationship. I really want to finish school and get good enough grades to get into graduate school someday.

I don't miss intercourse. It's not that I don't like sex. Before I got married, I used to really get off on sex with both men and women. My sex life with my daughter's father was really great, and eventually I stopped having sex with anyone else but him and got pregnant. Things between us were never the same after that and since we split up, I've just been burned out on the idea of starting a new relationship. I masturbate a couple of times a week and prefer to deal with my sexual needs that way. I can see this changing someday and hope to meet a woman who can love and satisfy me and love my daughter. For now, though, I'm not looking for a relationship.

Critical Thinking

Think about your own life and periods where you have chosen voluntary celibacy. What were the circumstances surrounding your choice, and was it the right decision for you? If you have never chosen celibacy, describe a future situation where this strategy might work for you.

Use your Virtual Workbook to explore your answers to these questions at **http://health.wadsworth.com/blonna1.**

cause they do not have the time or energy to sustain a commitment (sexual or otherwise) with another person. They think they need all of their energy for school or work, especially if they are beginning a new career or starting school. They don't want to divert time and energy from these areas.

The generic definition of **abstinence** is self-restraint or self-denial. Sexual abstinence, therefore, refers to self-restraint or self-denial of sexual activities. Many people assume that abstinence means denial of all forms of sexual behavior. Actually, one can choose to abstain from unprotected intercourse but not other forms of sexual behavior.

Abstinence usually is not discussed as a lifelong spiritual or religious commitment. It is more situational; a person can abstain for a day, a week, a month, a semester, and so on. It doesn't have to be an all-or-nothing proposition. Most of us have voluntarily chosen to abstain from sexual intercourse at various times during our lives. Once abstinence is viewed as a situational choice and not a lifetime commitment, it becomes easier to accept and understand as a viable sexual option. We also believe that although abstinence is a valid option for people, it is not the only option.

Abstinence Self-restraint or self-denial, as in not engaging in sexual activity

Nonpenetrative Sexual Activity

Nonpenetrative sexual activities offer a wide variety of pleasurable behaviors that can be carried out to the point of orgasm and involve little risk of pregnancy or disease. This activity has been called "outercourse" and includes options ranging from kissing and hugging to using sex toys. To us, nonpenetrative sexual activity includes any sexual behaviors that do not involve genital-to-genital, mouth-to-genital, or insertive anal sexual contact.

Kissing is an almost universal form of sexual expression.

Thinkstock/GettyImages

Kissing

Kissing can provide intense sensual and sexual delight. The sucking, licking, rubbing, and tongue probing associated with kissing is pleasurable and carries no risk for pregnancy. Volumes have been written about kissing.

As we age, we seem to become more genitally focused and lose some of our interest in kissing. Kissing becomes an ancillary activity associated with the real objective—orgasm—rather than a satisfying activity in and of itself.

healthy sex hints 8.2

10 Good Reasons for Choosing Abstinence

Abstinence has gotten a bad rap over the years. It's almost politically incorrect to talk about abstaining from sexual intercourse (and penetrative sex, if you're gay or a lesbian). Here are 10 good reasons to choose abstinence:

1. To retain your virginity for someone special
2. To get to know your partner better (you want to become more comfortable with your partner and come to trust him or her)
3. To ascertain your partner's STD/HIV status (you'd rather wait to have intercourse but might consider safer-sex options)
4. To wait to be in the mood (you'd rather be doing something else)
5. If you're heterosexual, to avoid pregnancy if neither of you has contraception (you might consider a low-risk sexual outlet other than intercourse)

6. To find a suitable partner (sure, you've had offers, but no one turns you on)
7. To recuperate from an illness or surgery (you're not feeling very sexy or are feeling downright lousy)
8. To get a medical opinion on unusual genital symptoms (these might represent an STD)
9. To get some sleep (you're tired and need sleep, not sex)
10. To adhere to your personal moral code (regarding premarital, extramarital, and other sexual taboos that make up your personal code of ethics)

What other good reasons for abstaining from intercourse can you come up with?

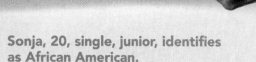

sex in society 8.1

Variations on Kissing

We asked our students to talk about kissing—their likes, dislikes, the role it plays in their relationships. Here's what they had to say:

Marcia 19, single, freshman, identifies as Latina.

I love kissing. I especially like long, deep, French kissing with my boyfriend. I really enjoy deep tongue thrusting—you know, like when he tries to run his tongue all the way down my throat. What a turn-on.

Mary 18, single, freshman, identifies as Italian American.

I like gentle kissing. I like lighter pressure—soft pecks, nuzzles, gentle tongue probing. I hate it when a guy tries to ram his tongue down my throat. It's disgusting. Oh, and I hate hickeys. Why do some guys feel compelled to leave their mark on my neck? I never go out with a guy again if he tries to lay a hickey on me. How gross.

John, 20, single, junior, identifies as Asian American.

I like kissing. It's kind of like a game, tongues darting back and forth, in and out. There's almost a rhythm or method to kissing. I like to work my tongue around my girlfriend's whole mouth.

Sonja, 20, single, junior, identifies as African American.

I personally think French kissing is overrated. I prefer lip action. I like to nip and suck, just using my lips. I like it when my boyfriend nibbles on my lips and when we just use the tips of our tongues around our lips and the outer parts of our mouths. I find this kind of darting tongue action preferable to all of that deep tongue thrusting. That makes me gag.

Glen, 41, married, nontraditional senior, identifies as African American.

At this point in my life, I find that my wife and I are more gentle in our kissing. We still get into all the deep French kissing every once in a while, but most of our kissing is more affectionate than passionate. Don't get me wrong—our sex is great, and intercourse is usually pretty passionate. We just seem to kiss more as an expression of love and affection. Kissing during sex is less frequent than when we were in our 20s.

Hugging/Rubbing

Kissing is usually associated with hugging and rubbing. These activities, once commonly called *petting*, can take on new meaning if we can visualize them as viable forms of sexual expression. Hugging and rubbing, even with one's clothes on, can be intensely pleasurable and can be carried to the point of orgasm with no risk of pregnancy or disease. These activities also can serve as a prelude to other noninsertive forms of sexual activity such as masturbation and use of sex toys. A delightful way to use rubbing as a safe sexual release is to rub against your partner to the point of orgasm. Typically this is done with both partners fully clothed. You rub your penis or vulva against your partner's groin, leg, arm (or another convenient body part) to the point of orgasm.

You control the pressure, rhythm, and intensity. Although students sometimes call this "dry humping," it doesn't have to be either. You can enhance your enjoyment by doing it with your clothes off and adding oil or lotion to the equation. Try spreading lotion on your partner's breasts or chest. Take your clothes off, lie on your back, and let your partner rub your penis or vulva back and forth and up and down between her breasts or his chest until you come. Try spreading some lotion or oil on your partner's buttocks and small of his or her back. Straddle the backside and ride back and forth to the point of orgasm.

If this seems too messy, try rubbing your penis or vulva through your partner's hair and against his or her head and neck. You can use hugging and rubbing in many ways to enjoy a highly erotic sexual episode without fear of disease or pregnancy.

Massage

Nongenital massage is one of the greatest sensual delights you can share with your partner. Massage can be a stand-alone sensual activity or be part of activities culminating with orgasm. Sex therapists often prescribe nongenital massage for clients as a way to help them reestablish touching each other's bodies again. Massage allows us to explore every nook and cranny of our partner's bodies in a relaxed, sensual way.

Separating our sensuality from our sexuality is sometimes difficult when it comes to massage. The only time many of us touch others in such an intimate way is when we are being sexual. Massage is not an inherently sexual activity. It *is* sensual, though. Kneading, stroking, and manipulating another person's flesh require us to be in tune with the sensation of touch. We must be acutely aware of pressure and motion when we give a massage. Also, many of the massage oils available are scented and bring into play our sense of smell. Visually, the sight of exposed flesh has the potential for arousal.

The ability to enjoy giving and getting a massage and viewing these as sensual delights that don't have to lead to sexual activity may take time. Of course, giving a massage with the intent to arouse your partner sexually is a natural way to initiate erotic activities if that is the intention. Being able to give and receive sensual pleasure without sexual release is excellent training in becoming a compassionate lover.

Giving a massage is a natural behavior. Instinctively, we believe that if it feels good to us, it will feel good to the person we are massaging. Usually, giving a massage is easier if you use some form of lubricating oil. Some people prefer powder to reduce friction, and they like the sensation of powder. Most people, however, prefer oil. Oil should be warm or at room temperature. Cold oil on the skin can get the massage off to a bad start. The oil should sit at room temperature or be warmed in the container under hot water in the sink before starting. The oil should be poured into the hands and rubbed onto the body rather than squirted directly onto the person's skin (Good Arts, 2003).

Massage should be done with sufficient room to get completely around the person without having to lean on or jump over him or her. When straddling a person, you should not sit directly on him or her. You should be able to position yourself over the person so you can apply firm pressure during some strokes. A massage table or high bed is ideal because it allows you to stand while giving a massage. You also could kneel next to the person receiving the massage. It allows the person to lie comfortably with the face down, facilitating easy access to the neck, shoulders, and head. A professional table isn't necessary. You could place a pillow under the person's head for support and have him or her rest the head gently to the side.

Most important in giving a massage is to take your time. The other person will sense if you feel obligated to do this and are rushing through it. Giving a massage is an act of kindness and must be done slowly, lovingly, with no expectations for getting anything in return.

Several types of strokes can be used in giving a massage. All of them require maintaining contact with the partner as much as possible while moving from one body part and stroke to the next. The strokes should merge to form a sense of continuous motion with the muscles. A visual image of the muscular system may help (see Figure 8.1).

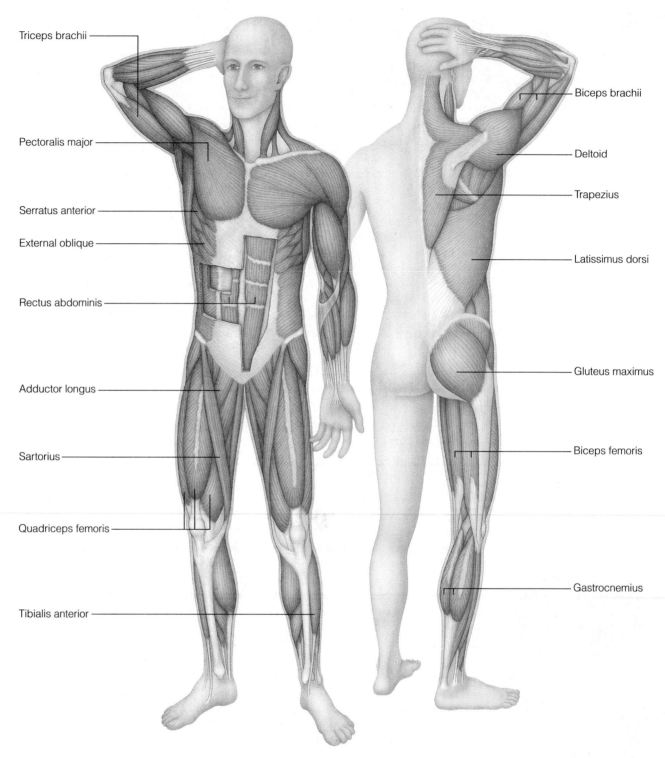

Triceps brachii

Pectoralis major

Serratus anterior

External oblique

Rectus abdominis

Adductor longus

Sartorius

Quadriceps femoris

Tibialis anterior

Biceps brachii

Deltoid

Trapezius

Latissimus dorsi

Gluteus maximus

Biceps femoris

Gastrocnemius

Figure 8.1 *Muscular System* Knowledge of the muscular system can help you when giving a massage.

Boost and Blocks to Arousal

There are so many differences in what each person finds sexually arousing and what blocks each person's arousal. Too often we don't even recognize what are our own boosts or turn-ons and our blocks or turn-offs to being aroused. Remember that arousal does not just happen as a prelude to sexual intercourse. Arousal can happen while we are walking across campus and notice a great body. The goal of this activity is to help you recognize what is sexually significant and important to you.

To identify your own personal boost and blocks to sexual arousal, keep a diary for 1 week where you list all the little things that sexually arouse you. Include not just physical but social and psychological factors that arouse you. (You can keep this in code if you don't want anyone to know what you are doing.) Notice all the little contributors such as reading an erotic passage in a novel, having someone you find attractive brush your hand, how you respond when you are being kissed, and so forth. When the week is finished, examine your list and star the ones that are the most effective in arousing you. These are the things you want to enhance in your sensual activities to increase your arousal. Next put an X by those that most effectively block your arousal, and try to eliminate these factors when possible. If you have a partner, you may want to share what you discovered about yourself and suggest he or she keep a diary for a week. Your partner can then share the findings with you. The two of you can use your list to enhance what is really important to both of you in your sensual life together.

The strokes should be rhythmic and symmetrical and will get better with practice. The whole hand should be used to master all of the strokes effectively. The fingers, palm, heel, and fist all come into play. The types of strokes are as follows (Inkeles & Austin, 1992):

1. *Kneading.* In kneading, you grasp the flesh with all four fingers of both hands and rotate your thumbs in opposite directions. Kneading works beautifully with the muscles of the arms, legs, hands, feet, back, and shoulders. You can practice kneading by making homemade bread and working on the dough.
2. *Pressing.* Pressing involves pushing against the body with the heel of the hand. For extra pressure, you can use your other hand to apply pressure against the heel of the hand involved in the pressing. Pressing can be used in long strokes or in a circular motion and is effective with thicker muscles such as those in the back.
3. *Stroking.* Stroking is done with the fingertips, either pushing away from you in circles or drawing toward you. Stroking also can employ all five fingers gently drawing flesh toward you. Stroking is good with the scalp, neck, and inner thighs and also works well as a long continuous motion along the back, torso, arms, and legs.
4. *Pulling.* Pulling is similar to stroking toward you except that it involves more pressure. Whereas stroking movements glide over the skin, pulling involves grabbing hold and gently tugging. You can pull with just your fingers, an entire hand, or both hands. Pulling is well suited for the head, hands, fingers, toes, feet, arms, and legs.
5. *Lifting.* In some cases, actually lifting a part of the body, such as the head, torso, or leg, and supporting it in your hands is relaxing. When lifting, the hands are cupped to cradle the part being elevated.
6. *Pounding.* Making a fist and gently pounding a body part can release accumulated tension. Pounding isn't for everyone or every body part. It is most effective on the back.

Kneading the back is a classic massage technique.

Anthony Saint James/Getty Images

Chrissy and Ken: Sensual Massage

Ken 23, is white; Chrissy, 22, is white.

Chrissy and Ken are single and in their senior year of college. They have been dating and having sex for 2 years and are planning to get engaged sometime before graduation in June. They have worked massage into their sexual lifestyle.

KEN: We got into massage as a way to relax and enjoy the sensual part of it. I didn't want Chrissy to think the only time she'd get a massage was when I wanted to have sex.

CHRISSY: We talk about what our needs are. If we want just a massage, we know this going into it, and that's what we do. If we're feeling sexy, we sometimes use massage to feel more sensual and get excited. We spend a lot of time massaging each other's erogenous zones.

KEN: I really get excited when Chrissy uses oil to massage my toes. I also love it when she uses long, slow strokes up my inner thighs and gently kneads the skin there.

CHRISSY: I really go wild when Ken uses small, circular strokes around my temples or kneads the base of my skull. I start to get wet when he spends a few minutes doing that.

Critical Thinking

How does your own background and upbringing affect your ability to give and receive sensual massages and derive the pleasure associated with this activity?

Use your Virtual Workbook to explore your answers to these questions at **http://health.wadsworth.com/blonna1.**

Masturbation

One of the first activities linking our sensuality to sexual behavior is **masturbation.** Masturbation usually evolves out of sensual exploration of our own body. We notice that it feels good when we unintentionally or intentionally rub (or rub up against) our genitals. In her book *Liberating Masturbation*, feminist writer, artist, and sex educator Betty Dodson (1996, p. 11) describes masturbation as "our primary sex life, our sexual base." According to Dodson, all other forms of sexual expression are a result of socialization. The expression of healthy sexual relationships between

Masturbation Individual or mutual stimulation of genitalia by hand or using other objects

healthy sex hints 8.3

Giving a Massage

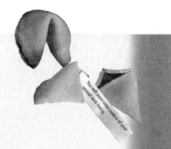

You can give full-body or partial massages. Sometimes just a back massage or a foot massage will do the trick. At other times, a full-body massage, complete with scented candles, is preferred. When giving a full body massage, try these pointers:

- Start anywhere. Wherever you start, move in the direction toward the heart to facilitate venous blood flow.
- If you start with the feet, work up to the head, and finish at the hands. Or work in the reverse order.
- Or start at the abdomen, as it is the center of the body and, when stressed, is the place where blood pools.

- Cover the entire body in a systematic way. Finish a part thoroughly, then move on to the next. Don't jump around from feet to head to toes. Massage both hands/arms or feet/legs before moving to the next body part.

After a massage, allow the person some quiet time to savor the results—and maybe even to reciprocate. Massage can be a prelude to other forms of sexual activity. In sensual massage, the focus shifts to providing more direct contact with the genitals and other erogenous zones.

individuals begins with self-exploration of sensual and sexual pleasure from the time of birth.

As described in Chapter 5, most of us learn the joy and security of cuddling, hugging, and warm, caring touch early in our lives, from contact with our parents and other caregivers. Although our earliest bonding experiences with our mother and father are not sexual in nature, they provide a sensual connection that leads to healthy sexuality.

Besides laying the foundation for developing trust and self-esteem, physical bonding with, and nurturing by, parents sets the stage for recognition and acceptance of our own body as a potential source of pleasure. Solitary sexual behavior, or masturbation, provides our first, and usually lifelong, source of sexual pleasure. Too many of us, however, associate masturbation with sinful, inappropriate behavior.

Masturbation can be a solitary sexual behavior or can be enjoyed with a partner. As a solitary behavior, masturbation may or may not be accompanied by sexual fantasy and other autoerotic activity. Couples can masturbate each other simultaneously, take turns pleasing each other, or masturbate themselves simultaneously.

Female Techniques   Masters and Johnson noted that women exhibit much greater variation in masturbatory behavior. Even when women had a similar style of stimulation, the tempo, timing, and approach to masturbation varied. The most common form of female masturbation is to stimulate the clitoris, labia, and mons by hand through stroking, pulling, or rubbing (Hite, 1976).

Most women prefer to masturbate while lying on the back. A smaller percentage chooses to sit or stand while stimulating the genitalia. Between 5 and 10 percent of women prefer to masturbate while lying on their stomach, either placing a hand between their legs to stimulate the clitoris or rubbing the vulva against a pillow or some other object (Hite, 1976). Figure 8.2 illustrates female masturbation.

Masters and Johnson reported the following patterns of masturbatory behavior in order of preference: (1) manually stimulating the vulva, (2) using a vibrator to stimulate the clitoris/vulva, (3) inserting something into the vagina, (4) rubbing up against an object, (5) pressing the thighs together, (6) using water massage, and (7) all other methods. About half of the younger women reported using sex toys (vibrators, dildos, or other devices) to

Figure 8.2 *Female Masturbation* Lying on the back and massaging the genitals with one hand is a common position for masturbation.

masturbate, choosing either to insert these or to use them to apply external vibration. A smaller percentage reports using these devices in a similar fashion to stimulate the anus during masturbation. The variety and complexity have increased markedly as more women (and their partners) express interest in these products.

Male Techniques   In her study of male sexuality, Shere Hite (1981) reports the following male masturbatory techniques in order of preference: (1) stimulating the penis by hand, (2) lying down on the stomach rubbing against a bed, and (3) with water in the shower.

Few men choose to masturbate using sex toys such as vibrators, dildos, plastic sleeves, penile pumps, and inflatable dolls, although these devices are readily available. Though still relatively uncommon, proponents of these sex toys claim that they can enhance sexual pleasure, provide a change of pace from routine masturbatory practices, and add variety to safe-sex options.

Masters and Johnson found that many men masturbate by rubbing, stroking, or pumping the shaft of the penis with one hand (Masters, Johnson, & Kolodny, 1996). The tempo of movement usually builds gradually in response to the increase in arousal. Slow, deliberate touch gradually gives way to more forceful, rapid movements, often accompanied by increases in pressure and tension. A small percentage of men studied spend time stimulating the frenulum on the underside of the glans of the penis.

Uncircumcised men seem to spend more time stimulating the glans and frenulum through pulling the foreskin back and forth. Ejaculation varies more, some men preferring

Figure 8.3 *Male Masturbation*

to slow down and relax their grip and others desiring to increase pressure, squeezing out the last drops of semen. Figure 8.3 illustrates male masturbation.

Because the male penis is not lubricated, and masturbation usually involves a buildup of heat and friction, most men use some form of lubrication while masturbating. Body lotion and baby oil are two commonly used lubricants.

Health Aspects of Masturbation   Early critics of masturbation posed pseudoscientific charges that masturbation was neither "healthy" nor "normal." In fact, masturbation has no adverse health consequences. It does not cause any physical problems. It carries no risk for any physical or psychological illness. Most safesex educators encourage their students to masturbate to relieve sexual tension or to enjoy an orgasm whenever they want one. It is also an excellent way to learn what feels good and how their own body responds.

From a physiological perspective, a person cannot masturbate to excess. It is a self-limiting behavior; we ultimately lose our interest in it. As long as people follow basic hygienic precautions (clean hands, toys, and so on) and have adequate lubrication, they can masturbate as often as they want to. Rather than being a source of problems, masturbation is a healthy outlet for sexual desire, can reduce risk for sexually transmitted diseases in people who don't have safe sexual partners, and is an alternative to having sex with prostitutes or anonymous partners.

Intellectual and Emotional Wellness

Intellectual wellness provides the objective basis for understanding sexual behavior. It allows you to separate fact from fiction, truth from myth, science from theology. It empowers you to gain access to information and make informed choices that are free from dogma and outside pressures. Emotional wellness allows you to understand your emotions about the information without being overwhelmed by them. Perhaps nothing illustrates this interplay more than the topic of masturbation.

Centuries upon centuries of misinformation based on religious dogma, pseudoscience, and Puritanism have clouded the truth about masturbation and shrouded the topic in a veil of shame, guilt, and punishment. While the scientific "truth" about the behavior (it is a harmless outlet for sexual tension and a viable sexual behavior in itself) is well documented, the emotions it arouses often makes it difficult for people to deal with masturbation honestly and openly. People with high-level intellectual and emotional well-being about masturbation realize that it is a normal, healthy sexual behavior, and they try to work with their emotions regarding it rather than to suppress them or feel worse because of them. They talk about these issues with their partner(s) and seek help if they need it.

Patterns of Masturbatory Behavior   Masturbation is a form of autoerotic behavior. **Autoeroticism** is the dimension of the sex life defined by sexual desire or gratification, or both, experienced by a person without the direct participation of another (Lauman, Gagnon, Michael, & Michaels, 1994). Even though autoerotic activities lack a sex partner, sexual fantasies always include the imaginary presence of another person. In addition, autoerotic activity follows a specific social script appropriate to the individual, even if he or she never wishes to act out the fantasy.

Autoerotic activities differ from partnered activities because they do not require coordination with another person, can avoid many of the reality-based features of sex with a partner, and are limited only by the person's imagination. A surprising finding of Laumann et al. was the lack of imagination and repetitiveness of pornographic and fantasy themes. Table 8.1 describes women's top 10 favorite fantasy themes. These common themes permeate various autoerotic media (adult books and magazines, films, CD-ROMs, videos, telephone and computer sex) and behaviors (use of sex toys, vibrators, dildos). Table 8.2 illustrates the use of autoerotic materials by gender.

Table 8.1 Women's Top 10 Fantasies

1. Sex with current partner
2. Sex with another man
3. Sex with another woman
4. Sex in embarrassing places/situations
5. Receiving oral sex
6. Romantic sexual scenarios
7. Forced sex
8. Being found irresistable by a man
9. Working as a prostitute
10. Sex with a stranger

Source: Tracey Cox, *Hot Sex*. New York: Bantam, 1998. (Cox is a former associate editor with *Cosmopolitan* and a freelance writer.)

Table 8.2 Autoerotic Activity by Gender

	Distributions (%)	
	Men	Women
Thinking about sex		
More frequently	54	19
Less frequently		
Rarely or never	4	14
Autoerotic material		
X-rated movies or videos	23	11
Go to a club that has nude or seminude dancers	22	4
Sexually explicit books or magazines	16	4
Vibrators or dildos	2	2
Other sex toys	1	2
Sex phone numbers	1	0
Any of the above	41	16

Note: Rarely or *never* refers to "less than once a month" or "never"; *less frequently* refers to "a few times a month" to "a few times a week"; *more frequently* refers to "every day" or "several times a day." Fantasy is measured by the frequency with which the respondent reported thinking about sex.

Source: The Social Organization of Sexuality: Sexual Practices in the United States, by E. O. Laumann, J. H. Gagnon, R. T. Michael, and S. Michaels. © University of Chicago Press. Reprinted with permission.

Even though the content of sex fantasies is similar for men and women, the most important finding in this area by Laumann et al. is the great disparity in levels of autoerotic activity between men and women. Men are much more likely to engage in autoerotic activities and to associate masturbation with these activities. Laumann et al. attribute this to the continuing social context of masturbation among men. Masturbation is a socially acceptable concept among adolescent males and almost completely absent in the social context of adolescent females.

A final finding of Laumann et al. concerning autoerotic activity is the lack of association between autoerotic behavior and not having a primary sex partner. In fact, higher levels of autoerotic activity were associated with higher levels of partnered sexual activity. Rather than being a way to compensate for the lack of a sex partner, autoerotic activity seems to be a source of additional sexual pleasure. Laumann et al. found that individuals with higher levels of autoerotic activity were more likely than those with lower levels to engage in a broader range of sexual activities. In a sense, they have a much more elaborate set of sexual scripts. The development of sexual scripts or scenarios is influenced by a variety of sources of information, including autoerotic activities.

Autoeroticism is highly correlated with an increased incidence of techniques such as fellatio, cunnilingus, and anal intercourse (Lauman et al., 1994). Men and women who reported the highest levels of autoerotic behavior were more likely to engage in these behaviors than their peers who had lower levels of autoerotic activity.

Autoeroticism The dimension of the sex life defined by sexual desire and/or gratification experienced by a person without the direct participation of another

Social Wellness

The quality of social relationships plays a big part in sexual behavior. The foundation of social well-being is a solid relationship with your sex partner. This relationship is built on caring, trust, mutual respect, equality, and openness. Within this type of relationship, sexual communication and experimentation will flourish. It allows you and your partner to explore and understand your sexuality in a safe, caring, disease-free way.

sex in society 8.2

Masturbation: Student Reports

Although masturbation is a generally accepted form of sexual expression for our students, their feelings about it vary considerable. Some are completely accepting and open about their masturbatory behavior. Others still feel guilty masturbating and hide their behavior from their partners and friends. Here are a few reports from our students concerning masturbation:

Susan, 21, senior, is white and identifies as lesbian.

I masturbate a couple of times a month, usually when I'm stressed out. I used to feel a little guilty about it, but I've found I can deal with things a lot better if I can get rid of my tension. Usually my lover and I make love when we see each other on the weekend, but sometimes she's away on business and we miss a week. I'll usually go home and take a nice bath, relax, and make myself come. My parents were very strict when I was growing up, and masturbation was a definite no. I don't think they could imagine that I do it, and I guess that's why I still feel guilty about it.

Tom, 18, freshman, single, identifies as African American.

I would say I masturbate once or twice a week. I'm a little nervous masturbating in my room because I can't really relax, having a roommate. I'm never sure when he's going to walk in. When I go home on weekends, I enjoy it more because I can lock my door, look at my magazines, and "get off" in private. My parents have never said anything, but I think they know I do it.

Edwardo, 25, senior, engaged, identifies as Hispanic.

I masturbate about two times a week. Sometimes my fiancée and I will watch X-rated films and then masturbate each other. She'll do me, and then I do her. Other times, if either one of us isn't horny, we'll masturbate the other to orgasm. Sometimes we won't even have intercourse. We masturbate each other and finish off with oral sex. I never have had any inhibitions about masturbation. My parents always told me it was normal and OK as long as I keep it private. I don't view it as second best to intercourse, just different.

healthy sex hints 8.4

Safe Fantasy

Sexual fantasy serves several important functions. Fantasies help us expand our sexual scripts. They help us explore and expand our sexual repertoire. Sexual fantasies are a healthy sexual outlet. Coupled with masturbation, they provide a safe, exciting release of sexual tension. Sexual fantasy provides a "practice arena" to work through sexual scripts and encounters that we eventually may want to enact in real life. This safe practice carries none of the interpersonal or health risks of an actual encounter. Fantasies allow us to experience activities that turn us on but are not things we want to experience in real life. Fantasies do not necessarily represent what we really want in reality.

Sometimes, however, the lure of living out our sexual fantasies is strong. When is turning a fantasy into a reality a good idea? The following criteria may help you determine when you may appropriately cross that line:

1. The nature of the fantasy
2. The strength of the turn-on
3. The social context of the fantasy
4. The nature of your partner(s)
5. Your level of control over the specific situation
6. Whether the person is willing to lose the fantasy (sometimes living out a fantasy makes it lose its fantasy appeal)

The nature of the fantasy refers to how unusual, bizarre, or dangerous the fantasy is. The more bizarre or dangerous the fantasy, the more cautious you should be about want-

Sexual Intercourse

Many people think that being a good lover means being particularly adept at sexual intercourse. Actually, being a good lover means having certain skills (knowing how to arouse your partner, using various sexual behaviors, and so on), as well as having good psychosocial skills (knowing how to communicate, when to initiate, and the like). In this section, we will focus on a variety of intercourse positions.

Spiritual Wellness

A key component of spirituality is the sense of being connected with something beyond the self. In one sense, a person can't become more "interconnected" with another human being than through sexual intercourse. When our sexual relationships are based on respect, mutuality, and caring, our union with another person creates something that we cannot experience as individuals. In contrast, when our sexual relationships are based on exploitation, power, mistrust, fear, or other destructive intentions, we become disconnected from others, mere sexual mercenaries, out for ourselves only. Regardless of whether we are religious, we each have a moral code, a sense of right and wrong that can enhance our connectedness to others or destroy it. Those with high-level spirituality view their sexual relations with others with integrity and morality.

Vaginal Intercourse

Vaginal intercourse, also known as **coitus,** is one of the most common forms of heterosexual sexual activity, although sexual paraphernalia (strap-on or hand-held dildos and the like) allow lesbian women to penetrate their partner's vaginas if they desire. The three starting points for vaginal intercourse are face-to-face,

Coitus Vaginal intercourse

ing to turn it into a reality. If you can control for some of the other variables (items 3, 4, and 5) and safety, you might want to act it out. If you can't control these variables, you're probably better off leaving it as a fantasy.

The strength of the arousal exerts a powerful influence on whether to act out the fantasy. If a strong desire isn't there, you may not want to turn it into reality at this time. The social context of the fantasy refers to the setting in which the fantasy plays out. For example, many people are turned on by the fantasy of having sex in a public place. Public places range from semideserted beaches (where the likelihood of discovery is minimal) to the elevator at your favorite hotel (where the chance of discovery is high). Combining the risk of exposure with the consequences of being discovered (being arrested, losing your job or public stature, and the like) will help you evaluate the social context of acting out the fantasy. Some fantasies are based on giving up control. The turn-on with dominance and submission lies in being vulnerable and letting someone have control over you. Other fantasies are more

amenable to control. The greater the control, the safer is the fantasy. In general, the less control you have in the situation, the greater is your need to act out the fantasy with a trusting partner in a familiar, safe environment.

The last warning concerns losing the turn-on after you act it out. Some sexual experiences are better left as fantasies. They provide a strong turn-on that is satisfying. When you turn this into reality, however, you run the risk that the reality won't be as exciting as the fantasy. When this happens, the fantasy often loses its appeal and its ability to turn you on.

The nature of your partner(s) will help you evaluate the safety and confidentiality of acting out your fantasy. Asking your wife to tie you to the bedpost and then acting out a dominatrix scenario in the safety of your own bedroom is vastly different from going downtown to Mistress Helga's illegal place and allowing her to put manacles on you. Fantasies acted out with a well-known partner whom you can trust are much safer than those with strangers and prostitutes.

side-by-side, and rear entry. We call these starting points rather than positions because each starting point offers a limitless array of positions depending on how you place the rest of your body (arms, legs, torso, and so on).

Face-to-Face   Face-to-face positions have two variations: man on top and woman on top.

Woman on Top. The woman-on-top position, shown in Figures 8.4 (heterosexual couple) and 8.5 (lesbian couple), allows women greater control in the depth, pace, and motion of her partner's thrusting. It allows the woman on the top the greatest control in clitoral stimulation and is the easiest intercourse position for manual clitoral stimulation. Orgasm rates for heterosexual women are better for this position than any other. This position is also good for helping heterosexual male partners control premature ejaculation. The woman can get to this position in two ways: She can start with her partner on top and roll over into this position or start with her partner on his or her back and move on top. In the latter case, the partners must have enough room on the bed so they won't find themselves rolling off the bed and onto the floor.

When starting with the man on his back, the woman kneels over him with one knee on either side of his legs. Either partner can part the vaginal lips as the woman lowers herself onto the erect penis, guiding it in with a free hand.

Figure 8.4 *Woman on Top Sitting; Heterosexual Couple* This position allows for the partner on the bottom to use his hands to massage his partner's breasts and upper body.

Figure 8.5 *Woman on Top Lying; Lesbian Couple* Lying on top of one's partner while facing her allows both partners to kiss as they make love.

With the penis inside, the woman can rock or thrust her hips or move them in a circular fashion. The rocking and thrusting motions allow maximum penile penetration, whereas the circular grinding motion stimulates the clitoris more directly. Each of these three creates entirely different sensations.

Lesbians can use this position in a similar fashion with the aid of a strap-on dildo. The motions, activities, and benefits are the same as those for heterosexual couples. The partner on the bottom can be passive and allow the woman on top to control all movements or move with her, synchronizing motion with hers. The bottom partner can also initiate thrusting and grinding if the woman on top becomes tired or desires it.

In this position the woman also has more freedom to use her hands in ways similar to those of the man-on-top position. From this position she can caress and manipulate either her partner or herself. One option that the woman-on-top position offers is the ability to rotate her torso, while still being penetrated by her partner, so that her back is to her partner. In this position she can lean forward or sit back and achieve different depths of penetration and sensations. Her partner can fondle her buttocks and back while maintaining penetration.

An interesting variation of the woman-on-top position is to move from kneeling or lying on to actually sitting on her partner. By sitting on her partner, the woman-on-top position affords maximum penetration and intimacy as the couple can embrace, kiss, and talk.

Man on Top (Missionary). The man-on-top position, illustrated in Figure 8.6, is also known as the "missionary position." It is the most commonly used intercourse position in the United States. In this position, the partners stimulate each other until they are sufficiently aroused. The man then moves on top of the woman. Either partner spreads the female's vaginal lips and inserts the penis into the vagina. The man supports his weight on his elbows, hands, knees, or across his partner's entire body as his penis moves in the vagina.

The most typical penile movements involve thrusting in and out as the female either remains still or moves her hips in concert with her partner's thrusting. These motions provide direct sexual stimulation of the male's penile nerve end-

Figure 8.6 *Man on Top, Heterosexual Couple* The man-on-top position is commonly referred to as the "missionary position" and is the most common heterosexual intercourse behavior.

ings (on the shaft, glans, and corona). The woman's clitoris usually is stimulated as the clitoral hood (top of the labia minora) pulls back and forth over it or the man's pubic area rubs against it. The vagina is stimulated as the penis slides in and out. The deeper recesses of the vagina (cervical area) may or may not be stimulated depending on the depth of the strokes and the positions.

An option to thrusting in and out is a circular motion, known as *grinding*, which involves more pubis-to-pubis contact and stimulates the female's clitoris differently. This provides more direct and intense stimulation of the clitoris and the base of the man's penis and can be done even if the man has ejaculated. If he hasn't withdrawn the penis before it has become limp, he can continue stimulating his partner with the circular motion. Sometimes this can go on through his refractory period, and he can achieve another erection without removing his penis. This allows his partner to be stimulated and have additional orgasms even though he has climaxed. Many men find this type of stimulation enjoyable even though they have a limp penis and already have had an orgasm.

Variations of this starting point involve changing the position of the legs and arms. The woman on the bottom can experience a variety of different sensations and depths of penetration by wrapping her legs around the partner's ankles, legs, or waist. Or she can throw her legs over her partner's shoulders as he thrusts in and out, which affords the deepest penetration.

One of the advantages of this position is that it allows the partners to look into each other's eyes and communicate. It also allows the partners to rub and caress each other's chest and shoulders. Furthermore, it allows use of the hands to enhance stimulation by touching or rubbing the partner's genitals during intercourse.

The woman may enjoy stretching her arms over her head, arching her back. This allows her partner better access to caress the breasts and nipples. She may enjoy having the partner pin her arms back over her head. This mild form of domination/submission allows her to "lose control" in a safe way. Individuals should participate in domination/submission only with someone they trust and must understand that "no means no" if either partner wants the activity to stop.

The missionary position can also be used by lesbian women if the partner on top is using a strap-on dildo to penetrate her partner's vagina. The positioning, motions, and benefits are similar to those experienced by heterosexual couples.

Figure 8.7 *Rear Entry, Heterosexual Couple* The rear entry intercourse position is commonly referred to as "doggie style."

Rear Entry The rear entry starting point (Figure 8.7) is also known as "doggie style" because it is the way in which dogs and most other animals have intercourse. In rear entry positions, the partner enters the woman's vagina from behind. This usually is accomplished with the woman kneeling on her hands and knees and the man kneeling behind her, either between or straddling her legs. Either partner parts the vaginal lips and guides the penis in.

This position creates deep vaginal penetration but little direct clitoral stimulation. For this reason, either the man or the woman stimulates the clitoris manually. This position also offers stimulation of the anus and perineum through pressure and friction from the man's pubis rubbing or grinding against it. Once engaged, the woman can lower her head and raise her hips higher to achieve maximum penetration.

The rear entry position can also be used by lesbian women with the aid of a strap-on dildo for vaginal penetration. The positioning, motions, and benefits are similar.

Two other rear entry position variations are (1) the couple can lie down with the man on top of the woman, or (2) they can lie on their sides. The latter is commonly known as the "spoon" position. One disadvantage of this position is that the partners do not face each other, which makes communication and kissing more difficult.

Side-to-Side The side-to-side vaginal intercourse can involve face-to-face positioning (Figures 8.8 and 8.9) or rear entry positioning. Because neither partner is bearing the full weight of the other, the side-to-side position is ideal for leisurely lovemaking or the rest period between more vigorous sessions. The easiest way to get into the side-to-side position is by rolling into it from the man-on-top or woman-on-top or the rear entry position.

Figure 8.8 *Side-by-Side, Heterosexual Couple* The side-by-side facing and rear entry intercourse positions are very comfortable and are often used to relieve pressure on the partner.

Figure 8.9 *Side-by-Side, Pregnant Heterosexual Couple*

Figure 8.10 *Rear Entry Anal Intercourse, Gay Couple* The rear entry position is commonly used by gay couples.

Besides being a comfortable position for leisurely lovemaking, the side-to-side variation has many advantages. It also is good for obese people, as it minimizes weight-bearing. The rear entry variation (Figure 8.9) is good for pregnant women whose developing fetus and protruding abdomen make the man-on-top position impossible. The side-to-side position also facilitates good communication and kissing while leaving the hands free for hugging and forms of manual stimulation.

Anal Intercourse

In anal intercourse, a man inserts his penis into his partner's rectum. Heterosexual and homosexual couples both practice anal intercourse. Like vaginal intercourse, anal intercourse can take place from the three starting points: side-to-side, rear entry, or face-to-face. The advantages and disadvantages associated with these starting points for vaginal intercourse are similar to those for anal intercourse. Rear entry is the most commonly used starting point for anal intercourse, although anal penetration can be accomplished through all of the positions previously described (Figure 8.10).

Oral Sex

Oral sex, also known as oral-genital sex, mouth-genital sex, giving head, and going down, is the stimulation of the partner's genitals with the lips, mouth, tongue, and face. The three main types of oral sex are fellatio (mouth-to-penis contact), cunnilingus (mouth-to-vulva contact), and anilingus (mouth-to-anus contact). All three are common forms of sexual expression for straight, gay, lesbian, and bisexual people.

Fellatio Oral stimulation of the penis

Fellatio   Also known as a "blow job," **fellatio** involves licking and sucking a man's penis. The term is derived from the Latin word *fellare,* which means "to suck." During fellatio, the partner begins by licking and sucking the flaccid penis while holding it. As the penis begins to grow, a man usually enjoys having his penis move in and out of his partner's mouth. The man can accomplish this by gently thrusting his hips, driving the penis in and out of his partner's mouth. The partner can do this by moving his or her head up and down, moving the penis deeper into the mouth and then letting it slide back again.

The sliding motion is accompanied by sucking, which can vary in intensity depending on the man's preference. The tongue is used to lick, flick, or swirl around the penis as it moves in the mouth. Using these tongue motions to stimulate the

healthy sex hints 8.5
Reducing Health Risks Associated with Anal Intercourse

Although the anus is richly endowed with nerve endings and has erogenous potential, it differs from other body parts and requires a few special considerations. One major difference between the tissue of the anus and rectum and that of the vagina concerns the blood vessels that supply the area. The blood vessels of the anus and rectum are very close to the surface. Any minor tearing or scraping of this tissue will result in bleeding and exposing these blood vessels to germs that could enter the bloodstream in this way.

Another major difference involves lubrication. Unlike the vagina, anal and rectal tissue does not produce natural lubrication as a product of vasocongestion. Therefore, care must be taken to adequately lubricate the anal opening and rectum with some other product. Saliva or a commercial water-based sterile lubricant is advisable. Saliva is not as slippery as most commercial products, such as K-Y Jelly, but it is free and can be used at any time. Because petroleum-based products can erode the latex in condoms, these products, such as Vaseline, should not be used in conjunction with a condom.

Lubricants should be spread liberally on the penis and the anus. Gently inserting a lubricated finger into the rectum will lubricate this area and relax the sphincter that keep the anus closed. (Make sure your fingernails are trimmed!)

The lubricated penis is inserted gently and begins controlled thrusting to work the penis deeper into the rectum. Once the penis is inserted comfortably into the rectum, the couple can decide on the nature and intensity of pelvic thrusting. From this rear entry starting point, couples can try most of the positions described in the section on vaginal intercourse.

Sex involving the anus and rectum also carries an increased risk for transmitting a range of infections ranging from hepatitis B to HIV. Organisms that are transmitted through contact with fecal matter or blood are easily transmitted through insertive or receptive anal intercourse or anilingus.

To reduce the likelihood of disease transmission and increase sexual response associated with anal stimulation:

1. Do not engage in anilingus or anal intercourse with an anonymous (don't know at all) or a casual (don't know that well) partner.
2. Before engaging in anal activities, be sure your sex partner is HIV-negative and free of other STDs. This means getting to know your potential partner better and sometimes being tested.
3. With disease-free partners, shower normally with soap and water before having sex to provide adequate hygiene.
4. Always use a water-based lubricant when anal penetration is involved.
5. Do not insert foreign objects (other than specially designed dildos, vibrators, and the like) into the rectum. Be careful not to let things you insert slip past the anal sphincter muscle. The object can get "lost" in the rectum and may require surgical removal.
6. If your partner's STD/HIV status is unknown, use a condom for anal intercourse.

glans and the coronal ridge (particularly the underside where the shaft meets the glans) provides maximum stimulation for the man.

These movements, if continued, usually provide enough stimulation to trigger orgasm. Many men find that a combination of oral and manual stimulation is necessary to provide enough stimulation for orgasm. The partner can grasp the penis at its base or along the shaft and pump it while simultaneously stimulating it with the mouth and tongue. Grasping the penis in one hand while licking and sucking it can also give the partner a sense of control over the depth and intensity of the man's thrusting.

When the penis is thrust into the throat, it typically initiates a gag reflex, which can be minimized by using your hand to control the depth of the partner's thrusting. To minimize this, the partner can relax the throat muscles and control the depth of thrusting by holding the penis.

Couples need to discuss their feelings about ejaculation. As discussed in Chapter 3, the male ejaculate is typically about 1 teaspoon of fluid when he comes. The ejaculate is milky-white in color, has a slippery texture resembling egg whites, and leaves a salty aftertaste. Most men enjoy the sensation of ejaculating into the partner's mouth. This also can be enjoyable to the partner. If the partner finds swallowing ejaculate distasteful, an alternative is fellatio to the point of orgasm, then to withdraw the penis and ejaculate outside the partner's mouth, or to switch to some other form of sexual behavior prior to the point of orgasm.

Environmental Wellness

In this chapter, we openly discuss sexual behaviors from a scientific/health perspective. We discuss the pros and cons of such things as oral and anal intercourse, heterosexual, homosexual, and bisexual variations on these behaviors, and how to engage in them with minimal health risks. We realize, however, that people don't engage in these behaviors in a vacuum. There are still places in the United States where century-old statutes regarding *sodomy* (a term that can be broadly interpreted to include such things as oral sex between consenting marital partners) laws are still enforced. You need to know what laws are still on the books regarding sexual behavior in your city, town, county, and state. This is vital information that can help you make informed choices about your sexual behavior and lifestyle.

Cunnilingus   The oral stimulation of a woman's vulva through licking, sucking, and nibbling or rubbing with the face is called **cunnilingus.** It is a common sexual practice of straight, lesbian, and bisexual men and women. Although cunnilingus (from the Latin words *cunnus* [vulva] and *lingere* [to lick]) by definition refers to oral stimulation of the vulva, often the perineum and outer parts of the vagina are also stimulated during this act.

Cunnilingus **Oral stimulation of the vulva**

Cunnilingus typically begins as the partner kisses and licks the partner's inner thighs, abdomen, and mons area. The partner then gently parts the labia majora and uses the tongue to lick, flick, or swirl around the vaginal lips, clitoris, and introitus. Pressure can be applied by pressing the tongue against the vulva with greater force. Circular motions are often used to stimulate the vulva in a somewhat different fashion. Care must be taken not to apply too much pressure directly to the clitoris, as it is the part of the female sexual anatomy that is most richly endowed with nerve endings.

The mouth can be used to gently suck on the vaginal lips and clitoris. Gently sucking one or more lips into one's mouth can provide intense pleasure. The clitoris also can be sucked on gently. Some women find it arousing to have their partner gently nibble the vaginal lips and clitoris. The tongue also can be used to penetrate the vagina with thrusting motions.

The face (chin, cheeks, and forehead) can become involved in cunnilingus while the mouth and lips are busy providing stimulation. A partner can intentionally use the face to provide additional stimulation through direct pressure or circular motion. For instance, the bridge of the nose can provide clitoral stimulation while licking or sucking on the labia.

As with fellatio, cunnilingus can be performed with or without manual stimulation. Many women derive pleasure from having their partner insert a well-lubricated finger into their vagina or anus while performing cunnilingus. Saliva or vaginal lubrication can be used to make the fingers slippery. The partner also can stimulate the woman's clitoris with manual stimulation while licking or sucking on another part of the vulva.

Anilingus Oral stimulation of the anus

Anilingus   Although it isn't as common as fellatio or cunnilingus, **anilingus,** also known as *rimming,* is another form of oral sex practiced by people of all forms of sexual orientation. During anilingus, a person kisses, licks, or sucks the partner's anus. The motions and activities of anilingus are similar to both cunnilingus and fellatio.

Performing anilingus affords a good opportunity to stimulate the perineum, an area richly endowed with nerve endings. Some men and women enjoy having their partners insert their tongues into their anus during anilingus. Others prefer that their partner insert a well-lubricated finger into the rectum. When performing anilingus on a woman, care must be taken to avoid spreading *Escherichia coli* bacteria into the vagina. The tongue or fingers never should be inserted directly from the anus to the vagina without first being washed.

Another concern is the spread of hepatitis and other STD organisms through anilingus. We do not recommend performing anilingus with a casual sex partner or someone whose STD status is unknown, as this could result in ingesting disease-causing organisms. (This topic is discussed in greater detail in Chapter 15.)

Figure 8.11 *Mutual Oral Sex, Heterosexual* Mutual oral sex is often referred to as *sixty-nine* because of the shape couples form when engaged in it.

Figure 8.12 *Mutual Oral Sex, Lesbian Couple*

Mutual Oral Sex   The term used to describe simultaneous cunnilingus and fellatio is *sixty-nine*. This usually is accomplished in the side-to-side starting point, with each partner's head at the other's genitals (see Figures 8.11 and 8.12). From this position, both partners have easy access to their partner's genitals. From the side-to-side starting point, it is easy to roll into the man or woman on either the top or bottom positions. By being on the top or the bottom, a person can control for deeper penetration of the tongue when performing cunnilingus, or the penis during fellatio. Mutual oral sex is enjoyed by heterosexual, gay, and lesbian couples.

Sexuality and Disability

Physical disabilities can manifest themselves across a broad spectrum of afflictions. People who are physically or developmentally challenged can maximize their sexual potential by being creative despite their limitations. They experience sensual and sexual pleasures the same way people without disabilities do. Although they may have some restrictions concerning what they can and cannot do, they still can enjoy robust sexual activity and satisfying relationships.

Disabilities, Body Image, and Self-Esteem

For some people with physical disabilities, the main obstacles to sexual activity are social—finding and attracting partners and overcoming self-imposed or societal attitudinal barriers to sex. For these people, sexual behavior is affected very little by the actual physical disability. Their disability affects their body image and their perception of themselves as desirable. Their disability doesn't create a physical barrier to engaging in specific sexual acts or behaviors. Rather, it is their perception of the disability that creates the barrier.

Ostomy is the perfect example of this and will be covered in greater detail in Chapter 11. A *colostomy* can be described as a resectioning of the colon to a stoma that empties the contents of the colon into a bag attached to the abdominal wall. This procedure does not normally affect sexual response, and it doesn't impede engaging in a variety of sexual behaviors ranging from oral sex to different forms of intercourse. However, learning to manage these and other sexual activities while wearing a colostomy bag (or temporarily removing it) depends on the willingness of the person with the disability to accept the colostomy and work around it (Chance, 2002).

Physical Wellness

Physical well-being implies the absence of sexually transmitted diseases, which can severely curtail sexual activity and pleasure. It also includes daily hygiene and health behaviors, both of which play a role in enjoying sexual behavior. High-level physical fitness can enhance sexuality, and nowhere is this more evident than in relation to sexual behavior. High-level physical wellness enhances everything related to sexual behavior. It influences our ability to perform sexually. Although the goal is not to become a sexual acrobat, a high level of fitness will increase our strength, flexibility, and endurance—all elements that can enhance sexual ability and creativity. People with physical disabilities or illnesses may not be able to achieve the same levels of fitness as those who are not disabled or ill. However, they can strive to get the most out of their abilities and maximize their individual fitness level to achieve their sexual potential despite their limitations.

Disabilities and Physical Barriers

For others, the disability directly affects sexual behavior. Arthritis and low-back injury/pain can be used to illustrate this. A woman with arthritis in her hands, for instance, might find masturbation difficult and have to adjust, perhaps enlisting the aid of a vibrator, dildo, or the willing help of a partner. The pain in her hands and fingers, her limited range of motion, lack of strength, and physical deformity (depending on the severity of her arthritis and her ability to control it with a therapeutic regimen) all affect her ability to stimulate herself sufficiently through masturbation.

A man with a lower-back disc-related injury can experience chronic pain which makes certain sexual behaviors impossible. For instance, positions that require him to support his partner's weight (partner-on-top vaginal intercourse, partner sitting on top while seated on a chair, and so forth) would be difficult, if not impossible, to accomplish. He might have to substitute side-by-side, rear entry vaginal intercourse, or mutual oral sex, behaviors that don't require him to support the full weight of his partner.

Neurological Disabilities

Some disabilities such as spinal cord injuries (covered in detail in Chapter 7) and Parkinson's disease will actually affect the transmission of nerve messages that trigger sexual response. Men with spinal cord injuries and Parkinson's disease rarely achieve erections except through reflexive neural activity, and they lose their ability to ejaculate. This makes vaginal intercourse difficult, if not impossible, for them. However, these men might find that although they can no longer get erections, they can still enjoy cunnilingus and other forms of nonpenetrative sexual pleasuring (Yang, 2000; Alexander, Sipski, & Findley, 1993). Chance (2002) reports that some men with spinal cord injuries pride themselves in their abilities to satisfy their partners orally.

case study 8.4

Charlotte: Spinal Cord Injury

Charlotte, 30, single, identifies as African American.

As a young woman, Charlotte was a promising athlete. She was a multifaceted track star who at 20, while on spring break, got into a serious automobile accident that put her into a coma for 4 days and left her paralyzed from the waist down.

I was very bitter for several months following the accident. I didn't want to talk to anyone and was angry all of the time. I broke off my engagement and retreated into a world of antidepressant drugs and disability checks. I hated rehabilitation and didn't work hard at all. I couldn't accept myself without my legs. They had been the source of my greatest accomplishments and my best feature.

After about 6 months, we had a guest lecturer at the rehabilitation center. A social worker spoke to us about redefining our selves, including our sexual selves. I hadn't even begun to think about redefining myself let alone redefining my sexuality. She made me realize how much I missed my partner and the intimacy and sex we had. I really used to love oral sex (giving and receiving) and how my partner kissed and caressed my breasts when we made love. I really began to wonder whether I could really recapture that again with another man.

I slowly came around and began to take my rehabilitation seriously. I also started paying attention to myself as a whole person, capable of satisfying myself and someday my partner. I started taking night classes again and eventually went back to college full-time where I met my present husband. He was a graduate student in the counseling department, and it took me a long time to believe that he really loved me and wasn't just looking to "help" some poor cripple out.

I'm glad I gave him a chance because he is the best thing that ever happened to me. He helped me rediscover the intimacy, passion, and sex in my life. Sure, there are things I can't do sexually any more, and I can't have vaginal orgasms like I used to, but that is becoming less and less important in my life.

We've adopted a little girl, and I am thoroughly enjoying motherhood and hoping I can still teach her a thing or two about running high hurdles.

Critical Thinking

When you strip away all of the emotions and take into account the energy needed to work through a situation like Charlotte's, it makes you think about how you would react if you were in her shoes. How do you think you would react if it were you instead of Charlotte who had gone through this ordeal? Is there really ever a good reason to react the way she did initially?

Use your Virtual Workbook to explore your answers to these questions at **http://health.wadsworth.com/blonna1.**

Chronic Lifestyle Diseases

Chronic illnesses such as cardiovascular disease, obesity, and diabetes can affect sexual behavior. These and other chronic diseases, besides influencing body image and sexual desire, impact strength, endurance, and coordination. People with these conditions can find themselves unable to sustain sexual activity for sufficient duration to achieve orgasm. They might also find certain sexual positions unattainable because of excess body weight.

Redefining Sex

The major challenge for people with disabilities is redefining sexual activity and the goal of sexual behavior. Most people in American culture define sexual activity as genital intercourse and orgasm the goal of sexual behavior. For certain people with physical disabilities, however, that activity and goal are unattainable (Chance, 2002). It is essential, then, that people with physical disabilities set their own activities and goals for sex and not evaluate their happiness in terms of societal expectations. We have seen that activities such as massage, masturbation, and oral sex, with or without orgasm, can be as satisfying as penile-vaginal intercourse.

In some cases, people with physical disabilities develop new levels of sensitivity and sensuality. Research has shown that people with spinal cord injury can develop new erogenous zones and are more than able to become aroused when stimulated (Chance, 2002).

Persons with developmental disabilities usually do not face the same limitations as those with physical disabilities. Rather, their greatest challenge is protecting themselves from unintended pregnancy, disease, and abuse. Care must be taken not to lump all developmentally disabled people together because their abilities vary across a broad spectrum. Many are able to make informed decisions about their sexuality and risk reduction.

In this book, we cannot describe all of the potential variations in lovemaking associated with a full range of physical disabilities. We suggest that people with disabilities use the information in this chapter as a starting point to experiment with different forms of sexual behavior. They may find that accessories such as chairs or stools can be helpful when trying various positions. Communication with the partner is of primary importance, to ensure that the erotic and safety needs of both are being met.

Your responses to the Personal Assessment, Thought Questions, and Test Yourself! quiz questions can be logged online in your Virtual Workbook at **http://health.wadsworth.com/blonna1.**

Personal Assessment

8.1 Online Sensuality Test

Take an online sensuality assessment developed by Discoveryhealth.com. The test is one of many contained on its Web site (see Web Resources). Go to **http://discoveryhealth.queendom.com/sensuality_abridged_access.html.**

8.2 Favorite Sexual Behaviors

People satisfy their sexual needs in a variety of ways. We each engage in unique activities and behaviors to satisfy our sexual desire. The purpose of this activity is to illustrate how different positions satisfy different sexual needs. This will enable you to take a personal inventory of your personal turn-ons and have the opportunity to exchange them anonymously with your classmates.

1. Which autoerotic sexual activity do you find most enjoyable, and why? (If you do not engage in autoerotic activity, simply state this.)

2. Which partnered sexual activity do you find most satisfying? Why? (You could also include masturbation in this category.)

3. Describe your favorite sexual position within this category (for instance, if you enjoy vaginal intercourse most, which starting point and position do you find most enjoyable?).

4. Describe your favorite sexual fantasy. (If you do not fantasize, simply state this.)

Thought Questions

1. What is sensuality? What does "sensual lover" mean?

2. What is Burnham's concept of integration? What contributes to adults losing this capacity?

3. What are some guidelines for giving a massage?

4. What is the difference between celibacy and abstinence? When are each appropriate?

5. What are five nonpenetrative forms of sexual activity?

6. What are the pros and cons of the man-on-top and woman-on-top intercourse positions?

7. What are the advantages of the side-by-side and rear entry intercourse positions?

8. Describe how a person with disabilities might "redefine" sexual behavior and the goal of sexual activity.

Test Yourself!

1. Burnham's concept of "integration" refers to
   a. interracial sex.
   b. a merging of the senses and the intellect.
   c. acting childlike in response to sexual stimuli.
   d. integrating childish things into sensuality.

2. Which of the following best characterizes the relationship between sensuality and sexuality?
   a. They are the same.
   b. Sexuality is an important part of sensuality.
   c. They are completely different.
   d. Sensuality is an important part of sexuality.

3. The major distinction between abstinence and celibacy is
   a. celibacy is something that only involves the clergy.
   b. celibacy is very rare while abstinence is much more common.
   c. abstinence is usually viewed as a situational choice, not a lifetime commitment.
   d. abstinence makes the heart grow fonder.

4. Which of the following is generally *not* considered outercourse?
   a. mutual masturbation
   b. sensual massage
   c. coitus
   d. use of sex toys

5. Most health experts would agree that masturbation
   a. is an acceptable sexual outlet for children and teens only.
   b. can be carried out to excess and needs to be controlled.
   c. is not acceptable adult sexual activity.
   d. is an acceptable sexual outlet for people of any age.

6. Lauman et al. found that adults who masturbated on a regular basis
   a. had higher levels of sex with their partners.
   b. had lower levels of sex with their partners.
   c. did not have steady partners.
   d. preferred solitary sex to partnered sex.

7. Which of the following statements best characterizes how sexual health experts perceive anal sexual intercourse?

a. It is a source of STDs and should be avoided.
b. It can be a pleasurable sexual activity if care and extra lubrication are used.
c. It is similar to vaginal intercourse because of the naturally occurring lubrication.
d. It is a homosexual activity.

8. Which response best characterizes sexual intercourse during pregnancy?
   a. Should be avoided
   b. Should be avoided after the first trimester
   c. Can be facilitated through side-by-side or rear entry intercourse positions
   d. Is best accomplished using the man-on-top position

9. Which answer best describes people with physical disabilities such as multiple sclerosis and Parkinson's disease?
   a. Are almost always unable to engage in sexual intercourse
   b. Are uninterested in sexual intercourse
   c. Can't make the necessary adjustments to enjoy sexual intercourse
   d. Can enjoy sexual intercourse if they are able to make the necessary adjustments

10. Which answer best describes people with developmental disabilities such as Down's syndrome?
    a. Are too immature to have sexual intercourse
    b. Do not respond sexually the way "normal" people do
    c. Have the same desires as people without such disabilities
    d. Can't be trusted to have sex and not get pregnant

Media Menu

You can link to the following online tools by visiting
http://health.wadsworth.com/blonna1.

InfoTrac Activity

Felleux, Z. (1998, October). A great week of sex. *Men's Health,* 13(8), 96–99.

Web Resources

Good Vibrations

www.goodvibes.com

This is the definitive site for all of your sexual aids. The site offers an online catalog for sexual toys, book, films, and related materials and information from the sensual to the erotic.

Discovery Health

http://health.discovery.com/tools/assessments.html

This is the Discovery Channel's health Web site. It contains a variety of assessments related to health.

Intimacy Institute Sexuality

www.bettersex.com/gateway.asp

This is the home page of the Sinclair Intimacy Institute. It provides products and information on sexual response and a host of other topics.

The Pantone Color Institute

http://cn.pantone.com/colorinstitute/colorj.html

This one of the institute's color pages that provides a quick game regarding color and its effects on us. Click on the icon and play the game, or go to the institute's home page: www.pantone.com/aboutus/aboutus.asp?idArticle=49.

The Celibate FAQ

www.glandscape.com/celibate.html

A personal Web page with frequently asked questions and answers on celibacy. The site gives reasons for celibacy, advantages, and disadvantages, plus booklists and other resources. Questions raised include, What kind of people are celibate? What are the advantages/disadvantages of celibacy?

National Abstinence Clearinghouse (NAC)

www.abstinence.net

An alliance of nationally known educators formed to promote the practice of abstinence. The NAC provides a resource center and training for educators and parents. Many links are provided for related topics in the area of abstinence.

The Kama Sutra

www.bibliomania.com/nonfiction/vatsyayana/kamasutra

The Kama Sutra, by Vatsyayana (1883), online and translated by Sir Richard Burton. The timeless Indian sex manual that merges yoga, spirituality, and sex.

Tracey Cox.com

www.traceycox.com

This is the home page for Tracey Cox, writer of *Hot Sex* and other self-help sex books.

References

Alexander, C. J., Sipski, M. L., & Findley, T. W. (1993). Sexual activities, desire, and satisfaction in males pre- and post spinal cord injury. *Archives of Sexual Behavior, 22*(3), 217–229.

Bender, M. (1999). The secret to living a sensuous life. *Cosmopolitan, 227,* 236–242.

Brand, H. (2001). Sexual chemistry (the use of pheromones). *Soap, Perfumery & Cosmetics, 74*(9), 19.

Burnham, W. H. (1932). *The wholesome personality.* New York: Appleton Century.

Chance, R. S. (2002). To love and to be loved: Sexuality and people with disabilities. *Journal of Psychology and Theology, 30*(3), 195–209.

Dodson, B. (1996). *Sex for one: The joy of selfloving.* New York: Crown.

Eiseman, L. (1999). *Colors for your every mood.* New York: Capitol.

Goins, L. (2001). 5 secrets for making sex supersensual. *Cosmopolitan, 230*(4), 156–160.

Good Arts. (2003). *Sensual massage* [Online]. Available: www.goodarts.com.

Hite, S. (1976). *The Hite report: A nationwide study of female sexuality.* New York: Dell.

Hite, S. (1981). *The Hite report on male sexuality.* New York: Knopf.

Inkeles, G., & Austin, K. K. (1992). *The new sensual massage.* Bayside, CA: Arcata Arts.

Kemp, K. (2000). How to touch a naked man. *Cosmopolitan, 228*(4), 194–206.

Kraus, D. K. (2000, October 27). Realm of the senses. *San Francisco Business Times,* pp. 29–33.

Laumann, E. O., Gagnon, J. H., Michael, R. T., & Michaels, S. (1994). *The social organization of human sexuality: Sexual practices in the United States.* Chicago: University of Chicago Press.

Marrone, S. (2002). Indulge your sensual side: Eat a mango, sniff some cinnamon, and other fun, fast ideas for putting more pleasure into your life. *Redbook, 198*(5), 84–86.

Masters, W. H., Johnson, V., & Kolodny, R. (1996). *Human sexuality.* New York: HarperCollins.

Norris, K. (1996, September–October). Celibate passion. *Utne Reader,* 51–53.

Yang, C. C. (2000). Female sexual function in neurologic disease. *Journal of Sex Research, 37*(3), 205–208.

chapter *nine*

Atypical Sexual Behavior

Student Learning Objectives

After reading this chapter, students will be able to

- Distinguish between normal, atypical, and paraphiliac sexual behavior.
- Describe the four typical measures used to assess normalcy.
- Assess their own attitudes, values, and beliefs about what is normal.
- Describe the key characteristics of a variety of paraphilias.
- Evaluate the paraphiliac risks associated with the Internet.
- Evaluate the health risks associated with body piercing.
- Differentiate transvestic fetishism and transsexualism (gender identity disorder).
- Describe the origins of atypical sexual behavior and paraphilias.
- Evaluate various ways of treating atypical sexual behaviors and paraphilias.

*Test your understanding of these objectives by taking the end-of-chapter quiz, available online at **http://wadsworth.com/blonna1**.*

activity teaser: *Discover your true feeling about different sexual behaviors in the Personal Exploration Activity on page 285.*

case study 9.1

Greg: Exhibitionism or Mooning?

Gregg, 20, single, is white.

Critical Thinking

Many people experiment with a host of sexual behaviors such as "mooning." What distinguishes Greg's mooning from someone else's prank?

Use your Virtual Workbook to explore your answers to this question at **http:// health.wadsworth.com/ blonna1.**

Greg was the first client assigned to Dr. Blonna during the supervised clinical training component of the master's degree in counseling. Greg was on probation as a first-time sex offender convicted of exhibitionism. As a condition of parole, Greg had to seek counseling for a proscribed period of time. In Dr. Blonna's words:

I'll never forget Greg. I was a 25-year-old man, not too much older than Greg. I was still working through issues related to my own sexuality and found Greg quite a challenge. He was referred to counseling because he had been arrested for exposing himself to a young woman.

It was hard for me to understand the significance of exhibitionism. I had been raised as a typical man of the 1950s and 1960s and viewed exhibitionism with amusement more than a clinician's understanding of it as a paraphilia. Indeed, I was only a few years removed from engaging in mooning and streaking as fraternity pranks. In time, my work with Greg crystallized the significance of his behavior and the furtive nature of exhibitionism.

Greg was a reluctant client at first. He did not want to be in counseling, and the first couple of sessions were almost totally devoid of any conversation. Gradually we began to establish a relationship, and Greg started to talk about his exhibitionism. It became quite evident after that point that Greg's behavior was vastly different from mooning and other juvenile sexual behavior that, although offensive, has an entirely different motivation. Mooning, streaking, and other prank public displays of nudity are not intended to serve as sexual come-ons. Greg's behavior had an entirely different purpose.

Greg was immature—both socially and sexually retarded. He was painfully shy, could not communicate with women effectively, and had limited dating experience. His sexual experience was limited to autoerotic activities and a handful of sexual liaisons with prostitutes. He lacked self-esteem and self-confidence and had a hard time maintaining eye contact. He also admitted, while in counseling, that he was a voyeur and had masturbated several times while watching a few women in his neighborhood get undressed. He had a couple of peeping vantage points that allowed him to peer into the windows of apartment buildings in his neighborhood.

After seeing Greg for several sessions, it was obvious that exposing himself was his way of coming on to women sexually. He really believed that women, upon seeing his nakedness (and throbbing erection) would literally throw themselves at his feet and perform oral sex on him or ask him back to their place to have intercourse. He believed that his "manhood" would speak for itself and make traditional forms of establishing a sexual relationship unnecessary. In reality, Greg lacked the conversational and other social skills necessary to meet women and establish a sexual relationship.

As we can see with the illustration of Greg, sometimes there is a fine line between what is considered "normal" sexual behavior and what isn't. Normative behavior can be classified as sociological, biological, psychological, and statistical. Sexual behavior that is *sociologically* normal falls within the laws, mores, and customs of a society. Most of this behavior is culturally defined and passed from one generation to the next as a result of socialization. *Biologically* normal behavior is characterized as healthy and natural and helps perpetuate the species in positive ways. *Psychologically* normal sexual behavior is sexual activity that does not result in emotional distress or in neurotic or psychotic functioning. Finally, behavior that is considered *statistically* normal is sexual behavior in which the majority of people engage.

Given these four categories of "normality," defining abnormal sexual behavior might seem easy. Anything falling outside the parameters established by these four categories would be considered "abnormal."

The words *normal* and *abnormal* are commonly used labels because they characterize sexual behavior in easy-to-understand, stereotypical patterns. Furthermore, dichotomizing normal and abnormal makes it easier to stigmatize and discriminate against people who are not in the norm. A more commonly accepted term to describe behaviors that the majority of the population does not practice is *atypical* sexual behavior. Atypical sexual behavior is described as behavior that is not statistically typical. The term *atypical* does not carry the same pejorative tone as *abnormal*.

Paraphilias

Paraphilias are atypical or unusual sexual behaviors that become the focal point for an obsessive preoccupation or need. The paraphilia is almost always the central focus of the person's sexual repertoire, and arousal and orgasm are difficult, if not impossible, in the absence of the paraphilia.

Paraphilias generally revolve around three common themes: (a) nonhuman objects, (b) suffering or humiliation involving oneself or one's own partner, and (c) children or other nonconsenting persons. In addition, to qualify as a paraphilia, a behavior has to occur over a period of at least 6 months and cause clinically significant distress or impairment in social, occupational, or other important areas of functioning (American Psychiatric Association [APA], 2000).

The fourth edition, text revision, of the *Diagnostic and Statistical Manual of Mental Disorders* (DSM-IV) lists eight categories of paraphilias and one catchall category. The eight officially recognized categories are as follows:

exhibitionism
voyeurism
fetishism
frotteurism
pedophilia
sexual masochism
sexual sadism
transvestic fetishism (APA, 2000)

The catchall category "not otherwise specified" includes the following paraphilias, which are less common and don't meet the criteria to be included in any of the other eight categories:

telephone scatologia (obscene phone calls)
necrophilia (sex with a corpse)
partialism (focus on certain parts of the body)
zoophilia (sex with animals)
coprophilia (contact with feces)
klismaphilia (enemas)
urophilia (undue attention to urine) (APA, 2000)

A person often exhibits more than one paraphiliac behavior (APA, 2000). Also, someone who exhibits true paraphiliac behavior and someone who casually experiments with atypical behavior are different. True paraphilia creates almost obsessive recurring, intense sexually arousing fantasies, urges, and behavior, and it is the main focal point for sexual arousal.

In addition, the person recognizes that the paraphilia causes significant enough emotional, social, occupational, or other distress to interfere with daily functioning. Someone who casually experiments with episodic paraphiliac behavior (such as occasionally liking his lover to tie him to the bedpost) and does not suffer negative emotional or other consequences is considered a person who simply enjoys occasional atypical sexual behavior.

Paraphilia An unusual or atypical sexual behavior that becomes the focal point for an obsessive preoccupation or need

Exhibitionism

Exhibitionism Deriving sexual pleasure from exposing one's genitals to unsuspecting strangers

The paraphiliac focus of **exhibitionism** involves deriving sexual arousal by exposing one's genitals to unsuspecting strangers. The overwhelming majority of people with this paraphilia are men between 18 and 40 years of age. Sometimes the person masturbates while exposing himself or fantasizing exposing himself (APA, 2000). Often the sexual gratification is derived from the sheer shock value of the act and the reaction from the victim. The greater the reaction, the more the person has proven his masculinity.

Men who reveal exhibitionism tend to be shy, passive, and sexually inhibited. Exhibitionism is generally perceived to be unrelated to rape or sexual assault. In some instances, the man with this paraphilia believes that his victim will be sexually aroused by his nakedness and that it will provoke a sexual encounter with her.

Exhibitionism is often confused with "mooning" (baring one's buttocks to unsuspecting passersby). Generally, those who moon do not derive sexual gratification from the act, and it usually is a prank typically associated with adolescents. In a sense, exhibitionism is culturally disparate. Male and female exotic dancers get paid to expose themselves. Nude or partially nude dancing and other forms of exotic entertaining are designed to be sexually arousing and are legal, yet streaking, which is not sexual, is illegal.

Voyeurism

Voyeurism Deriving sexual pleasure from observing unsuspecting individuals undressing or engaging in sexual activities

The paraphiliac focus of **voyeurism** is exactly the opposite of exhibitionism. The voyeur derives sexual excitement and pleasure from observing unsuspecting people (usually strangers) who are naked, disrobing, getting dressed, or in the act of having sex. The pleasure is derived from the act of "peeping" and is not intended to lead to an encounter with the unsuspecting stranger. Sexual release usually occurs through masturbation either while peeping or later with the voyeuristic memory of the encounter. The person may fantasize having sex with the stranger (APA, 2000).

Voyeuristic behavior can be depicted along a continuum. At the extreme is the person who can achieve sexual release only by observing others having sex. At the other end of the continuum is the person who watches others to augment sexual pleasure with a partner. This person might get turned on by watching exotic entertainers to fuel a sexual episode with a partner.

Fetishism

Fetishism Deriving sexual pleasure from inanimate objects

The paraphiliac focus of **fetishism** is deriving sexual arousal and gratification from nonliving objects. The overwhelming majority of people with fetishes consists of men who derive sexual pleasure from items of women's clothing such as underwear, bras, stockings, shoes, and boots. Typically, the man with paraphiliac fetishism masturbates while holding, stroking, smelling, or licking the object. To a lesser extent, the person may ask his partner (or pay a prostitute) to wear the item of clothing while they engage in sex or he masturbates (APA, 2000).

A person with a true paraphiliac fetish usually strongly prefers and needs the object to experience sexual desire. Often, a person with a fetish is unable to obtain or sustain an erection without the object being present. Fetishes often are linked to significant childhood experiences and are in place by adolescence (APA, 2000).

Frotteurism

Frotteurism Deriving sexual pleasure from rubbing up against unsuspecting and unwilling victims

The paraphiliac focus of **frotteurism** is deriving sexual arousal and pleasure from rubbing one's genitals against an unsuspecting, nonconsenting person. The male rubs his genitals against his victim's buttocks and thighs while simultaneously fondling her breasts or genitalia, or both. This typically occurs in crowded public places such as busy sidewalks, subways, buses, and other public places where the perpetrator can make a quick escape and avoid arrest (APA, 2000).

Environmental/Occupational Wellness

The overwhelming majority of paraphiliacs are harmless, and as long as their behavior is private and with consenting adults, it does not represent a threat to society. In other instances it does. Legislation was passed in New Jersey and a host of other states to protect children from sex offenders in their communities. The New Jersey legislation, "Megan's Law," was enacted in response to the brutal murder of a young girl, Megan Kanka, by a neighbor who was a known sex offender. Essentially, the new law requires that neighbors be notified that a convicted sex offender has moved into their neighborhood. The hope is that such notification will enable parents and other neighbors to protect their children by keeping them away from the sex offender. In 1994, 12 new laws were enacted in California specifically targeting sex offenders. Provisions of these laws include, among others, a state-maintained toll-free phone number that alerts people to registered sex offenders living in their area, stiffer penalties for first-time offenders convicted of child molestation or rape, and the barring of unsupervised visits of sex offenders to their children.

The workplace can present many challenges to persons with atypical behavior. Transsexuals, and those with certain paraphilias such as fetishism, face daily stress (and often outright discrimination) as they struggle to earn a living and cultivate a career while living with atypical sexual desires and behavior.

Pedophilia

The legal aspects of **pedophilia** are discussed in detail in Chapter 16. The paraphiliac focus of pedophilia is fantasizing about engaging in sexual activity with a prepubescent child. Those sexually attracted to girls, in general, prefer 8- to 10-year-olds. Those attracted to boys favor slightly older children. The two subtypes of pedophilia are (a) exclusive (individuals who are sexually attracted to children only) and (b) nonexclusive (individuals who are sexually attracted to both adults and children) (APA, 2000).

Pedophilia Engaging in sexual activity with or fantasizing about prepubescent children

Individuals with pedophilia show a wide range of sexual activity with their victims. Not all pedophiles are child molesters. According to the law, a pedophile is an individual who fantasizes about sexual contact with children, whereas a child molester actually commits that act in some form (Davis, McShane, & Williams, 1995).

Most pedophiles masturbate while watching their victims undress, fondle themselves, or engage in sexual activities with another child or an adult. These activities can be live (paying children to perform in person or observing live sex shows broadcast over the Internet) or available through print (magazines, newspapers, and the like) and other electronic media (including movies, videotapes, and CD-ROMs).

Child molesters engage in a variety of sexual activities with their victims. This may consist of rubbing or fondling the child. Other child molesters penetrate the child's mouth, vagina, or rectum with their fingers, penis, or a foreign object. Some people with pedophilia obtain these sexual favors by gaining their victims' trust, affection, or loyalty. Others use physical force and psychological pressure and terror to obtain sex and control their victims.

The Internet and Pedophilia

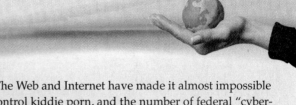

The Internet and the World Wide Web have become a major source of concern for law enforcement officials around the world trying to stem the tide of child pornography and pedophilia-related abductions and murders that originated in chat and other services available on the Web. The cases of Marc Dutrox of Belgium and Ronald Riva of California are just two of many that have brought attention to the problem of pedophilia and its many manifestations on the Internet.

Dutrox was convicted of kidnapping and murdering young girls in Belgium. The suspected head of a Europe-wide pedophile sex ring, Dutrox used the Internet to meet and lure his victims.

Riva, an unemployed truck driver, former prison officer, and father of four, was discovered when the mother of one of his victims (a 10-year-old girl) pressed charges of child abuse against him. The girl claimed that Riva had abused her when she stayed overnight at a slumber party for one of his daughters.

The case broke wide open when detectives discovered that Riva's house contained equipment (similar to that used in videoconferencing) that was set up to broadcast live "photo shoots" on the Internet. Police also discovered computer files containing child pornography and links to another man, Melton Lee Myers, who had similar equipment.

The investigation ultimately linked the two to a worldwide pedophile ring with members based in the United States, Finland, Australia, and Canada. The group was abusing children as young as 5 years old and broadcasting pictures and live child-sex shows on the Internet (Cusack, 1996).

The Web and Internet have made it almost impossible to control kiddie porn, and the number of federal "cyber-cops" (federal agents who scour the Internet for such material) has increased from a handful to more than 100 operating in the United States alone (Kaplan, 1997). Besides having a voracious appetite for pornography, which has contributed literally tens of thousands of child sex visual images to the Internet, pedophiles and child molesters have taken advantage of sophisticated broadcasting techniques to stay ahead of the law. Child pornographers often "morph" the head of one child onto the body of another, making identification of the child and proof of sexual abuse almost impossible. The naked images of adults in child pornography are limited almost exclusively to shots from the torso down.

Additional obstacles to tracking pedophiles, child molesters, and child pornographers include the sheer volume and worldwide scope of their activities. Keeping abreast of new sites, linking perpetrators, and identifying victims is indeed difficult. Often, just as investigators are making progress, a site closes down and relocates with a new Web address or country of origin.

One potential inroad being explored is forcing service providers to sever relationships with sites that have been known to contain child porn. A key component of the Communications Decency Act, which the U.S. Supreme Court struck down as unconstitutional in 1997, was the provision to hold providers (such as America Online) liable if their customers could gain access to obscene and indecent material. At present, a global effort is under way to come up with a way to control access of child pornography via the Internet.

Numerous state and federal laws have made the possession of any sexual image of kids under age 18 illegal. Nonetheless, the underground market for all forms of child pornography and prostitution is thriving (Kaplan, 1997). Pedophiles have victimized their own children, stepchildren, foster children, or relatives' children. Less often victims are children adopted through foreign services, bought through underground slave trade, or exchanged with other pedophiles. People with pedophilia have been known to use extraordinary means to obtain child pornography or actual live victims. In recent years, several pedophiles have made headlines by arranging encounters with children while posing as adolescents in Internet chat rooms.

Pedophilia usually is chronic and is more difficult to treat than other paraphilias. The recidivism rate for men attracted to boys is more than twice that of men attracted to girls (Davis et al., 1995).

Sexual Masochism

The paraphiliac focus of **sexual masochism** is deriving arousal and pleasure through being beaten, bound, humiliated (physically or mentally), or made to suffer in some other fashion (APA, 2000). Although fantasizing about being the victim of masochistic acts is common, true paraphilia involves engaging in the behaviors.

Many different masochistic acts typically are sought with a partner. These include being bound (physical restraint involving being tied, strapped, taped, chained, or handcuffed), spanked, bitten, paddled, whipped, beaten, shocked with an electrical current, cut, or pierced/pinned (infibulation). Another common masochistic desire is to be humiliated by being urinated or defecated on, to be forced to crawl and bark like a dog, and to be verbally abused. **Infantilism** involves being treated like an infant and forced to wear a diaper.

The last category of masochistic paraphilia involves **hypoxyphilia** (also known as *autoerotic asphyxia*), or oxygen deprivation, by noose or wire (ligature), chest compression, plastic bag, mask, or chemical (such as amyl nitrate, a powerful vasodilator that reduces the flow of oxygen to the brain). This behavior is particularly dangerous because mishaps in applying these procedures for sexual arousal could result in death. Little is known about this behavior since information about individual cases is usually derived from postmortem physical and psychological evaluations of the victim. Investigation is made even more difficult by the victim's family attempting to cover up the sexual nature of the death (Friedrich & Gerber, 1994). It does not seem that hypoxyphilia is attempted suicide (Hickman, 2002). Rather, in most cases it is accidental, a result of ritualized autoeroticism where oxygen deprivation is part of the sexual attraction and risk taking. Most people who engage in autoerotic asphyxia are males with a history of sexual abuse, physical abuse, choking behavior (sometimes associated with asthma), exposure to traumatic family experiences, and other risk taking (Friedrich & Gerber, 1994).

Many sex shops cater to sexual paraphernalia associated with sadism and masochism.

Edward Holub/CORBIS

Sexual masochism Deriving sexual pleasure from being humiliated or forced to suffer pain

Infantilism Deriving sexual pleasure from being treated like an infant

Hypoxyphilia Deriving sexual pleasure from activities that involve oxygen deprivation

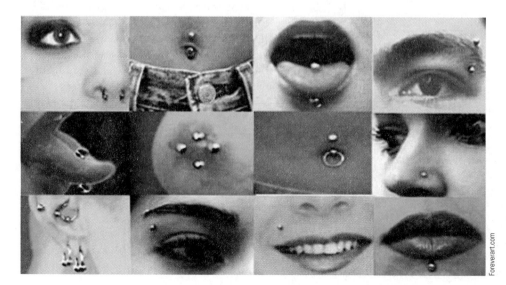

Foreverart.com

Piercing has become so popular that many states have adopted guidelines for ensuring the health and safety of the practice.

Sometimes, individuals with sexual masochism engage in masochistic acts by themselves. They self-inflict pain and humiliation through pinning, binding, shocking, or engaging in hypoxyphilia. Men with sexual masochism often concurrently have fetishism, transvestic fetishism, or sexual masochism (APA, 2000). The practice of body piercing has its etiology in sexual masochism. Piercing erogenous body parts such as the labia, nipples, and scrotum by paraphiliacs represents self-mutilation associated with masochism and the desire to humiliate and injure oneself. Most body piercers, however, have the procedures done for personal adornment, a reflection of style (Association of Professional Piercers [APP], 2002).

Physical Wellness

The continuum of atypical sexual behavior, as we've discussed, ranges from the relatively benign (occasional use of a fetish object) to the very dangerous (sadomasochistic beatings and torture). As we've mentioned throughout this text, healthy sexuality promotes physical well-being and behaviors that enhance health. Engaging in many of the atypical sexual behaviors can put your physical health in jeopardy. It is crucial to follow all of the warnings associated with these behaviors. There are ways to reduce the physical health risks associated with atypical sexual behavior.

healthy sex hints 9.1
Reducing the Health Risks Associated with Body Piercing

Body piercing, like other forms of adornment such as tattooing, branding, and ear piercing, carries some risk. The risks vary and are related to the body part being pierced, the piercing equipment, sterilization procedures used (or lack thereof), and the skill of the provider. The following hints can help reduce the risks associated with body piercing:

1. Think long and hard about your motivation for getting your body pierced. Make sure you understand the risks associated with the procedure.
2. Talk with people who have had piercing done. Ask what kind of experiences they had.
3. Before getting pierced, ask your physician about vaccination for hepatitis B, a blood-borne infection passed through contaminated needles.
4. Do not pierce yourself or let an inexperienced person (such as your best friend, who pierced her own ears) pierce you.
5. Go to a reputable piercing parlor that has been in business for some time. Ask for references from former customers.
6. Make sure the piercing parlor you choose uses an autoclave (a tabletop sterilizing device that uses heat and pressure to kill germs) to sterilize equipment. Ask to

see the certificate verifying that the autoclave has been recently inspected. If only boiling water is used to clean equipment, head for the door.
7. If a tattoo artist uses individually sealed, sterile needles, ask him or her to open these in front of you. Request the same for the containers of ink being used for your tattoo.
8. Talk to your physician to learn about special considerations concerning the body part being pierced. Particularly risky parts (because of increased likelihood of infection or permanent damage) are the eyelids, the tongue, the nipples, the clitoris, and the frenulum of the penis.
9. Don't have piercing done if you are pregnant or nursing.
10. Follow after-care instructions to the letter. If you suspect infection, consult a doctor immediately.
11. Wear only jewelry that is 14K gold, niobium, or surgical-grade stainless steel. These contain fewer alloys and are less likely to cause allergic reactions.

Source: Association of Professional Piercers (2002), *Procedure manual* (Chamblee, GA: Author).

Sexual Sadism

The paraphiliac focus of **sexual sadism** involves deriving sexual arousal and pleasure by inflicting physical or psychological pain and suffering on another person. The person may engage in sadistic activities with either a willing victim (usually someone with sexual masochism) or a nonconsenting victim (APA, 2000). Sexual sadism incorporates a range of acts, including all of those discussed previously under the topic of sexual masochism. In extreme cases, people with sexual sadism seek sexual arousal through extreme brutality, torture, mutilation, and murder. Typically, they engage in such behavior with nonconsenting victims and have had the condition for several years. The fantasies of sexual sadism usually are present in childhood, and the behavior begins in early adulthood and becomes chronic.

Sexual sadism Deriving sexual pleasure from inflicting pain or humiliation

Emotional Wellness

The difference between someone who engages in atypical sexual behavior and the true paraphiliac is in the emotional distress and social dysfunction the latter experiences. An individual or couple can engage in almost all of the atypical behaviors of paraphiliacs without this representing a paraphiliac sexual condition. A person can be emotionally healthy and still enjoy an occasional walk on the wild side. Actually, some people engage in atypical sexual activities to add a spark to their sex lives. When the behavior becomes an obsession, however, and carries with it emotional distress and social dysfunction, it becomes a paraphiliac sexual disorder.

Transvestic Fetishism

Transvestic fetishism differs from other forms of fetishism in that the fetishist derives sexual arousal by cross-dressing (dressing up as a female or wearing an article of female clothing). The transvestic fetishist typically masturbates to orgasm while dressed in that clothing.

The disorder is known only in males. It runs the full spectrum of behavior from routinely wearing a single item of female clothing (such as silk panties) under the male clothing to spending thousands of dollars on customized gowns and makeup and participating in the transvestic subculture (APA, 2000).

Men with transvestic fetishism do not have gender identity disorder (think they are really females), and most are heterosexual in sexual orientation. When not cross-dressed, men with transvestic fetishism look like the average man. Men who do not have transvestic fetishism but occasionally like to put on articles of female clothing often do so with the willing participation of their female partners.

Transvestic fetishism Deriving sexual pleasure from wearing women's clothing

Gender Identity Disorder

Gender identity disorder (GID) is also known as **transsexualism.** Gender identity disorder is characterized by four criteria:

- a strong and persistent cross-gender identification;
- persistent discomfort with his or her sex or a sense of inappropriateness in the gender role of that sex;
- the absence of any genetic or physical abnormality (intersex condition such as androgen insensitivity);
- significant accompanying clinical psychological distress and impairment in social, occupational, or other functioning.

Transsexualism (a gender identity disorder) A strong and persistent cross-gender identification

From James to Jenny

Jenny, 46, is white.

Critical Thinking

Should the medical profession be engaged in helping people change their biological gender? Why?

Use your Virtual Workbook to explore your answers to these questions at **http://health.wadsworth.com/blonna1.**

James Finney Boylan was living an idyllic life. He was a successful novelist and a professor of creative writing at Colby College in Maine. He was a loving husband with two sons. There was just one thing wrong. Since childhood, James felt he was living the wrong life. James had a secret: He was a woman trapped in a man's body.

In her book, *She's Not There: A Life in Two Genders*, Jennifer Finney Boylan chronicles her journey to womanhood. In 1998, James accepted the reality of his situation and began the process of transition, including psychotherapy, hormone treatments, electrolysis, and voice coaching. She underwent gender reassignment surgery in 2002.

Boylan began his transformation by telling his wife "Grace" about the psychological torment he was enduring because of his gender identity issues. In one particularly poignant moment, Boylan apologizes to his wife for all that she is enduring as they are watching the first *Lord of the Rings* movie: In the words of Bilbo, "I am sorry. Sorry you have come in for this burden, sorry about everything."

Boylan's children seem to take the metamorphosis in stride, even inventing a name to call her that makes sense: "Maddy," a combination of *Mommy* and *Daddy*.

Boylan takes a leave of absence from his duties at Colby, announcing to his colleagues via a letter that when he returns he will be Jennifer Finney Boylan. Boylan's close friend and colleague at Colby, Pulitzer Prize–winning novelist Richard Russo, initially cannot accept his friend's decision and evokes him to "be a man." Eventually, however, Russo comes to support his friend's decision and even accompanies Boylan and Grace to Wisconsin for the surgery.

Now Boylan notices that as a female her moods are more wide-ranging; she often feels more vulnerable and cries easily. She also deals with body image issues, being more conscientious about ordering a salad rather than the slab of ribs James would have requested. She also says that she is now attracted to men.

Today Jenny and Grace are in a new kind of relationship. Not husband and wife, or lesbian partners, but something different. They are still legally married and are committed to being partners in parenting. They are not currently seeking relationships with other people. At the end of this particular personal journey, Jenny Boylan is finally enjoying the life that she always felt was meant to be.

A strong and persistent cross-gender identification has several markers for children. The following constitute evidence for a strong and persistent cross-gender identification:

- a repeated stated desire to be, or insistence that he or she is, the other sex;
- in boys, a preference for dressing in female attire or simulating girls' clothing; in girls, wearing only stereotypical boys' clothing;
- a strong and persistent preference for cross-gender sex roles in make-believe play or fantasy;
- desire and participation in the stereotypical games and pastimes of the other sex;
- a strong preference for playmates of the other sex.

In adolescents and adults, the criteria for a strong and persistent cross-gender identification are met by the following symptoms:

- stated desire to be the other sex,
- frequent passing as the other sex,
- desire to live or be treated as the other sex, and
- conviction that he or she has the typical feelings and reactions as the other sex.

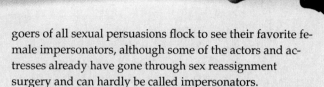

sex in society 9.2

The Underground World

In the 1970s Lou Reed, an avant garde artist and the lead singer for the Velvet Underground, sang about taking a walk on the wild side. The wild side in this case was the underground world of transsexuals—a world replete with its own bars, clubs, magazines, and clothing outlets.

Today you still can experience this underground world on certain streets in every major city in the United States, from New Orleans to New York City to San Francisco, and find a world filled with all of the transpeople—transsexuals, transvestites, and the transgendered. You'll find boutiques catering to transsexuals that carry everything in "women's" clothing from panties to feather boas in sizes designed to fit the average truck driver. You'll also find shoe stores that cater to spiked heels in sizes 10, 11, and 12 in every width. At night these districts come alive as club-

goers of all sexual persuasions flock to see their favorite female impersonators, although some of the actors and actresses already have gone through sex reassignment surgery and can hardly be called impersonators.

The World Wide Web has opened the globe to the transcommunity. You now can view entire catalogs of merchandise on your computer and shop from the privacy of your own home. There are social organizations, self-help groups, political action committees, legal aid societies, chat rooms, list serves, travel clubs (they find the best places for transpeople to vacation), auto clubs, discount purchasing cooperatives—and the list goes on and on. The amazing thing is that most of these people, places, and services operate outside the realization of mainstream society.

Supporting the second criterion is discomfort and inappropriateness with one's gender role. Boys strongly and persistently assert that their penis and testes are disgusting and wish they would disappear. They also have a strong aversion to typical rough-and-tumble play and stereotypical boys' toys, games, and activities. Girls have a strong and persistent resistance to sitting while urinating and assert that they do not want to grow breasts or menstruate. They also have an aversion to feminine clothing (APA, 2000).

Adults with gender identity disorder are preoccupied with ridding themselves of their primary and secondary physical sexual characteristics through hormone therapy and surgery. Transsexuals feel, and have always felt, that they were literally born the wrong sex, as if nature had made some mistake with their genitals.

Leavitt and Berger (1990) identify two forms of transsexualism: primary and secondary. *Primary* transsexuals are individuals who feel strong cross-gender identification from their earliest recollections of their childhood. Often, these individuals have clear cross-gender identification by age 3. *Secondary* transsexuals begin to develop strong cross-gender identification in adulthood. Because secondary transsexuals have gone through infancy, childhood, adolescence, and early adulthood with same-gender identification, shifting to their new cross-gender identification is more difficult.

There is much controversy surrounding the classification of GID, especially among secondary transsexuals. Transgender activists and those who serve transgendered clients claim that the "significant enough emotional, social, occupational, or other distress" that "interferes with their daily functioning" (quotes indicate DSM-IV criteria necessary for diagnosis) experienced by most transgendered men and women is not due to their gender identification but by societal reaction to it (Carroll, Gilroy, & Ryan, 2002; Klein, 2002; Isay, 1997). Citing this and other controversies

Jennifer Finney Boylan recently wrote about her journey from male to female in the book She's Not There: A Life in Two Genders.

Bruce Strong

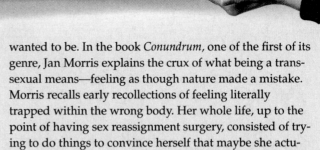

sex in society 9.3

Jan Morris: A Conundrum

Jan Morris started out in life as John Morris, later to be knighted and become Sir John Morris. John Morris—man, husband, father, athlete, soldier, explorer, writer, world traveler, climber of Mount Everest—was the epitome of every man's fantasy. He had power, prestige, wealth, and fame. Beautiful women wanted to be around him. He held the world in his hands.

John Morris had everything he wanted except for one thing: he really wanted to be a woman. He'd gladly have given it all up (and did) to become the woman he always wanted to be. In the book *Conundrum,* one of the first of its genre, Jan Morris explains the crux of what being a transsexual means—feeling as though nature made a mistake. Morris recalls early recollections of feeling literally trapped within the wrong body. Her whole life, up to the point of having sex reassignment surgery, consisted of trying to do things to convince herself that maybe she actually did belong in that body. Ultimately she realized that she didn't, and she had the surgery necessary to become a female.

---

surrounding the diagnostic category, Isay (1997) appealed to the American Psychiatric Association for the removal of the classification gender identity disorder. In a rebuttal to Isay (1997), Friedman (1998) acknowledges the problems associated with misdiagnoses of some transgendered persons (especially adult, homosexual men) but supports the continuation of the inclusion of the classification in the DSM-IV. Friedman notes that children with GID have much more psychopathology compared to other children. Elimination of the GID classification, Friedman claims, would cause these children to fall through the cracks and not receive the psychiatric care they need.

The Origin and Treatment of Atypical Sexual Behavior

Many different theories abound about the causes and treatment of atypical sexual behavior and paraphilias. Implied in "atypical" is the need to fix something that is wrong. Therefore, we reemphasize the difference between individuals who occasionally engage in behaviors that are atypical and cause no harm to another person and individuals who have paraphilias that cause themselves and others pain and suffering. The difference lies in the psychological distress and impairment in social, occupational, and other functioning between the two types of behavior.

Ethical Considerations

Society has an ethical and moral obligation to protect paraphiliacs and their victims from harm, even if they do not realize they are at risk. A sexual masochist, for instance, should be protected from the violence and suffering that may coexist with that paraphilia.

The need for treatment is less clear with problems such as gender identity disorder. Is this really a psychological disorder? Is the condition really a problem that requires treatment, or should their desire to be the other sex be respected? Many question the essential duality of maleness and femaleness. As mentioned in Chapter 4, gender is best viewed as a continuum rather than an absolute value (100 percent male versus 100 percent female).

The ethics of sexual reassignment surgery (surgically removing the genitals and reconstructing the genitalia of the desired, opposite sex) has been the subject of much debate. Should people who have GID be allowed to have sex reassignment surgery? Would it make more sense to try to help these people learn to accept both the fact that they have the genitalia of one gender and the identity of another? Why do we have to fit them into only one neat niche? These and other questions related to the diagnosis and treatment of atypical and paraphiliac sexual behavior are still being debated and may never be fully resolved.

Spiritual Wellness

When discussing spiritual wellness, we must take care to separate people who engage in occasional atypical sexual behavior from paraphiliacs. Spirituality, as we've mentioned throughout the book, emphasizes the interconnectedness of people and treating all people with respect and dignity. Paraphilias such as sadism, masochism, and pedophilia are based on seeking gratification by inflicting pain, humiliation, or dominance over another. Hurting others represents an absence of spirituality.

Etiology

Many explanations have been set forth for the causes of atypical sexual behavior and paraphilias. Three of the more commonly accepted views revolve around a psychoanalytic appraisal, a behaviorist explanation, and an eclectic etiology.

Psychoanalytic Appraisal A classic psychoanalytic explanation for atypical or paraphiliac sexual behavior is the fixation of libidinal energy at a specific point in development. An individual becomes "stuck" and, with advancing age, constantly regresses to that point in psychosexual development. The immature level of sexual development is a result of not having been allowed the full expression and passage of libidinal energy at the age-appropriate stage.

Sexual masochists' need to be humiliated by having their partner urinate or defecate on them, for instance, is attributed to unresolved issues at the anal stage. Perhaps this person was rushed through toilet training or belittled for soiling his underpants. Whatever the specific issue, the unresolved transition through this period results in the fixation of sexuality at this stage of development.

Behaviorism The behaviorist focuses on some facet of learning and argues that atypical sexual behavior and paraphilia stem from some associative learning experience. Perhaps it was extremely harsh parental punishment for some minor sexual act such as observing Mom in the shower or being caught masturbating. Or it may be pairing an act (observing a woman undressing, for instance) with a pleasurable sexual experience (such as masturbation) that is positively reinforcing. This type of behavior is likely to be repeated.

Eclectic Perspective John Money (Money & Lamacz, 1989) offers an eclectic explanation to atypical sexual behavior and paraphilia. He has developed a biosocial theory of sexual and gender development (see Chapter 4) based on what he called "lovemaps" ("templates" in the brain for patterns of eroticism and love). These templates, according to Money, are developed between 5 and 8 years of age as a result of biological and psychosocial forces.

During this period of development, Money believes children begin to link sex, love, and lust. The child usually develops a normal, healthy connection between romantic love and lust (sexual desire). Each of us has a unique lovemap based on

case study 9.3

The Marv Albert Case

Marv, 66, married, is white.

Critical Thinking

Because most paraphilias are deeply ingrained and difficult to extinguish, what do you think the goal of treatment should be? Why?

Use your Virtual Workbook to explore your answers to these questions at **http://health.wadsworth.com/blonna1.**

The sporting world was shocked when Marv Albert, a longtime radio and television sportscaster, was arraigned in Virginia on charges of forced sodomy and a variety of other lesser charges. Albert's more than 30-year career as the play-by-play announcer for NBC and other networks made him a celebrity, and his trademark "Yes-s-s-s!" following key baskets during New York Knicks broadcasts was known across the United States.

Albert's accuser, a longtime lover, charged him with biting her in several places on the back and forcing her to perform fellatio on him. She claimed that Albert's behavior was in response to his disappointment in the woman's unwillingness to bring a third partner in a ménage à trois, another man, to a rendezvous at a local hotel. The woman further asserted that she had a long history of such trysts with Albert, even several years ago while he was still married. She also claimed that Albert had a penchant for cross-dressing, watching X-rated videos, and biting during sex.

Albert countered by claiming that the woman liked "rough sex," and the biting was part of their sexual repertoire. He confirmed their long-term relationship but claimed that he never had forced her to do anything. Her accusations, Albert asserted, were in response to his informing her that he would be getting engaged and married and would be ending their relationship.

During the investigation, a second woman, a hotel manager from Washington, DC, surfaced, claiming that Albert had tried to force her to have sex with him also. She claimed that Albert had placed a call for room service, and when she arrived, Albert met her at the door wearing only women's panties and a garter belt. He had an obvious erection and tried to force her to have sex with him. She said she fought him off and left the room.

The case ended with Albert's and the woman's attorneys working out a plea bargain in which the sportscaster agreed to a lesser charge of assault (a misdemeanor) in exchange for dropping the forced sodomy charge (a felony). Albert eventually received a suspended 12-month sentence with a promise to expunge his record of all charges if he would seek counseling and honor all of the conditions of his probation.

The case sent shock waves throughout the United States, touching off a flurry of talk-show programs concerning rough sex, biting, cross-dressing, and other paraphiliac behavior. Included in the debate was a discussion of whether someone like Albert could ever be "rehabilitated." Experts testified claiming that the goal of Albert's treatment would be to teach him how to control his urges to engage in such behavior in public with strangers or nonmarital partners. Albert is now back on the airwaves.

a combination of biology (genetic inheritance, gonadal and hormonal influences) and psychosocial learning (parental and other models of love and affection). Healthy lovemaps are imprinted in our brain and create our idealized lover, love affair, and erotic imagery.

Atypical sexual behavior and paraphilia, according to Money, are a result of a distorted or "vandalized" lovemap that does not make a healthy connection between romantic love and lust. Love and lust are imprinted as disparate entities. Because the two are not linked, sexual desire (lust) is not attached to normal romantic involvements but, rather, becomes attached to the inanimate objects, humiliating behavior, and the like, that evolve into paraphilias. Sexual desire is something apart from intimacy and affection. Lovemaps can become distorted for a variety of reasons including incest, physical abuse, extremely harsh parental punishments for normal sexual activity in childhood, repressive parental attitudes, and lack of displays of affection between parents.

Is It Really So Bad?

It is really easy to react negatively when we hear of some "different" sexual behavior and to immediately label it as harmful. However, even though we may never want to engage in any paraphiliac sexual behavior, many of the behaviors cause no real harm to the person or others. The goal of this activity is to try to identify those behaviors that are truly harmful from those that, however odd they seem, are really rather harmless.

Take a sheet of paper and label three columns—one "harmless," one "harmful," and one "both harmful and harmless." As you continue to read about the different behaviors, try to keep an open mind and forget the judgments you have already formed about these behaviors. After reading about each behavior, list it in the column where it seems to fit the best. Notice what factors cause you to give each the label you assign. Based on what label you give each behavior, do you think there should be criminal penalties for the behavior? Keep in mind that many of these behaviors carry severe criminal penalties or at least very negative social attitudes. Is it possible that our society is overreacting because the behaviors do not fit what most consider to be normal? Should our laws and attitudes be changed for those you listed in the harmless category?

Treatment

Most paraphiliacs enter treatment as a result of being arrested for their behavior. They do not seek treatment on their own or enter willingly. Paraphilias are extremely difficult to treat, and "cure rates" are low. Regardless of which view one holds regarding the etiology of paraphilias, most experts agree that atypical and paraphiliac behavior originates early in life, manifests itself in fantasy and desire, and evolves into full-blown behavior and lifestyle by young adulthood. As such, the person has a long history of behavior that has been reinforced over time through pleasure (masturbation or other sources of orgasm). The prognosis for eliminating such behavior is not good.

Biomedical and Surgical Treatment   One way to treat people with paraphilia is to attempt to lower their level of sexual desire through chemical (drugs) and surgical (castration) procedures. Drug therapy consists of administering drugs that either inhibit the production of testosterone or block its effects on the brain. As we discussed in Chapters 2 and 3, testosterone is the main androgen linked to sexual desire in men and women. Drugs such as cyproterone acetate (CPA) and medrohxyprogesterone (MPA-Depo-Provera) interfere with the effects of progesterone. They have been shown to have limited effectiveness in treating pedophiles, rapists, and other male sex offenders (Wincze, Bansal, & Malamud, 1986; Cooper, 1986). Until the 1980s, castration was used to reduce the sexual desire of sex offenders. The surgical removal of the testicles eliminates the production of most testosterone but does not prevent sexual excitement and erection.

Although decreasing testosterone levels lower sexual desire, it does not eliminate desire entirely. Also, no evidence is available to show that reducing testosterone levels, and thus sexual desire, has any permanent effect on the focus of sexual behavior. Testosterone is linked with sexual desire, not sexual orientation or the focus of sexual activity. Drug therapy seems to work by lessening the compulsion to engage in paraphiliac behavior (Walen & Roth, 1987). It doesn't eliminate the desire but, in conjunction with other approaches invoking the patient's support system, helps control the desire enough to allow intervention.

Treatment for transsexualism (gender identity disorder) often involves surgically reconstructing the patient's genitalia. The overwhelming majority of transsexual surgical reassignments involve male-to-female transitions. In male-to-female transsexual reassignment surgery, a new clitoris, vulva, and vagina are constructed from penile and scrotal tissue. Internal structures remain the same. In female-to-male surgery, a penis and scrotum are constructed from vulval and vaginal tissue. In this case, artificial testes (with implants) are constructed, and removable penile implant rods can be inserted into the structure to achieve an erection.

Transsexual reassignment surgery is part of a four-part treatment process that also involves psychotherapy, hormone therapy, and living as the other gender. The goal of psychotherapy is to help the client readjust in his/her new role. The client begins taking hormones of the new gender to either "feminize" (in male-to-female reassignment) or "masculinize" (in female-to-male reassignment) the client's body. Lastly, before surgery is performed, clients must live as the new gender (complete with cross-dressing) for a year to learn what it is like to function as a member of society in one's new gender (Meyerowitz, 2002; Money & Wiedcking, 1980).

Aversion therapy A behavior modification technique that pairs an aversive stimulus with the behavior targeted for change

Covert sensitization A type of behavior modification in which an aversive fantasy is paired with the paraphiliac fantasy in an attempt to extinguish it

Behavior Modification   Behavior modification is used to desensitize paraphiliacs to their paraphilias and sensitize them to new, aversive stimuli. **Aversion therapy** is a behavior modification technique that pairs an aversive stimulus (such as electric shock) with the behavior that is targeted for change. Covert sensitization is a type of aversion therapy sometimes used with paraphiliacs. In **covert sensitization,** an aversive fantasy (not behavior) is paired with the paraphiliac fantasy in an attempt to extinguish it. For example, a voyeur is asked to visualize a past fantasy that accompanied one of the voyeuristic episodes. As the person visualizes the pleasing fantasy (say, peeping on an unsuspecting woman), the therapist introduces an aversive fantasy image (such as vomiting uncontrollably). By pairing the new aversive image (the vomiting) with the previously arousing image (peeping at the victim), the therapist links the negative image to the paraphilia.

Intellectual Wellness

High-level intellectual functioning can help a person know when an atypical behavior pattern represents a true paraphilia. Knowledge can help people understand that they have a problem and how to seek help in dealing with it. Paraphilias, however, tend to have such a strong hold over people that knowledge alone usually isn't enough to motivate them to seek help. Even so, knowledge can play a part in helping them learn how to live with their obsession and channel it into more acceptable forms of expression.

Skills Training   The focus of skills training is to enhance interpersonal skills. Paraphiliacs often rely on the paraphilia because of their inability to engage in satisfying interpersonal sexual relationships. Often they lack the self-esteem, confidence, and behavioral skills to meet potential sex partners and cultivate sexually satisfying relationships.

In skills training, they learn a variety of behaviors ranging from communicating (how to initiate conversations, meet new people, and the like) to coping with stress. As individuals become more proficient with these skills, they can learn to rely less and less on their paraphilia for sexual arousal (Zilbergeld, 1992).

Social Wellness

People who engage in atypical sexual activity (particularly partnered activities) can be socially healthy. They may engage in atypical activities to add spice to their sex lives. Most people with full-blown paraphilias, however, are not doing well socially. Their paraphilia often originated from disordered social functioning and learning. The paraphilia takes the place of functional adult social and sexual relationships. Many paraphiliacs experience sexual release through solitary masturbation in the presence of their paraphiliac object of desire.

Your responses to the Personal Assessments, Thought Questions, and Test Yourself! quiz questions can be logged online in your Virtual Workbook at **http://health.wadsworthcom/blonna1.**

Personal Assessment

9.1 Values Continuum

Instructions: For each of the 10 sexual behaviors listed here, mark the appropriate spot on the continuum indicating your level of approval/disapproval.

1. Heterosexual vaginal intercourse

   strongly disapprove   **strongly approve**

2. Being tied to a bed, chair, or other structure during sex

   strongly disapprove   **strongly approve**

3. Being spanked or paddled during sex

   strongly disapprove   **strongly approve**

4. Being pinched or bitten during sex

   strongly disapprove   **strongly approve**

5. Masturbating or having sex with the aid of a special object (a shoe, for example)

   strongly disapprove   **strongly approve**

6. Being totally submissive during sex (must follow your partner's instructions or be punished)

   strongly disapprove   **strongly approve**

7. Being totally dominating during sex (your partner must follow your instructions or be punished)

   strongly disapprove   **strongly approve**

8. Watching someone else (or a couple) get undressed or have sex

   strongly disapprove   **strongly approve**

9. Intentionally get undressed or have sex in public view (with shades open and the like)

   strongly disapprove   **strongly approve**

10. Masturbating while looking at pictures of children

    strongly disapprove   **strongly approve**

There are no right or wrong answers. By examining your position on the 10 different continua, you will know where your values lie regarding atypical sexual behavior. The important point is understanding your values and sharing them with your sex partner. You may wish to have your partner take this assessment and discuss your results with each other.

Thought Questions

1. What are some of the many facets of "normal" sexual behavior?

2. What does "atypical" sexual behavior mean?

3. When does atypical sexual behavior become a paraphilia?

4. How do a person's morality and ethics influence atypical sexual behavior?

5. How have the media treated some of the more common paraphilias such as voyeurism and exhibitionism?

6. What is the difference between a true transsexual and someone with transvestic fetishism?

7. What are the origins of paraphilias?

8. What are three treatment approaches for paraphilias?

9. Describe the controversy associated with sexual reassignment surgery.

Test Yourself!

1. Which of the following is *not* considered a category of normative sexual behavior discussed in this chapter?
   a. Biological norm
   b. Anthropological norm
   c. Statistical norm
   d. Sociological norm

2. *Abnormal behavior* is generally considered
   a. an outdated term, replaced by *atypical behavior*.
   b. an outdated term, replaced by *nonnormative behavior*.
   c. an acceptable term synonymous with *atypical behavior*.
   d. an acceptable term still widely used by most experts in the field of human sexuality.

3. Atypical sexual behavior becomes paraphiliac when
   a. it is the major recurring theme in the person's sexual fantasies.
   b. it is obsessive and interferes with a normal sex life.
   c. it becomes repetitive and obsessive.
   d. it causes obsessive preoccupation or need and interference with daily functioning.

4. Occasionally tying your lover to the bedpost to simulate loss of control during sex is an example of
   a. a fetish related to rope.
   b. an atypical sexual behavior.
   c. a paraphilia.
   d. an abnormal sexual behavior.

5. Which behavior is often mistaken for mooning or other forms of consensual public sexual activity with a partner?
   a. voyeurism
   b. frottage
   c. urophilia
   d. exhibitionism

6. A sexual sadist is someone who derives sexual arousal and pleasure from
   a. inflicting pain and/or humiliation on sexual partners.
   b. experiencing pain and/or humiliation at the hands of sexual partners.
   c. "snuffing" a partner with no direct sexual involvement.
   d. torturing a partner with no direct sexual involvement.

7. A sexual masochist is someone who derives sexual arousal and pleasure from
   a. inflicting pain and/or humiliation on sexual partners.
   b. experiencing pain and/or humiliation at the hands of sexual partners.
   c. "snuffing" a partner with no direct sexual involvement.
   d. torturing a partner with no direct sexual involvement.

8. The best answer to describe the major differences between transsexuals and transvestites is
   a. transsexuals derive sexual arousal and pleasure from cross-dressing.
   b. transvestites derive no sexual arousal and pleasure from cross-dressing.
   c. transvestites feel they are members of the opposite gender and are "trapped" in the wrong body.
   d. transsexuals feel they are members of the opposite gender and are "trapped" in the wrong body.

9. John Money's "lovemaps" theory of atypical sexual behavior and paraphilia says that paraphilias develop as a result of
   a. neurolinguistic programming that distorts lovemaps.
   b. unhealthy lovemaps that link love and lust.
   c. unhealthy lovemaps that imprint love and lust as distinct entities.
   d. people who vandalize other people's lovemaps.

10. The prognosis for treatment of people with paraphilias is
    a. excellent over time using conventional behavioral modification.
    b. fair using short-term aversion therapies such as electric shock.
    c. not good regardless of the treatment modality.
    d. pretty good if the patient is highly motivated.

Media Menu

You can link to the following online tools by visiting
http://health.wadsworth.com/blonna1.

Film

Gender Identity Disorder

 InfoTrac Activity

Kinnon, J. B. (2000, April). Pierced to death. *Ebony, 55*(6), 142–146.

 Web Resources

The American Psychiatric Association (APA)

www.psych.org/index.cfm

A medical specialty society recognized worldwide. Its 37,000 U.S. and international member physicians work together to ensure humane care and effective treatment for all persons with mental disorder, including mental retardation and substance-related disorders. The APA is the voice and conscience of modern psychiatry and envisions a society that has available, accessible quality psychiatric diagnosis and treatment.

Above & Beyond

www.abgender.com

This outrageous site is a smorgasbord of resources (everything from shopping to emotional support) devoted to the transgender community.

Transgendered Suite

www.tgni.com

A major site for transgender information, support, and services. It provides everything from general information to a transgender dating service.

The Association of Professional Piercers (APP)

www.safepiercing.org

An international nonprofit association dedicated to the dissemination of vital health and safety information related to body piercing to piercers, health care providers, and the general public. The group believes that it is the obligation of all professionals in the field to assume responsibility for their continued education. The organization dedicates itself to enabling this responsibility to be met.

The New Zealand Edge; John Money Page

www.nzedge.com/heroes/money.html

The New Zealand Edge is a nonpolitical organization dedicated to fostering understanding of the country and its contributions to the world. This linked page is their page devoted to John Money.

References

American Psychiatric Association. (2000). *The diagnostic and statistical manual of mental disorders* (4th ed., text revision). Washington, DC: Author.

Association of Professional Piercers. (2002). *Procedure manual*. Chamblee, GA: Author.

Carroll, L., Gilroy, P. J., & Ryan, J. (2002, Spring). Counseling transgendered, transsexual, and gender-variant clients (practice and theory). *Journal of Counseling and Development, 80*(2), 131–140.

Cooper, A. J. (1986). Progesterone in the treatment of male sex offenders: A review. *Canadian Journal of Psychiatry, 31,* 73–79.

Cusack, J. (1996). The murky world of Internet porn: The "Orchid Club" shakes up the law. *World Press Review, 43*(11), 8–10.

Davis, L., McShane, M. D., & Williams, F. P. (1995). Controlling computer access to pornography: Special conditions for sex offenders. *Federal Probation, 59*(2), 43–48.

Friedman, R. C. (1998, January 19). Gender identity. *Psychiatric News: Viewpoints* [Online]. Available: www.payxh.org/pnews/98–01019/gender.html.

Friedrich, W. N., & Gerber, P. N. (1994, September). Autoerotic asphyxia: The development of a paraphilia. *Journal of the American Academy of Child and Adolescent Psychiatry, 33*(7), 970–975.

Hickman, W. (2002, August 8). A real swinger—Part IV (autoerotic asphyxiation cases). *Mondau Business Briefings.*

Isay, R. A. (1997, November 21). Remove gender identity disorder from DSM. *Psychiatric News: Viewpoints* [Online]. Available: www.psych.org/pnews/97/-11-21/isay.html.

Kaplan, D. E. (1997). New cybercop tricks to fight child porn: Police struggle against an online onslaught. *U S. News & World Report, 122*(20), 29.

Klein, J. A. (2002, December). A sex of one's own. *The Nation* [book review, *How Sex Changed: A History of Transsexuality in the United States*], *274*(19), 33–39.

Leavitt, F., & Berger, J. C. (1990). Clinical patterns among male transsexual candidates with erotic interest in males. *Archives of Sexual Behavior, 19*(5), 491–505.

Meyerowitz, J. (2002). *How sex changed: A history of transsexuality in the United States.* Boston: Harvard University Press.

Money, J., & Lamacz, M. (1989). *Vandalized lovemaps.* New York: Prometheus.

Money, J., & Wiedcking, C. (1980). Gender identity/role: Normal differentiation and its transpositions. In B. B. Wolman & J. Money (Eds.), *Handbook of human sexuality.* Englewood Cliffs, NJ: Prentice Hall.

Walen, S., & Roth, D. (1987). A cognitive approach. In J. H. Geer & W. T. O'Donohue (Eds.), *Theories of human sexuality.* New York: Plenum.

Wincze, J., Bansal, S., & Malamud, M. (1986). Effects of medroxprogesterone acetate on subjective arousal, arousal to erotic stimulation, and nocturnal penile tumescence in male sex offenders. *Archives of Sexual Behavior, 15,* 293–306.

Zilbergeld, B. (1992). *Male sexuality: A guide to sexual fulfillment.* Boston: Little, Brown.

chapter *eleven*

Sexual Communication

Student Learning Objectives

After reading this chapter, students will be able to

- Compare a variety of communication models.
- Describe some of the key elements that make sexual communication different and difficult.
- Assess the importance of communication in sexual relationships.
- Describe a variety of verbal sexual communication techniques.
- Describe a variety of nonverbal sexual communication techniques.
- Compare and contrast verbal and nonverbal sexual communication techniques.
- Describe some barriers to effective sexual communication.
- Describe how disabilities impact sexual communication.

*Test your understanding of these objectives by taking the end-of-chapter quiz, available online at **http://health.wadsworth.com/blonna1.***

activity teaser: *Are you comfortable with the language of sex? Find out with the Personal Exploration Activity on page 334.*

case study 11.1

Sirahana

Sirahana, 22, single, identifies as Iranian American.

Critical Thinking

How have your cultural beliefs and traditions influenced your relationships with current or former partners?

Use your Virtual Workbook to explore your answer to this question at **http://health.wadsworth.com/blonna1.**

Sirahana was a senior with a major in finance, enrolled in the human sexuality class to fulfill her free elective requirement and to learn more about herself. Normally an "A" student, Sirahana was having trouble with a couple of assignments that required her to write brief reactions about the influence of culture and religion on her sexuality.

She came to see Dr. Blonna about this matter and explained that the assignments forced her to examine things about her life and culture that were painful to her. She had been able to avoid these subjects because she had lived away from home for the past 4 years and was able to hide them from her parents. In a couple of months, however, school would be ending, and her parents expected her to move in with her Iranian family.

Sirahana would have to make some tough choices. She had a steady boyfriend, Sean, who was Irish Catholic. She had never told her parents about Sean because their relationship started out as a casual, lighthearted romance that neither thought would last. Little by little, it blossomed as their attraction for each other grew. She practically lived at his off-campus apartment and wanted to move in full-time once school ended in the summer. They had talked seriously about marriage and eventually children, neither one wanting to let their religious beliefs stand in the way of their love.

Sirahana explained that she was feeling a tremendous amount of guilt over her desire to live apart from her family with Sean. Her parents, culture, and religion all expected her to follow tradition by living at home and ultimately marrying someone of her own faith. It was such a strong expectation that she felt utterly paralyzed at the thought of talking to her parents about it. She also knew that she loved Sean and wanted to start a new life with him. She didn't want to move back home.

She liked the freedom of her current life and felt less and less drawn by the covenants and traditions of her religion and culture. She also loved and respected her parents and deeply appreciated all they had done to put her through school and rear her. She wanted to talk to them, explain exactly what she was feeling, and help them understand, but she didn't know how or where to begin.

Communication

Communication The process by which information is exchanged between individuals through a common system of symbols, signs, and behaviors

Communication is defined as the process by which information is exchanged between individuals through a common system of symbols, signs, or behaviors. It involves all the modes of behavior that an individual uses to affect another person. It encompasses spoken and written words as well as nonverbal messages such as gestures, facial expressions, bodily messages or signals, and artistic symbols (Watzlawick, Beaven, & Jackson, 1967).

Communicating, as Sirahana has shown us in Case Study 11.1, involves a whole range of issues from emotional comfort and security, to cultural considerations, and finally to discrete behavioral skills. Communicating about sexuality-related issues is even more complex and often more difficult because of this. Communication is the foundation of healthy sexuality. It is essential to obtaining sexual information for oneself as well as communicating information to others. Sexual communication poses unique challenges because of the difficulty of communicating in general, plus the personal nature of sexuality. Communicating effectively requires skill, patience, and commitment as well as an understanding and mastery of sexual information. Honest and accurate sexual communication is essential in developing and maintaining good relationships and fostering healthy sexuality.

Metacommunication

Communication also includes the interpersonal relationship between communicators. When we are in the presence of others, it is impossible not to communicate. Activity and inactivity, speech and silence—all communicate messages. Communication occurs at two levels: the *content* level (what is actually being said) and the *relationship* level (what is going on between the communicants). This second relationship level is referred to as **metacommunication,** or communication about communication. **Pragmatics** refers to the relationship between communicators, and relationships are of two types—symmetrical and complementary. **Symmetrical relationships** are based on equality. Each communicator treats the other in a like fashion, minimizing differences and conflict. Symmetrical relationships are comfortable and facilitate communication. When we are involved in symmetrical relationships, we are relaxed, our conversation is not forced, and we perceive periods of silence as comfortable and not awkward (Watzlawick et al., 1967).

Complementary relationships are based on differences. Communicators maximize their differences, causing inequality and disharmony. Complementary relationships crackle with the tension in the air. Communication is forced, and periods of silence seem interminable. Complementary relationships often result in stress (Watzlawick et al., 1967).

Metacommunication Communication about communication

Pragmatics The relationship between communicators

Symmetrical relationships Relationships based on equality

Complementary relationships Relationships based on differences

Social Wellness

All interpersonal communication has a social basis. It is not just about putting thoughts and feelings into words. It also is about the relationship between you and the person with whom you are communicating. As we have seen, metacommunication proposes a framework for communicating based on symmetrical (equal) and complementary (confrontational) relationships. Symmetrical relationships foster good communication, whereas complementary ones discourage effective dialogue.

Transactional Analysis

Eric Berne's (1960) **transactional analysis** (TA) model examines relationships that are either symmetrical or complementary. Berne proposed that all of us have three sources of behavior, or ego states: child, adult, and parent. Each ego state manifests itself in a different communication style. Figure 11.1 illustrates the three ego states of TA.

1. *The child.* The child manifests itself through childish use of verbal and nonverbal communication. The child uses coyness, naiveté, charm and seduction, boisterousness, giggling, and whining and is spontaneous, irresponsible, and manipulative. Our childish ego state is playful and free of restraint.
2. *The adult.* The adult is rational and objective, uses logic and analysis, and exhibits sound decision making based on accurate perception and analysis. The adult is fair, responsible, sociable.
3. *The parent.* The parent incorporates feelings and behaviors learned from authority figures. The parent communicates the conscience of the person through words, actions, postures, behaviors, expectations, and the use of guilt or reward. The parent can be nurturing (protects, cuddles, and cares for) or critical (corrects and condemns).

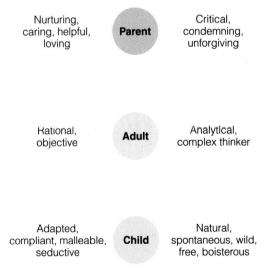

Figure 11.1 *Berne's Three Ego States*
Berne identified three ego states: the parent, the adult, and the child.

Source: Transactional Analysis in Psychotherapy, by Eric Berne (New York: Grove Press, 1960).

Figure 11.2
Transactional Mismatch
Miscommunication occurs
when people talk to each
other using different ego
state levels.

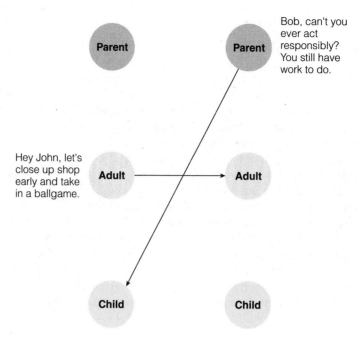

One adult addresses another adult. The second adult
receives the message in an adult ego state and
responds as if to a child ego state.

Transactional analysis (TA)
Eric Berne's communication
model based on three ego
states—parent, adult, and
child

According to Berne, when we communicate, our message is sent from one of
our three ego states and is received by a specific ego state of another. Ideally, the
ego state from which we send messages matches that of the person to whom we
are talking. Thus, if we are speaking from our adult state to another person, that
person should be receiving our message in his or her adult state. If this is not the
case, a mismatch occurs. A mismatch is similar to the complementary message in

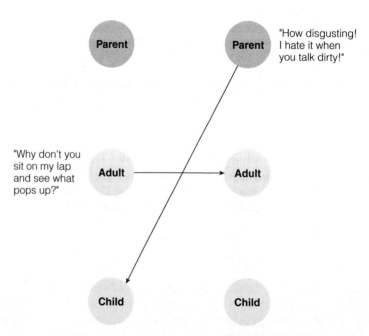

Figure 11.3 *Sexual
Transactional Mismatches*
Sexual transactional
mismatches occur when
lovers communicate about
sex using different ego state
levels.

One person initiates from his adult state, using humor to signal his sexual
interest. His partner responds sternly from her critical parent state,
treating him like a child.

case study 11.2

Susan: An Awkward Communication Circumstance

Susan, 37, single, and lesbian, is white.

Susan, a professor, is attending an out-of-town conference with some friends. She is sitting at the bar in her hotel, waiting for friends to come down and go out to dinner with her. She is nursing a drink, trying to relax.

A man seated two stools to her right tries to draw Susan into a conversation he is having with a group of his friends about the sexual differences between men and women. Susan doesn't know any of these people. She finds them not only a little drunk but also pretentious, shallow, and untrustworthy. She immediately feels uncomfortable. Susan feigns interest in what they are talking about, nodding her head while looking over their shoulders to try to spot her friends. She politely adds a comment here and there but can't relax around them as they carry on about a variety of issues she doesn't care about and trade barbs with each other. She also feels uncomfortable talking about this subject with a group of strangers who don't realize she is gay. These are characteristics of a complementary relationship.

Eventually Susan's friends arrive, and she quickly excuses herself and joins them. She is able to let down her guard, be herself, and enjoy the rest of the evening in symmetrical conversation among peers she respects and feels comfortable around.

> ### Critical Thinking
>
> We are often forced to endure social situations like the one Susan encountered that made her feel uneasy. How would you have responded to the man at the bar if you were Susan?
>
> Use your Virtual Workbook to explore your answer to this question at **http://health.wadsworth.com/blonna1.**

Watzlawick et al.'s (1967) metacommunication model. Mismatches between messages sent from one state and received by another can be a source of stress and sexual miscommunication.

Figure 11.2 illustrates a mismatch that occurs when we are talking to a peer and we use our parent ego state instead of our adult state. Our friend, receiving in an adult ego state, expects us to send an adult message. Instead, we send a parent message assuming we are sending to an assumed child ego state, which creates a mismatch and is a source of stress.

Figure 11.3 illustrates another mismatch between two lovers. One is in a playful mood and communicates a sexy message from his adult state. His lover, in an adult state, receives the message, is confused, and sends back a parent message. The critical nature of the message and the condemning tone send a stressful message that resonates within the partner's child state. Mismatches like this can cool the fires of desire if they are not cleared up.

Forms of Communication

The basic forms of communication are one-way and two-way.

One-Way Communication

One-way communication is an information-giving process that does not involve or rely on feedback. Speeches, lectures, movies, TV programs, concerts, and radio broadcasts are examples of one-way communication. One-way communication is a direct and powerful way to transmit information about sexuality. Much of what we learn about sexuality in our culture is disseminated through one-way communication.

Print and broadcast media use sexual themes in their programming and to sell their products. Movies, TV programs, and music videos weave visual sexual images into their plots. Song lyrics provide auditory sexual information. We absorb most of what we learn about the cultural context of sexuality through this passive transfer of sexual information through mass media. Mass media convey messages about how our culture views sex. Mass media communicate sexual information to entertain or sell products, not to inform and educate us. Although the impact of this exposure is powerful and conveys messages about sex, the portrayal is often shallow and inaccurate and doesn't offer the opportunity for a dialogue. It also doesn't afford the opportunity to personalize the information and explore how it relates to us as individuals.

Two-Way Communication

Feedback A verbal or nonverbal response sent from a person receiving a message to the person sending that message

Dialogue An exchange of information in communication

Encoding Selecting the signs, symbols, emotions, and words to transmit a message

Decoding The use of knowledge, memory, language, context, and personal history and experience to interpret a message

Two-way communication goes beyond information-giving by including **feedback.** Feedback ensures a dialogue, the key component of two-way communication. It gives us the opportunity to share information, ask questions, seek clarification, and explore ideas and feelings that go beyond those initially presented. **Dialogue** represents a true exchange of information. This is why two-way communication is essential for communicating about sexuality. Two-way communication increases the likelihood that each person will express his or her needs and wants and will understand each other clearly. One way to explain two-way communication is through a circular model of communication.

A Circular Model of Communication   Effective communication is a circular process that involves sending and receiving coded messages, as illustrated in Figure 11.4. A sender, wishing to communicate, puts the idea and feeling of the message into a form that can be transmitted. This process of formulating a message, choosing appropriate words, symbols, tone, and expressions to represent it is called **encoding.** The receiver perceives and translates the message using his or her personal storehouse of knowledge and experience in a process called **decoding.**

Encoding and decoding take place within the context of the communicator's interpersonal and physical relationship. What is being said involves not only the

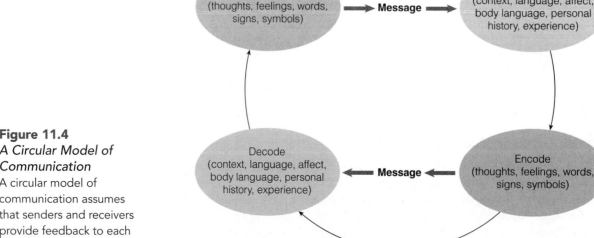

Figure 11.4
A Circular Model of Communication
A circular model of communication assumes that senders and receivers provide feedback to each other.

actual message but also the physical environment of the communication as well as the relationship of the sender and receiver. A sender might alter the message depending on whether the environment is friendly or unfriendly, familiar or unfamiliar, safe or unsafe, formal or informal (Sawyer & Behnke, 2002).

In addition, a sender might send a different message in the same environment depending on the nature of the relationship with the receiver. The message might be affected by whether the sender and receiver are friends or enemies, strangers or known to each other, peers or of unequal status (Sawyer & Behnke, 2002). Communication involves sending and receiving both verbal and nonverbal messages. Each type of message is capable of transmitting information and is part of the encoding and decoding process.

Verbal Communication

Verbal communication is two-dimensional in that it involves transmitting both thoughts and feelings through words. The *cognitive* domain is concerned with communicating our thoughts about things. The *affective* domain involves putting our feelings into words. Many people find communicating cognitive information easier than expressing feelings.

Specificity   Specificity is crucial in effective verbal communication. The more specific the message, the more likely it is to be transmitted clearly. Vocabulary plays a big part in the specificity of our verbal communication. Having a large working vocabulary allows us to specify exactly what we want to say.

Sexual Vocabulary   One of the things that makes sexual communication difficult is the lack of a common sexual vocabulary. U.S. culture has no uniform set of agreed-on words, phrases, and sexual language level. Often we are unsure of the proper terminology for sexual topics such as anatomy and physiology and sexual behaviors. Insecurity about sexual terminology, coupled with emotional discomfort, makes talking about sex difficult.

Language Level   The level of language we use also plays a part in effective verbal communication. The four levels of language are childhood, street, everyday discourse, and scientific language (Mandel, 1980).

1. *Childhood language* is simple, cute, and fun and often is used to disguise embarrassment. Lovers have their own brand of childhood language. They may use it to describe their sexual anatomy and physiology, sexual desire, or need for pleasure. Pet names and phrases are part of this language. Lovers often use childhood language to refer to their genitalia or sexual desire. People also use childhood language when they make mistakes and seek forgiveness. "Ooops, sowwy about that," we might say in mock childhood tones.
2. *Street language* is tough, expressive, and emotional. Street language can be disarming and often is used to level the playing field when communicators do not share equal power or prestige. Tough talk can bestow power and superiority. Street language also serves to create bonds between members of subcultures by sharing a language that members of mainstream society do not understand. Rap music incorporates the power and raw sensuality of street language into a unique art form.
3. *Common discourse* is the language level of mainstream society. It is the generally accepted form of language with which most of us communicate. Most people use its words, expressions, and speech patterns in communicating information that is neither intimate nor scientific. It is the language taught in schools and used in most communications.

sex in society 11.1

He Said/She Said

Do men and women communicate differently? Research about this subject over the past 20 years has yielded mixed results. Men and women are socialized differently, and many researchers believe this difference emerges in the way we communicate. Women are socialized to show their feelings, whereas men have been taught to keep their feelings hidden (Michaud & Warner, 1997). Men have been taught to keep their fears and doubts disguised, because showing these is considered a sign of weakness. Men are socialized to believe that admitting weakness is unmanly (Tannen, 1990).

These beliefs can affect the way we communicate with our partners. Wives send clearer and more emotional messages than their husbands do (Noller & Fitzpatrick, 1991). Wives tend to frame their message in an emotional context, whereas husbands deemphasize affect and focus instead on issues and facts. Husbands send more neutral, less expressive messages that are harder to interpret (Tannen, 1990).

Michaud and Warner (1997) found that men and women communicate differently when dealing with problems. When dealing with "troubles talk," these researchers found that women were much more likely to offer sympathy than men were. Men were much more likely to tell a joke. Women were much more likely to be supportive, whereas

men were more likely to avoid the trouble. Lastly, Tannen (1990) found that women were much more likely to listen as a way to offer support, whereas men were much more likely to try to "solve" the problem by offering advice.

McGinty, Knox, and Zusman (2003) found that female college students were more likely to engage in nonverbal feedback and were more proficient at using it than their male counterparts. Female college students in the study were also more proficient at decoding nonverbal feedback than the males who participated. McGinty et al. (2003) also found that males and females differ in how they communicate according to the nature of the relationship. There were significant differences in the communication patterns of students in "involved" versus "casual" relationships. The former group was significantly more concerned about nonverbal communication than the latter. The involved students also demonstrated greater skill in communicating nonverbally with their partners than the casual daters did (McGinty et al., 2003). Involved daters were also "less confused" about their communications than the casual daters were and reported "working harder" on communicating (both verbally and nonverbally) clearly (McGinty et al., 2003).

4. *Scientific/professional language* is the discourse of the work world and professional community. It is the language that professional peers use as they communicate about the subtleties of their chosen professions. Like street language, it usually is understood only by those who share its culture. Computer programmers, doctors, and other professions have unique vocabularies, complete with acronyms only they understand.

When we communicate with our partners, we must use the level of language with which they are most comfortable. Miscommunication can occur when the language levels of two communicators are not the same. A language level in common is a good starting point for effective sexual communication.

Nonverbal Communication

Body language Sending intentional or unintentional messages through body postures and movements

How we say things is just as important as *what* we actually say. **Body language** describes the nonverbal messages we send through posture, gestures, movement, and physical appearance, including adornment. Our body language intentionally or unintentionally sends messages to receivers (Andersen 1999).

Lovers use nonverbal communication to express feelings, ask for things, and reinforce pleasurable activities. A moan, a hug, a seductive look—these can speak a thousand words. Placing a partner's hand in the correct spot or squeezing it when you are being touched as you want can accomplish as much as explaining these things through words.

Body Language

Positive, or open, body language is demonstrated by a relaxed posture, steady eye contact, nods of the head, and an occasional smile or happy expression. These are cues that you are an approachable sender or a receptive receiver (McGinty et al., 2003).

Negative, or closed, body language has visible signs of tension such as clenched fists or tight jaw muscles, a closed posture (arms folded, body shifted sideways, and the like), and facial expressions ranging from anger to disbelief. Negative body language can indicate either apathy or disturbance about something.

Physical Appearance

Physical appearance can convey a variety of messages. A messy, sloppy, or un-groomed appearance may send encoded messages ranging from positive ("I'm comfortable enough in your presence to relax") to negative ("I don't care enough about you or myself to pay attention to my appearance"). Clothing and adorn-ment might intentionally or unintentionally be erotic and seductive. This can af-fect both the encoding and the decoding process, as the sender might be trying to convey one message ("I'm trying to look my best"), while the receiver may per-ceive another ("This person is trying to manipulate or come on to me sexually").

Silence

Silence is a form of nonverbal communication that can be either a source of stress or a sign of comfort. Silence also can be used to hurt and control people. Silence is a stressor when wordless pauses are perceived as signs of a breakdown in com-munication. Conversely, silence communicates comfort and acceptance between friends and lovers who understand that a loving bond is present despite a lack of conversation. Silence is a necessary part of effective communication that is often overlooked. We need time to listen, digest, and understand messages. Silence al-lows us time to reflect as we formulate our thoughts and words.

Touch

A firm handshake, a reassuring touch on the arm, a gentle squeeze of the but-tocks, the placing of a partner's hand on the genitals or breast—all convey messages without speaking a single word (McBurney, 2002). Appropriately used, touch adds another dimension of communication that sometimes reaches deeper than mere words.

Often we find it easier to communicate our sexual desires through touch than words. For instance, a man might take his partner's hand and place it on his penis and squeeze it rather than ask, "Please squeeze my penis this hard." A woman might draw her partner's head upon her breast rather than ask, "Please suck on my nipples." A person might moan or groan rather than say, "I like it when you suck on my penis like that," or "It feels good when you rub my clitoris like that."

When used inappropriately, however, the effects of touch can be devastating. A pat on the head can be a sign of endearment to a child but can embarrass or in-furiate another adult. A squeeze on your friend's shoul-der can show him you understand his problems and care about him. The same squeeze on your secretary's

True intimacy doesn't require constant talking. Holding hands and walking silently can communicate love, trust, and a variety of other emotions.

Professionals use desk and chair placements as a way to establish comfortable space requirements.

shoulder, however, can convey an entirely different meaning. A pat on a teammate's buttocks can show appreciation of a great play or an extreme effort. The same pat on a coworker's buttocks can be perceived as sexual harassment.

Space

The space between sender and receiver also affects communication. Four space zones common to communication in North America are as follows (Hall, 1973):

Intimate space (less than 18 inches)—space reserved for communication between intimate partners
Personal space (18 inches to 4 feet)—space appropriate for close relationships that may involve touching
Social-consultive space (4 to 12 feet) space for non-touching, less intimate relationships that may involve louder verbal communication
Public space (more than 12 feet)—space used for formal gatherings such as addressing a large group.

Stress and sexual tension can arise when we violate these commonly accepted space parameters. For example, we find ourselves backing up to reclaim our violated space when a nonintimate person gets within the boundaries of our intimate space. Sometimes we place objects as barriers between us and other people to define our space and set allowable communication zones. Culture plays an important part in determining what is acceptable and unacceptable concerning space.

Intellectual Wellness

Intellectual wellness can facilitate communication. Effective communication, whether of a generic or sexual nature, involves three sets of skills: initiating, listening, and responding. Because these are skills, they can be developed and improved, regardless of one's current level of functioning.

Initiating Skills

Initiating sexual communication is different for new and for established relationships. Initiating skills are critical in meeting new people. Initiating skills also are important for discovering what our partners desire, as well as for communicating our own wants and needs, likes and dislikes. Partners in established relationships have a history of intimacy and trust that foster communication. The context of their communication differs greatly from that of two people who are attracted to each other but have not established an intimate relationship yet.

Despite the nature or length of the relationship, however, research shows that men and women often misread emotional cues and misinterpret nonverbal messages (Senecal, Murard, & Hess, 2003). This makes it particularly important to take responsibility for any perceived miscommunication and initiate a dialogue with one's partner to clear this up.

Nonverbal Initiating Skills

Initiating communication starts with nonverbal messages. Think about how you act when you meet for the first time someone to whom you are attracted. You make eye contact and hold it a little longer than you would if you were not interested in meeting the person. Eye contact leads to a smile, a brush of the hair, followed by another look that signals approachability.

Take the case of John and Susan. They are in the same biology lecture class of 150 students. For a couple of weeks they have noticed each other and seem mutually attracted. Today Susan decides she wants to meet John. She intentionally sits closer to him—about four seats down in the same row. She smiles at him as she takes her seat. She sees that he notices her and returns her smile. Buoyed by this, she glances over again, tossing back a long shock of hair while reestablishing eye contact—this time for a moment longer. She decides to approach John after class and initiate a conversation with him. If John hadn't noticed Susan, returned her glance, or maintained eye contact, she might have received a different message and decided not to pursue meeting him any further.

Nonverbal communication between lovers in a long-term relationship is similar—but different because of their shared intimacy, comfort level, and experience together. Nonverbal messages are still important, though, to signal approachability and desire to communicate. They still need to establish eye contact, set the appropriate distance, and adopt a relaxed and approachable posture. Lovers can soften or strengthen their intentions with techniques such as a flirtatious look, lingering eye contact, a smile, or a serious look

Initiating nonverbal communication also can involve props for both new and established lovers. Peering over the top of a book you are reading or the drink you are nursing provides a small security blanket. The feigned dropped handkerchief is the quintessential prop that heroines in classic movies used to gain the attention of their heroes.

Leaving on the table a magazine opened to a story about sex is one way to send a message that you are interested in discussing the subject. Putting a sex manual on your coffee table or bedstand is a way to send messages of interest and approachability to your partner. Renting an erotic or romantic video is a way to introduce the topic of sex without saying a word.

Verbal Initiating Skills

Whether a person is trying to meet someone for the first time or to talk to a partner of 15 years about a sexual topic, he or she has to initiate the communication. Waiting and hoping that your partner or someone in whom you are interested will initiate is a sure way to end the communication before it begins.

Take the case of Susan and John again. Clearly, from his nonverbal messages, John is at least approachable. Susan now is responsible for initiating. Deciding what to say in first-time encounters can be excruciating. A simple rule of thumb is to be honest. Susan could simply say, "Hi, I'm Susan. I'm a little embarrassed, but I've noticed you for the past couple of weeks, and I'd like to meet you." It's now up to John either to reinforce his nonverbal display interest or to pass it up. Susan also could draw from their shared experience of the biology lecture. She might initiate by saying something like, "Hi, I'm Susan. I'm having trouble understanding something the professor just said. Can we talk?"

Four common initiating techniques that can be used in both first-time and longtime relationships are open-ended questions, paraphrasing, declarative statements, and simple yes/no questions.

sex in society 11.2

Cultural Considerations in Communication

Communicating effectively requires awareness of, and sensitivity to, various cultural influences related to verbal and nonverbal communication. The following are a few examples of common cultural consideration to keep in mind.

Verbal Communication

Cultural groups and subcultures do not necessarily share a common language. Although English is the first language spoken by most Americans, and common discourse is the level most frequently used to communicate, this is not the case for many individuals and groups. For many Americans, English is a second language, and common discourse (including slang) is often misunderstood. For these Americans, certain subjects, words, and gestures may be misunderstood or taboo.

For Americans traveling abroad for pleasure or business, this consideration is even more important. Sharing personal information, using hand gestures, squeezing an arm, and giving a peck on the cheek are all examples of communication behaviors that are common to everyday discourse among Americans. These would be consider major gaffes when used by Americans traveling in such places as China and Japan (Dou & Clark, 1999).

Perception of time and the relationship of the past, the present, and the future also vary by culture. The predominant culture in the United States is time-urgent and future oriented. Being aware of the present and doing something now to plan for the future (such as exercising now to prevent heart disease in the future) are commonly accepted. In daily life, people are oriented to specific times of the day and strict schedules. Some other cultures are much less interested in time and are not as oriented to specific schedules. For example, many Native American homes do not even have clocks, as people of some tribes are more concerned about the present and live one day at a time (Ivey, D'Andrea, Ivey, & Simek-Morgan, 2002).

Nonverbal Communication

A variety of nonverbal factors also vary from culture to culture. Cultures differ in their norms for territoriality and personal space. In general, people of Arabic, Southern European, and African origins sit or stand relatively close to each other when talking. People of Asian, Northern European, and North American countries are more comfortable being farther apart when they are talking (Ivey et al., 2002).

Body language varies significantly according to culture. The dominant U.S. culture places a high value on direct eye contact when speaking. In contrast, Native Americans consider continuous direct eye contact to be insulting and disrespectful. Rules about eye contact also vary by gender in certain cultures. In Islamic cultures, women are taught to avert the eyes, whereas eye contact is OK for men. The meaning and acceptability of a myriad of other nonverbal behaviors, such as pointing fingers, shaking hands, and other forms of touch, vary by culture (Ivey et al., 2002).

The following general suggestions can be helpful in verbal and nonverbal communication with people from cultures different from one's own:

- *Slow down.* People for whom English is a second language sometimes have a hard time keeping up with and understanding English when it is spoken too rapidly.
- *Minimize nonverbal distractions.* Be conservative rather than flamboyant in your use of gestures, personal space, and other nonverbal communication.
- *Look for feedback.* People who don't understand, can't keep up, or are uncomfortable with something you do or say often give nonverbal or verbal cues. These can be as overt as asking for clarification or as subtle as a turned head or lack of eye contact. Seek clarification of these cues.
- *Avoid talking louder.* Sometimes, when we are not sure we are being understood, we raise our voice, assuming that the person can't hear us. Talking too loudly, however, can be perceived as threatening or condescending and is rarely helpful.
- *Show respect.* Being humble and respectful of cultural differences conveys the message that you care and want to understand and improve communication.
- *Use an interpreter.* If necessary, get someone to translate your message into the person's primary language.
- *Seek information.* Take advantage of opportunities to learn more about cultural differences in communication (read, travel, go to workshops, and so forth).

Open-Ended Questions **Open-ended questions** are excellent for initiating a dialogue because they cannot be answered with a simple yes/no response. Imagine that you want to explore how your partner likes to be touched. You initiate using an open-ended question such as, "Tell me more about how you like to be touched," or "What else can I do to make you feel good?" Open-ended questions require information from the other person. Your partner can't respond with a simple yes/no answer. Open-ended questions will get your partner talking and draw out additional detail and emotion.

Open-ended questions Sentences that require information from the other person

Paraphrasing **Paraphrasing** means interpreting the meaning of a message and restating it in one's own words. Paraphrasing is another way to initiate a conversation and obtain additional information by getting a person to talk. Imagine that you want to follow up on something your partner said about sex last night. You could initiate a conversation by paraphrasing your partner's comments from the previous evening. For instance, in discussing last night's conversation about sexual technique, you might say, "I was thinking about what you said last night. What I heard you say was that you like it when I squeeze your scrotum firmly," or, "So, what you were saying last night is that you really enjoy it when I bite gently on your nipples," or, "I sense from last night that you don't like it when I put my tongue in your ear." Paraphrasing requires interpretation, or reading between the lines. Your partner usually will let you know if you are on target or off base in your interpretation of the initial message.

Paraphrasing Restating a message in one's own words

healthy sex hints 11.1

Open-Ended Questions to Keep a Sexual Dialogue Flowing

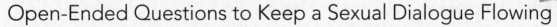

Close-ended questions provoke simple answers. Most closed-ended questions tend to be answered with one- or two-word replies. Open-ended questions (often referred to as *open-ended statements*) require the person to elaborate. They usually cannot be answered with a simple response.

Close-Ended

"Did you do like this/that?"
"Do you still love me?"
"Can you remember the last time we made love?"

Open-Ended

"Tell me more about. . . ."
"How do you feel about. . . .?"
"Describe that more fully."
"What are your thoughts about. . . .?"
"Explain that more completely."
"What made you decide to do that?"

My Personal Sexual Dictionary

Sexual communication is made even more difficult by the lack of a comfortable vocabulary that does not offend anyone. Most of us have heard an amazing number of different words for the various sexual anatomy and sexual acts. To make our own sexual communication easier, we may find it helpful to identify which words we are comfortable using and hearing used. In this activity, you will create your own personal list of sexual terms that you like and enjoy using.

For the following sexual terms, list all the words you feel comfortable using and enjoy hearing. These can be words you have made up, words from your childhood, slang, words you as a couple have made up, or technical terms. The terms for making your list are *vagina*, *penis*, *intercourse*, *masturbation*, *breast*, and *testicles*. When you have listed all your favorites, ask your partner to do the same and then compare your list. If one of you has listed a word that the other finds offensive, discuss what about the word offends. Decide as a couple what words you want to eliminate and what words you want to use together. You may find this activity makes asking for what you want and need sexually a little easier when you have a comfortable communication tool. If you are not in a relationship now, do this exercise with a friend. You may find you are quite different in your likes and dislikes.

Declarative statement A verbal initiating technique that does not require a response to a message

Simple Declarative Statements Sometimes simple **declarative statements** about a sexual topic can initiate a dialogue. These are not as direct as the previous two techniques because they do not specifically require a response. They can be useful, however, especially to test the waters to see how someone feels or what he or she thinks about some sexual topic. Imagine you just read some sexually provocative story in a magazine and are interested in discussing it with your partner. You could simply state this as a declarative sentence: "I just read a fascinating story in this magazine about what men desire most in sexual relationships." By tossing out this simple declarative statement, you could assess whether your partner wants to pursue the discussion and gauge his or her feelings about it. You might follow up with an open-ended statement or let it pass if your partner shows no interest.

Yes/no questions A verbal initiating technique involving a question that requires only a yes or no response

Yes/No Questions The weakest way to initiate a dialogue—and the way most of us start conversations—is to ask direct **yes/no questions.** These are questions that can be answered by a simple yes or no. They don't require explanation or embellishment in the way that open-ended statements and paraphrasing do. Although they are useful for verifying facts ("Do you like it when I touch you like this?" "Does this feel good?"), when they are overused, they can shut down a dialogue.

Listening Skills

Passive listening One-way listening; provides no feedback

There are two types of listening: passive and active. In **passive listening** the listener merely soaks in what the initiator of the message is sending. Passive listening is what we do when watching television, a movie, the radio, and so on. It is one-way communication. Although passive listening can be an effective way to receive sexual information, it is not the most effective form of listening to another person when trying to establish or maintain a dialogue.

Active listening Listening with understanding and providing feedback

Active listening is much better than passive listening for dealing with interpersonal communication because, by definition, it requires feedback. Active listeners show that they are listening by providing both nonverbal and verbal feedback. For this reason, active listening is demanding. It takes a lot of energy and concentration, and the listener can easily get distracted and lose interest.

Letting the sender know that the receiver is listening actively can be accomplished through a variety of nonverbal cues. First, the listener adopts a relaxed pose and maintains eye contact. Additional techniques include nodding the head and smiling. Simple verbal cues such as "uh huh," combined with eye contact and head nodding, are enough to let the speaker know the receiver is listening.

Responding Skills

The message receiver reacts to the initiator's message and encodes some type of feedback using verbal or nonverbal communication. If the message was understood and no further clarification is necessary, the receiver can make a simple declarative statement, acknowledging the message with agreement, disagreement, or new information. If the receiver disagrees, or has problems, he or she can use **"I" language** to express opinions. An example is "I hear what you're saying, and I understand your point, but I disagree with that position. I see it differently."

"I" language Taking responsibility for feelings by saying "I feel . . ." versus "You make me feel . . ."

Often, responding skills go beyond merely providing feedback and are used to get additional information needed to understand an issue or to solve a problem. Keeping the conversation going or requesting more information relies on being able to draw more information out of the initiator. Open-ended statements, paraphrasing, and simple yes/no questions, discussed earlier in the chapter, can be used to respond as well as initiate. An additional responding technique that can be powerful is mirroring.

Open-Ended Statements

The open-ended statement is an excellent responding technique because it provides feedback and also keeps the dialogue going. A response such as, "I hear what you're saying—tell me more about how you feel about masturbation," lets the sender know you are with him or her and want additional information.

Paraphrasing

Paraphrasing lets senders know you are listening but goes one step further by giving them an idea of how you interpret their message. For instance, a response such as "What I heard you say is that you can accept masturbation as a form of sexual release in general but personally don't feel good about it" lets the sender know you are listening and also provides the opportunity for the sender to know what you think he or she said. The sender usually will let you know if your interpretation is accurate or if you missed the point.

Mirroring

A powerful technique for providing feedback and keeping a person talking is **mirroring**—restating the person's exact words while mimicking the body posturing. This is done intentionally for impact. Mirroring is useful when someone says something that has strong emotional connotations. The message was so powerful that you do not want to risk weakening or misinterpreting it. Let's say a friend tells you she was so angry at the lewd comments a stranger made to her as she walked by him that she felt she could kill him. You would mirror it by saying, "You were so angry you felt you could kill him!" This usually prompts the person to continue and go into the greater detail you desire.

Mirroring Restating the message exactly, including body language

Yes/No Questions

The weakest type of response in a dialogue—and the way most of us seek additional information about something—is to ask direct yes/no questions. Although these are useful for verifying facts ("Do you like it when I touch you like this?" "Does this feel good?"), they are easy to overuse, can make people feel defensive, and can shut down a dialogue.

Once the receiver encodes a response, the communication process shifts back to the sender. We have now come full circle from sender encoding, receiver decoding, receiver encoding, and providing feedback that now becomes information to be decoded by the sender. And the cycle begins all over again.

Barriers to Sexual Communication

Impediments to communicating sexually include failure to initiate, picking an inappropriate time or place, not being specific enough, lack of active listening and assertiveness, saying no when we mean yes, and failing to make requests.

Failing to Initiate

One of the biggest barriers to effective sexual communication is failing to initiate. Whether you want to meet someone or discuss a problem with something your long-term lover says or does, you are responsible for bringing it to the person's attention. Failing to initiate is the initiator's problem, not the receiver's.

The best time to address issues and problems is when they occur. Taking time to clear things up, before they are allowed to progress, can prevent problems from escalating. Often, however, situational constraints prevent this. Other people may be around, you're in the middle of something else, or you don't have enough time right then. In these cases, you should tell the other person you need some time alone with him or her to discuss something important. The two of you should be in a neutral territory where you feel safe and emotionally strong, with enough time so neither of you feels rushed. In the case of meeting someone new, initiators should wait until they can speak to the person alone, away from friends.

When using "I" language, communicators take responsibility for their feelings. This is especially important when discussing sexual concerns. For example, let's say your boyfriend has made fun of your outfit in front of three other mutual friends. Rather than blame your boyfriend by saying, "You really made me feel bad," you could say, "I felt bad when you criticized my outfit in front of our friends." Rather than blame your friend for what you are feeling, you own your feelings and state them in "I" language.

The situation and feelings about what happened should be stated in clear, simple terms. General statements like "I hate it when you treat me like a sex object" or "I hate it when you do things like that" should be avoided. Good communicators specify exactly what the other person did that they dislike. It's better to say things like "I don't like you to talk about my sexual behavior or level of desire in front of your friends," or "I really feel like a fool when you talk about my sexual needs in front of my friends." Specifying exactly *what* you dislike (talking about sexual needs) and the context (in front of your friends) clarifies the situation and leaves no room for misunderstanding.

Using "I" language when trying to meet others shows the other person that you are being responsible for your feelings and you really care: "Hi, I'm Rich. I find myself agreeing with a lot of your viewpoints about things. I really liked what you said in political science class today. Can we talk about it over a cup of coffee in the Student Center?"

Physical Wellness

Good communication takes time and energy. Often we are too tired, too stressed, and too busy to communicate effectively. Sometimes when our energy level is low, we simply don't have the energy to think clearly and communicate well. Spending our energy on talking and active listening seems beyond our ability during times of low energy. Stress also robs us of energy, puts us on edge, and contributes to our being overly defensive. It's hard to communicate effectively when we are on edge. We don't listen effectively and have empathy when we are stressed out.

Inappropriate Time and Place

Choosing the appropriate time and place to initiate a discussion about sexuality is important. To be able to relax, each person needs to feel safe and secure. This is important for establishing new relationships as well as strengthening existing ones.

In new relationships, talking in public in less intimate settings is sometimes better. A booth in a restaurant, a bench in the park, under a tree on campus all afford privacy yet are public enough to ensure safety and security until you get to know each other better.

When dealing with problems or concerns in an established relationship, time should be sufficient to discuss the issues completely. Privacy and undisturbed time are ensured by shutting off the TV, putting the answering machine on the phone, closing the door to your room, and giving each other undivided attention. Some people prefer the privacy of their bedrooms when talking about sex. As one student explained, "I like to talk about sex in the bedroom—not when we're making love, but at other times. I like to close the door, prop up a few pillows, unplug the phone, and talk. Sometimes we'll have a glass of wine, relax, and let our feelings flow."

Other people prefer discussing sex outdoors. A student described it this way: "I like to get outdoors to talk to my wife about sex. We go for a long walk somewhere in the mountains or in a local park along the canal. There's something open but private about strolling slowly, hand in hand, and discussing our feelings. It works for us."

Environmental/Occupational Wellness

Some of the barriers to effective communication are environmental in nature. Privacy, safety, and a nonthreatening, nondistracting environment are essential for effective sexual communication. Most people find that talking about intimate personal issues in public places is somewhat threatening. A walk in the woods or along the beach or in a park sometimes can create a facilitative setting and mood for communicating about sexual matters.

The workplace can be a particularly challenging place to communicate. Men and women of different cultures and ages all come together around a common work theme. The potential for miscommunication is great, so extra care must be taken to communicate effectively and to take responsibility for miscommunication.

Lack of Specificity

Being critical of a partner's behavior at times is normal in any long-term relationship. Being critical of someone's *behavior*, however, is different from being critical of the person. A sure-fire way to sabotage an attempt to discuss sexual concerns is to criticize the partner rather than the behavior. It is important to criticize the behavior, not the person. People have to understand that the other still loves them but does not like a certain behavior. The partner probably is unaware of how the behavior affects the other. The more precision in describing exactly what a person did or said, the better is the chance of clearing up the problem without hurting the person's feelings. "I really feel hurt when you reject my sexual advances" is a lot easier to deal with than "You're a jerk for rejecting me."

Sexual messages are difficult to interpret clearly, even under the best of circumstances. People in long-term relationships are no exception. Mixed messages—contradictory messages—usually are a result of nonverbal cues not matching verbal messages or people saying something they don't really mean. For instance, if a partner asks, "Do you like it when I do this?" and the response is, "Yeah, sure," while the body is tight and the facial expression is pained, the message is mixed.

We send mixed messages for various reasons. In some cases, we are unsure where we stand or how we feel. The message is mixed because feelings are mixed. Sometimes we send mixed messages because we are unable or unwilling to be assertive and say no or tell the other person how we really feel. In the worst case, we send mixed messages because we play games and deliberately want to keep people off balance and unsure of our position. This approach may be linked to unhealthy sex role stereotyping based on positioning for power and control in relationships.

The bottom line in mixed messages is that they impair the communication process, making it difficult to understand the true meaning of what is going on. Healthy sexuality revolves around effective communication, based on personal knowledge and the desire to communicate honestly.

Failing to Listen Actively

Many sexual communication problems, too, revolve around failure to listen actively. Instead of giving undivided attention and providing feedback, we get caught in a variety of bad listening habits that impair our ability to listen actively.

healthy sex hints 11.2

How to Be a Better Listener

1. *Keep yourself in good mental and physical shape.* We listen better when we are mentally and physically alert.
2. *Keep eye contact with the speaker whenever possible.* This will assure the speaker that what he or she is saying is being heard.
3. *Listen actively rather than passively.* In other words, exert energy and use body language to reflect what the speaker is saying. Nod in agreement, smile or laugh at the speaker's humor, and the like.
4. *Avoid distracting mannerisms.* Things such as hair twirling, fingernail inspecting, and similar behaviors convey boredom or disinterest.

5. *Ask questions* when you don't understand something the speaker is saying. Repeat what the speaker has said, in different words, to convey understanding.
6. *Resist the temptation to let your mind wander.* It's easy to do considering that a person can think much faster than he or she can speak.

The best listeners make the speaker feel like he or she is the only person in the world at that moment. By following these tips, you can join the ranks of good listeners.

Lack of Assertiveness

Assertiveness is a positive attribute, based on mutual respect and democracy in relationships. Assertiveness means understanding one's own wants and needs and pursuing these without infringing on others' ability to do the same. **Aggressiveness,** on the other hand, means pursuing one's needs and wants without regard to how this affects the rights of the others. Often, aggressive people get their needs met at the expense of others. Nonassertive people fail to pursue their needs and wants while allowing others to meet theirs. They fail to stick up for their rights and allow others to take advantage of them, often denying what is going on (Smith, 1993).

Assertiveness is important to effective communication. Many people are not assertive because they confuse assertiveness with aggressiveness. In an attempt to control what they perceive as aggressiveness, they act nonassertively and fail to meet their needs while allowing hostility and frustration to build up inside themselves, weakening their communication and relationships.

Assertiveness Pursuing one's own needs and wants without infringing on others

Aggressiveness Pursuing one's own wants and needs without regard for the rights of others

Saying Yes When We Mean No

When people are nonassertive, they say yes to others' demands when they really want to say no. They spend an inordinate amount of time pleasing others without being reciprocated. They forsake their sexual needs and wants while granting the partner's desires. Although sharing and sacrificing are important to relationships, they become a problem when this behavior is always one-way and not reciprocated.

When people are nonassertive, they are filled with resentment and hostility toward their partner as a result. It's a vicious cycle. Originally, in an attempt to avoid conflict, discomfort, or hurting the partner's feelings, they say yes when they really mean no. This response temporarily relieves them from feeling guilty. Unfortunately, however, when they do this, they get trapped into doing things they really don't want to do. When this result happens, they begin to feel miserable because they've lost control of their lives and lost their self-respect. Not only do they feel stressed because of this situation, but it also affects their sexual response. Desire and arousal are difficult when a person feels stressed and angry.

healthy sex hints 11.3

Assertiveness Bill of Rights

The following "Assertiveness Bill of Rights" may help strengthen your resolve to speak up for yourself:

You have the right to judge your own behavior, thoughts, emotions and to take responsibility for their initiation and consequences upon yourself.

You have the right to offer no reason or excuses for justifying your behavior.

You have the right to judge if you are responsible for finding solutions for other people's problems.

You have the right to change your mind.

You have the right to make mistakes and be responsible for them.

You have the right to say, "I don't know."

You have the right to be independent of the goodwill of others before coping with them.

You have the right to be illogical in making decisions.

You have the right to say, "I don't understand."

You have the right to say, "I don't care."

Source: Terrap Treatment Centers, Menlo Park, CA, 1999.

The only way to stop the cycle is to begin to say no. This brings us full circle to the same situation as the initial one: having to say no. If people are assertive to begin with, they can avoid the aggravation and stress.

Failing to Make Requests

Assertiveness is directly related to requesting things you desire and saying no to things you don't want to do. People have many reasons for not making explicit sexual requests. As we've already discussed, language poses a unique barrier. Feeling comfortable with sexual language is important, and finding a comfortable language level helps. If sex has been a taboo topic of conversation while growing up, it may be difficult to talk about openly. People enter their first relationship without having had the benefit of knowing that talking about sex is OK. Shaking this taboo is sometimes difficult. You can become more comfortable by proceeding slowly, acknowledging your fears and discomfort, and allowing yourself to take chances and grow out of your old ways of thinking and feeling.

Another barrier is not taking responsibility for one's wants, needs, and feelings. First, the individual has to find out who he or she is as a sexual person. Then the person has to accept this. The third step is to share it with the partner. The partner can't know who the other is, what he or she needs, and how to please that person without the other person's taking responsibility to communicate this.

Our sexuality is continually growing and evolving. A married student expressed it this way in class:

My wife is always saying that she shouldn't have to explain what she wants sexually. We've been together for 10 years, and I should know how to please her and what her needs are. I

healthy sex hints 11.4

Saying No

Saying no isn't always easy, but it is essential if you are to be assertive and reduce your stress. You have the right to say no. The following are clear guidelines:

1. *Face the other person from a normal distance.* If you are too far away, you may appear timid. If you crowd the person, you border on aggressiveness.
2. *Look the person directly in the eyes.* Averting eye contact is a sure giveaway that you'll cave in.
3. *Keep your head up and your body relaxed.* Don't be a shrinking violet.
4. *Speak clearly and firmly, at a volume that can be heard clearly.*
5. *Just say no.* You don't have to clarify why.
6. *Be prepared to repeat it.* Sometimes people are persistent. Be prepared to say it again.
7. *Stick to your guns.* Don't give in. It gets easier with practice.

If you feel a need to explain why you are declining, here are a few tips for setting the stage:

1. Thank the person for the offer: "Gee, thanks, but *no*. I really can't [don't want to] . . ."
2. Express appreciation: "I really appreciate the offer, but *no*. I'm not interested/too busy/don't want any . . ."
3. Affirm your friendship: "I enjoy your company, and I'd like to do something together, but *no*."
4. Reject the offer, not the person: "Please don't take this personally. I like you, but *no*, I don't . . ."

have a hard time with this. My own needs change from day to day and from sexual encounter to sexual encounter. One day I may want her to take the lead and initiate sex and be dominant while I lie back and let her take me. The next time we make love, I might want to initiate. I know she's the same way, but I can't tell in advance without her communicating her desires to me.

We need to take responsibility for what we're feeling and make requests accordingly, using "I" language.

Gender and Cultural Considerations

Often, lack of assertiveness is based in religious, cultural, or gender role expectations and transcends lack of skill or desire to assert oneself. Some cultures require subjugating one's personal desires to those of the dominant partner in the relationship. In many cultures, the male partner is the dominant member of the couple. Women are expected to put their needs behind those of their partner and behave in ways expected of them. Respecting the wishes of the partner and the culture is taught to be more important than one's own needs. The conflict between these traditional ways of behaving and U.S. cultural values focusing on the individual and self-actualization is a source of stress and sexual dissatisfaction for many women.

Models of Communication

Two models relevant to sexual communication are the DESC model and rational emotive behavior therapy.

The DESC Model

A useful model that combines assertiveness and effective verbal communication is the DESC model (Bower, 1976; Greenberg, 2003). It is a powerful tool that helps a person make requests, deliver criticism more effectively, and become more precise in assertiveness.

The DESC model has four parts:

D—*describe:* Paint a verbal picture of the situation or the other person's behavior that is a source of stress. Be as precise as possible: "Honey, when you use language like 'I'm feeling horny—let's fuck,'. . . ."

E—*express:* Express your feelings about the incident using "I" language: "I feel seedy and cheap" or "I feel very uncomfortable."

S—*specify:* Be specific in identifying alternative ways that you would prefer the person to speak or behave: "I'd like you to soften your language and say, 'I'm feeling sexy—let's make love.'"

C—*consequences:* Identify the consequences that will follow if the person does (pro) or doesn't (con) comply with your wishes: "In the future, if you do soften your language, I'll be much more likely to get in the mood and want to make love with you (pro)." "If you don't, and you continue to use such crude language, I can't guarantee that I won't be turned off and not feel sexy."

When using this model, precision is important in describing the other person's offending behavior or actions. Again, the offensive behavior, not the person, should be the object of criticism. And the person should take responsibility for his or her feelings and use "I" language when describing them. Rather than blaming the partner and saying, "You make me feel cheap and seedy," the person should be clear and take responsibility by stating, "I feel cheap and seedy when you use those coarse words."

Emotional Wellness

Emotional wellness affects the ability to communicate clearly. Communicating effectively is difficult even under the best of circumstances. Communicating about sexuality poses unique challenges because of the sensitive nature of the topic. Even though people may want to communicate more effectively, emotions sometimes get in the way. They might feel embarrassed talking about their most intimate desires, thoughts, and feelings. They also might feel guilty about some of these things. These emotions often make it difficult to think clearly and logically. A first step in sexual communication is to identify how we are feeling and to take responsibility for owning these feelings. Once we assume ownership for our feelings, we can use "I" language to communicate them to our intimate partner.

Rational Emotive Behavior Therapy (REBT) and Irrational Thinking

Sometimes we fail to communicate clearly because our sexual thinking is irrational or illogical. Our sexual perspective, or belief system—as Albert Ellis (1993), the father of rational emotive behavior therapy (REBT), calls it—is disordered. Ellis believes that our *perception* of our partners and specific sexual situations (not the actual person or situation) gives them meaning and determines whether they become a source of dissatisfaction and miscommunication.

For instance, Khalid and Teri have been lovers for a year and have been happy with their sexual lifestyle. They make love about once a week and engage in a variety of sexual behaviors they find enjoyable. Last night, after they came home from the movies, Khalid wanted to make love and Teri didn't. She was tired and wanted to get to bed early. Feeling rejected, Khalid began to have doubts about their sexual relationship, wondering, "What's wrong with her? Teri should be in the mood when I am. What's wrong with our relationship?" In reality, nothing is wrong with their relationship. They are happy, enjoy each other's company, and have a satisfying sex life together. The only problem is Khalid's perception of this specific situation.

In their clinical work with neurotic patients, Albert Ellis and Robert Harper (1998) identified a group of 10 commonly held irrational or illogical beliefs about life. These beliefs form the basis of a belief system that gives one a distorted perspective for assessing potentially stressful situations. Using and understanding Ellis and Harper's theory can be simplified by grouping the 10 illogical/irrational beliefs into four categories (Walen, DiGuisseppi, & Wessler, 1980).

Awfulizing statements: These exaggerate the negative aspects/impact of a situation.
Shoulds/musts/oughts: These are beliefs that put illogical demands on oneself and others.
Evaluation-of-worth statements: These imply that some people or things are worthless or a complete waste of time.
Need statements: These are beliefs that set unrealistic, unattainable requirements for happiness.

We often blow things out of proportion, set unrealistic demands for our behavior and that of our partners, misinterpret sexual comments, or have irrational fears about discussing our wants, needs, desires, or problems with our partners. These illogical/irrational beliefs result in undesirable emotional, intellectual, physical, social, and behavioral consequences. Ellis and Harper (1998) use an ABC model to describe this interaction. In this model, the presence of an activating event, A, triggers a series of irrational/illogical beliefs, B, about A. These illogical beliefs about A (not the activating event itself) are the cause of a variety of negative consequences, C. We'll illustrate the model again using Khalid and Teri:

A—activating event:
> Khalid wanted to make love with his girlfriend Teri when they came home from the movies, but she didn't. She said she wasn't in the mood and wanted to get to bed early.

B—irrational/illogical beliefs:
> "My girlfriend should always be in the mood."
> "My girlfriend should always be in the mood when I am."
> "Partners should always be sexually available."
> "People who are in love should always please their partners sexually."
> "She must not love me anymore."
> "She must be having an affair with someone else."
> "I'm not good enough for her."

C—Consequences
> Physical—muscle tension, upset stomach, tension headache
> Emotional—anger, depression
> Mental—irrational thoughts
> Social—retreating into isolation, breaking off all physical touching
> Behavioral—starting to drink to excess

REBT uses logical thinking and positive self-talk as an aid to reducing sexual problems. Ellis and Harper's (1998) ABCDE technique attempts to help us understand our illogical beliefs and self-talk and learn to substitute more rational thoughts in their place. The ABCDE technique builds upon Ellis's ABC model of **illogical thinking** by adding D (dispute) and E (evaluate). D involves disputing each illogical B and substituting a more logical belief in its place. When all of the illogical beliefs have been disputed, the effectiveness of the dispute in defusing the consequences is evaluated.

The ABCDE technique would work like this:

A—Khalid's girlfriend Teri rejecting his offer to make love
B—Khalid's irrational beliefs about A
> "My girlfriend should always be in the mood."
> "My girlfriend should always be in the mood when I am."
> "Partners should always be sexually available."
> "People who are in love should always please their partners sexually."
> "She must not love me anymore."
> "She must be having an affair with someone else."
> "I'm not good enough for her."

C—Consequences of B
> Physical—muscle tension, upset stomach, tension headache
> Emotional—anger, depression
> Mental—irrational thoughts
> Social—retreating into isolation, breaking off all physical touching
> Behavioral—starting to drink to excess

Illogical thinking Thought based on inaccurate or irrational perception of information

sex in society 11.3

Ellis and Harper's 10 Illogical Beliefs

Often we are sexually dissatisfied because of illogical or irrational beliefs and expectations we have about sex and our relationships. Ellis and Harper found that when these beliefs form a belief system that is predominately irrational, we are more prone to stress and sexual dissatisfaction. Throughout the course of their clinical work, Ellis and Harper noticed recurring themes or patterns. They distilled these beliefs into 10 that form the basis of an irrational belief system or way of viewing the world. This way of viewing the world could relate to any subject. When it forms the basis of our sexual belief system, it can create sexual problems and make it difficult to communicate effectively. The beliefs are the following:

1. You must have love or approval from all the people you find significant.
2. You must thoroughly prove adequate, competent, or achieving.
3. When people act obnoxiously or unfairly, you should blame and damn them and see them as bad, wicked, or rotten individuals.
4. You have to view things as awful, terrible, horrible, and catastrophic when you get seriously frustrated, treated unfairly, or rejected.
5. Emotional misery comes from external pressures, and you have little ability to control or change your feelings.
6. If something seems dangerous or fearsome, you must preoccupy yourself with it and make yourself anxious about it.
7. You can more easily avoid facing many life difficulties and self-responsibilities than undertake more rewarding forms of self-discipline.
8. Your past remains all-important, and, because something once strongly influenced your life, it has to keep determining your feelings and behavior today.
9. People and things should turn out better than they do, and you must view it as awful and horrible if you do not find good solutions to life's grim realities.
10. You can achieve maximum human happiness by inertia and inaction or by passively and uncommittedly enjoying yourself.

Source: Guide to Rational Living, by A. Ellis and R. Harper (Hollywood, CA: Wilshire Book Company, 1998). Reprinted with permission.

D—Dispute

Khalid decides to tackle this problem by analyzing each of these illogical beliefs and substitute more rational thoughts in their place.

1. "It's irrational for me to think that Teri should always be in the mood."
2. "It's impossible for us both to always be in sync with our sexual desire."
3. "Each partner has the right to say no when he or she is not in the mood to make love."
4. "People can be in love but on any given day not feel sexually responsive."
5. "Teri's not wanting to have sex doesn't necessarily mean she doesn't love me."
6. "Her not wanting to have sex with me doesn't necessarily mean she's doing it with someone else."
7. "I'm great for Teri. This has nothing to do with that."

E—Evaluate

As a result of working through the dispute and coming up with a more rational belief system concerning what happened, Khalid experiences the following changes: Physically, his muscles begin to relax and he can get to sleep again. His tension headache subsides. Emotionally, Khalid feels like a tremendous weight has been lifted from his shoulders. He feels he is thinking clearly again. Khalid stops drinking and asks Teri whether she wants to snuggle and fall asleep while he reads his book.

Communicating About Disabilities

As we have discussed, communicating sexual needs and wants is often difficult for many people because of their upbringing, the uniqueness of the subject, and the lack of a uniform language of sex. Communicating about special sexual considerations due to disabilities presents a unique challenge for the person with disabilities and his or her partner. Not only does the person have to work through personal issues surrounding sexuality in general, but he or she also has the added challenge of describing how the disability impacts sexual needs and wants (Bullard & Knight, 1981).

As we've seen, disabilities can affect sexual anatomy and physiology, sexual response, and sexual behavior. Describing these effects and the special considerations they bring to the sexual encounter can be a daunting experience for the most proficient communicator. We'll use colostomy as the disability to illustrate these challenges.

Ostomy

Ostomy is a general term used to describe an artificially created opening in the body. The prefix associated with the ostomy denotes the organ where the opening is. A *colostomy* is an opening of the colon, for example, and an *ileostomy* is an opening to the ileum (Alterescu, 1981). The actual connection of the opening to the abdominal wall is referred to as the *stoma*.

Many people are squeamish about the association of an ostomy to organs associated with human waste (urine and feces), and they have a hard time discussing the impact of the ostomy on their sexuality. A colostomy, for instance, redirects the movement of feces from the rectum and anus to the colostomy bag, which is attached to the stoma through a ring and sealed bag secured to the abdominal wall with adhesive material. The bag fills up with waste on a schedule that coincides with the person's bowel movement behavior. The consistency of the fecal material and the frequency of accumulation will vary according to the person's diet, exercise behavior, and overall health. Assuming the person with the colostomy returns to a normal lifestyle following surgery, eventually the person can expect a bowel pattern similar to what he or she experienced prior to the surgery. A person with a colostomy can learn how to clean, change, sanitize, and maintain the colostomy bag to ensure a return to a normal life and control of bowel functioning with normal hygiene.

In reality, having a colostomy does not necessarily impact sexual response and behavior. The physiological changes that occur during arousal and orgasm are, in most cases, unchanged by the procedure. A person who has undergone a colostomy may experience nerve damage, pain, and the development of scar tissue. These can impact sexual arousal and the enjoyment of sexual activities (Alterescu, 1981). These complications can occur with any surgery, however, and are not exclusive to colostomy. A person with a colostomy can also have temporary mechanical problems associated with securing the ostomy bag to the abdominal wall and securing a leak-free attachment between the ring and the collection bag.

In most cases, sexual problems associated with colostomy are due to psychosocial factors related to the patient's self-perception, depression, and relationship concerns or problems. Desire and the frequency of sexual activity can be affected if the person with the colostomy perceives it negatively and as something that interferes with sexuality in a negative way. Alterescu (1981) has compiled the following list of questions that many colostomy patients have:

Will my partner(s) still consider me desirable and attractive?
Will I still be capable of maintaining social usefulness as a worker and mother/
    father?

Will I (male patient) be capable of achieving/maintaining an erection and ejaculating?

Will I be able to make adjustments in clothing?

Will I experience pain during intercourse?

Will my pouch interfere with my sexual activities?

How will I explain the existence of my pouch to my new partner?

Will my ostomy keep me from being the person I want to be?

Questions like these must be answered honestly and completely by the person with a colostomy and his or her partner in order to have a satisfying sex life. The communication skills discussed in this chapter will help people with a colostomy or other disabilities understand these concerns, transmit them to their partner(s), and keep the dialogue open regarding these issues so they don't lead to deeper response and relationship problems.

Foremost, this chapter has demonstrated how the responsibility for sexual communication lies with the individual. People with a colostomy or any other disability must discuss the nature of their disabilities with their intimate partners and helping professionals if necessary. They must seek to learn all they can about how their disability impacts their sexuality and take responsibility for transmitting this information to their intimate partners.

Your responses to the Personal Assessment, Thought Questions, and Test Yourself! quiz questions can be logged online in your Virtual Workbook at **http://health.wadsworth.com/blonna1.**

Personal Assessment

11.1 Sexual Communication Satisfaction Questionnaire

This questionnaire assesses your satisfaction with your sexual communication with your partner. Use the following scale to indicate how strongly you agree or disagree with each statement:

1 = Strongly agree	4 = Disagree
2 = Agree	5 = Strongly disagree
3 = Neither agree nor disagree	

1. I tell my partner when I am especially sexually satisfied.
2. I am satisfied with my partner's ability to communicate his/her sexual desires to me.
3. I do not let my partner know things that I find pleasing during sex.
4. I am very satisfied with the quality of our sexual interactions.
5. I do not hesitate to let my partner know when I want to have sex with him/her.
6. I do not tell my partner whether or not I am sexually satisfied.
7. I am dissatisfied over the degree to which my partner and I discuss our sexual relationship.
8. I am not afraid to show my partner what kind of sexual behavior I find satisfying.
9. I would not hesitate to show my partner what is a sexual turn-on to me.
10. My partner does not show me when he/she is sexually satisfied.
11. I show my partner what pleases me during sex.
12. I am displeased with the manner in which my partner and I communicate with each other during sex.
13. My partner does not show me things he/she finds pleasing during sex.
14. I show my partner when I am sexually satisfied.
15. My partner does not let me know whether sex has been satisfying or not.
16. I do not show my partner when I am sexually satisfied.
17. I am satisfied concerning my ability to communicate about sexual matters with my partner.
18. My partner shows me by the way he/she touches me if he/she is satisfied.
19. I am dissatisfied with my partner's ability to communicate his/her sexual desire to me.
20. I have no way of knowing when my partner is sexually satisfied.
21. I am not satisfied in the majority of our sexual interactions.
22. I am pleased with the manner in which my partner and I communicate with each other after sex.

Source: "Sexual Communication, Communication Satisfaction, and Solidarity in the Developmental Stages of Intimate Relationships," by Lawrence R. Wheeless, Virginia Eman Wheeless, and Raymond Baus (1984), *Western Journal of Speech Communication, 48* (3), 224. Copyright © 1984 by Western Speech Communication Association. Reprinted by permission.

Thought Questions

1. What makes communicating about sex different from communicating about other subjects?

2. Define metacommunication. What are the parts of a metacommunication model?

3. What four sets of skills are involved in two-way communication?

4. What is "I" language? Give examples of using "I" language.

5. How do we communicate about sexuality nonverbally? Is nonverbal sexual communication accurate?

6. What is the best thing to do if miscommunication becomes apparent? Whose responsibility is it? Why?

7. Give examples of four open-ended sexual statements.

8. What is the impact of language level on sexual communication?

9. What are three barriers to effective listening?

10. What are two barriers to correcting miscommunication?

11. What should you do if you reach a communication impasse?

12. Describe the effects of a disability such as colostomy on sexual communication.

Test Yourself!

1. Which statement best characterizes communicating about sex?
   a. It is easier than communicating about other topics because everyone likes sex.
   b. It is harder than communicating about other topics because of the subject and the personal nature of the material.
   c. It is easier because of the personal nature of the subject matter.
   d. It is harder because the subject is personal and immaterial.

2. Metacommunication focuses on
   a. the actual content being discussed.
   b. the content and the relationship between the communicators.
   c. the content and the metaphysical nature of human sexuality.
   d. the relationship between the communicators.

3. The key to successful communications using Berne's transactional analysis model is
   a. communicating on the same ego state as your partner.
   b. communicating on a different ego state than your partner.
   c. trying to keep your ego state out of objective communication with your partner.
   d. keeping your ego out of communications.

4. Which of the following represents a true exchange of information between two people?
   a. Selflessness
   b. Monologue
   c. Dialogue
   d. Information giving

5. Which statement best describes how men and women communicate?
   a. Research shows that men tend to focus more on wanting to solve problems, whereas women want to share emotions.
   b. Research shows that men and women are very similar in their communication patterns.
   c. Research shows that women tend to focus more on wanting to solve problems, whereas men want to share emotions.
   d. Research shows that women and men focus equally on problem solving and sharing emotions.

6. Nonverbal forms of sexual communication
   a. generally are not very useful in communicating sexual content.
   b. are often just as effective in communicating sexual needs and wants as verbal forms.
   c. should be avoided until you get to know a person better.
   d. have no place in effective sexual communication.

7. What is the relationship between language level and sexual miscommunication?
   a. Miscommunication can occur when the language levels of the two communicators differs.
   b. Miscommunication occurs because people from different countries have different words to describe things.
   c. It is easiest to avoid miscommunication by using scientific/professional language, which is the most precise language level.
   d. Miscommunication is less likely to occur if both partners use a lower language level.

8. "I" language refers to
   a. maintaining eye contact when you are communicating.
   b. being very assertive about your sexual needs and desires.
   c. taking personal responsibility for feelings.
   d. putting blame for problems on others where it belongs.

9. Using open-ended statements is effective when you want your partner to
   a. expand on how he or she feels about an issue.
   b. get a simple yes or no answer to a simple question.
   c. leave things kind of open to debate.
   d. put off closure on the subject.

10. DESC is a communication model that is useful for
    a. using verbal aggressiveness to resolve communication problems.
    b. using verbal assertiveness to resolve communication problems.
    c. describing communication problems that are descriptive in nature.
    d. expressing deep-seated sexual problems to your partner.

Media Menu

You can link to the following online tools by visiting
http://health.wadsworth.com/blonna1.

InfoTrac Activity

Van Gorp, K. (2001, Fall). You're not hearing me! Communication problems within a couple. *Marriage Partnership, 18*(3), 18.

Web Resources

General Communication Skills

http://discoveryhealth.queendom.com/access_communication_skills.html

This site presents a test that evaluates your general level of communication skills and offers detailed, personalized tips.

Communication in Sexual Behavior

www.couns.msu.edu/self-help/suggest.htm

Michigan State University Counseling Center site with a wide range of topics to improve communications: asserting your interpersonal rights, improving communication skills, maintaining a relationship, communicating in sexual behavior, establishing sex guidelines, saying no without feeling guilty, criticizing others, blaming, and avoiding the self-defeating "should."

Manhattan College Counseling Center

www.mancol.edu/stntlife/relcom.html

Suggestions for improving communication skills in relationships. These hands-on exercises provide sentence completion methods in which students complete statements with their partner.

RealWorld University

www.rwuniversity.com/articles.cfm?cid=28

RealWorld University's (RWU) mission is to help students succeed in college and in life by helping them identify and pursue their purpose, strengthen their character, overcome life's obstacles, and maximize their potential. RWU addresses some of the toughest challenges facing college students today by sharing proven strategies, solutions, and advice from some of the country's leading educators, authors, speakers, and college graduates.

DiscoveryHealth.Com's Love and Relationships Page

http://health.discovery.com/centers/loverelationships/loverelationships.html

This is the love and relationships page of DiscoveryHealth.Com. It offers a variety of assessments and links to other pages devoted to this subject.

References

Alterescu, V. (1981). Sexual functioning following creation of an abdominal stoma. In D. G. Bullard & S. E. Knight (Eds.), *Sexuality and physical disability*. St. Louis: Mosby.

Andersen, P. A. (1999). *Nonverbal communication: Form and function*. Mountain View, CA: Mayfield.

Berne, E. (1960). *Transactional analysis in psychotherapy*. New York: Grove.

Bower, S. A., & Bower, G. H. (1976). *Asserting yourself: A practical guide for positive change*. Reading, MA: Addison-Wesley.

Bullard, D. G., & Knight, S. E. (Eds.). (1981). *Sexuality and physical disability*. St. Louis: Mosby.

Dou, W. L., & Clark, W. (1999, Summer–Fall). Appreciating the diversity in multicultural communication styles. *Business Forum, 24*(3–4), 54–62.

Ellis, A. (1993). Reflections on rational emotive therapy. *Journal of Consulting and Clinical Psychology, 61*(2), 199–201.

Ellis, A., & Harper, R. (1998). *A new guide to rational living*. North Hollywood, CA: Wilshire.

Greenberg, J. S. (2003). *Comprehensive stress management* (8th ed.). Boston: McGraw-Hill.

Hall, E. (1973). *The silent language*. Menlo Park, CA: Cummings.

Ivey, A. E., D'Andrea, M. D., Ivey, M. B., & Simek-Morgan, L. (2002). *Theories of counseling and psychotherapy: A multicultural perspective* (5th ed.). Boston: Allyn & Bacon.

Michaud, S. L., & Warner, R. M. (1997, October). Gender differences in self-reported troubles talk. *Sex Roles: A Journal of Research, 37*(7–8), 527–541.

Mandel, B. (1980, Summer). Communication: A four part process. *Hotliner, 1*(4), 6.

McBurney, L. (2002, Spring). Touch me—not there! How to be sensual without necessarily being sexual. *Marriage Partnership, 19*(1), 26–29.

McGinty, K., Knox, D., & Zusman, M. E. (2003, March). Nonverbal and verbal communication in "involved" and "casual" relationships among college students. *College Student Journal, 37*(1), 68–72.

Noller, P., & Fitzpatrick, M. A. (1991). Marital communication. In A. Booth (Ed.), *Contemporary families: Looking backward, looking forward*. Minneapolis: Council on Family Relations.

Sawyer, C. R., & Behnke, R. R. (2002, Fall). Behavioral inhibition and the communication of public speaking state anxiety. *Western Journal of Communication, 66*(4), 12–23.

Senecal, S., Murard, N., & Hess, U. (2003, January). Do you know what I feel? Partners' predictions and judgements of each other's emotional reactions to emotion-eliciting situations. *Sex Roles: A Journal of Research*, 21–38.

Smith, J. C. (1993). *Creative stress management*. Englewood Cliffs, NJ: Prentice Hall.

Tannen, D. (1990). *You just don't know: Women and men in conversation*. New York: Morrow.

Walen, S., DiGuisseppi, R., & Wessler, R. (1980). *A practitioner's guide to RET*. New York: Oxford University Press.

Watzlawick, P., Beaven, J. H., & Jackson, D. D. (1967). *Pragmatics of human communication*. New York: Norton.

chapter *fifteen*

Sexually Transmitted Diseases (STDs)

Student Learning Objectives

After reading this chapter, students will be able to

- Describe the major STD trends of the past decade.
- Diagram and describe the Pyramid of Risk for STD/HIV infection.
- Explain how demographic variables are related to STD/HIV risk.
- Describe how sexual orientation affects STD/HIV risk.
- Describe the characteristics of core transmitters of STD, including HIV.
- Evaluate the relationship between sexual/medical history and STD/HIV risk.
- Assess a variety of sexual lifestyles and the continuum of risk for STD that they represent.
- Evaluate the risks inherent in a variety of sexual behaviors.
- Develop a personal plan for reducing the risk for STD/HIV infection.
- Describe the major modes of STD/HIV transmission.
- Describe the major symptoms associated with STD/HIV infection.
- Describe the epidemiology of a variety of STDs.

Test your understanding of these objectives by taking the end-of-chapter quiz, available online at **http://health.wadsworth.com/blonna1.**

activity teaser: *Why should you wait to have sex? Find out with the Personal Exploration Activity on page 481.*

Yolanda: Assessing the Risk

Yolanda, 22, single, identifies as Latina.

Yolanda, a student in a human sexuality class, expressed the following concerns about finding out about her sex partners' medical histories:

It looks like I'm going to have to spend a lot more time getting to know my sex partners before I take a chance of having sex with them without condoms. Up until today I thought I was a responsible lady because I'm on the pill and take responsibility for my sexuality. I always thought the pill would protect me against STDs. Boy, was I wrong. I never realized that there was so much to find out about a guy before you could tell if he was a threat to you.

I used to try to sneak a look to see if he had any symptoms, but now you're saying there are lots of other things that are important about his sexual past that I need to know about. I'm not sure what I'm going to do, but I know I'll never let any guy in there bareback until I can answer all those questions about him.

Critical Thinking

How does one actually acquire from a potential sex partner the type of detailed sexual/medical information necessary to make an informed decision about the STD risks posed by that individual?

Use your Virtual Workbook to explore your answer to this question at **http://health.wadsworth.com/blonna1.**

Sexually transmitted diseases (STDs) Diseases that are spread from person to person through sexual contact

Sexually transmitted diseases (STDs), also known as sexually transmitted infections (STIs), are infections that are almost always contracted through sexual contact. We will continue to use the term *STDs* because it is the term of choice used by the Centers for Disease Control, the lead agency in the United States for the control of infectious diseases. Although STDs theoretically can be transmitted via any form of sexual contact, vaginal and anal intercourse are much more *efficient* modes of transmission than is oral-genital sexual contact. Some STDs, such as HIV and hepatitis B, also are transmitted by contaminated blood through needle sharing associated with injection drug use (Eng & Butler, 1997).

More than 65 million people in the United States are currently infected with an incurable sexually transmitted disease, and each year an additional 15 million people develop new cases of one or more of the 25 diseases categorized as STDs. Of these new cases, roughly half are incurable, lifelong infections (Division of STD Prevention [DSTD], 2000; Cates et al., 1999). STDs represent 87 percent of the cases of the diseases reported to the Centers for Disease Control and Prevention. Five of the top 10 most frequently reported diseases in the United States are STDs (DSTD, 2002). The STD **epidemic** is really a series of epidemics since we are really talking about over two dozen different types of infections, many of which are asymptomatic (without symptoms). Because of the asymptomatic nature of many STDs, many of those who are infected go undiagnosed. This situation has led public health officials to refer to the problem as the "hidden epidemic" (DSTD, 2000).

Epidemic Levels of infection in populations that exceed those normally expected for that population

Tracking the hidden epidemic is difficult to do because individuals with asymptomatic diseases do not even know they are infected. Their infections go undiagnosed as they continue to infect others. For a variety of public health reasons, not all STDs are reportable by law. Consequently, surveillance of these diseases by public health officials requires periodic surveys of health care providers to assess the full magnitude of the problem. Often, STDs and other communicable diseases present trends that help enable us to understand who is at greatest risk and what the key risk factors are.

Table 15.1 Estimated Incidence and Prevalence of Common STDs

STD	Incidence (estimated new cases every year)	Prevalence (estimated number of people currently infected)
Chlamydia	3 million	2 million
Gonorrhea	650,000	Not available
Syphilis	70,000	Not available
Herpes	1 million	45 million
Human papilloma virus (HPV)	5.5 million	20 million
Hepatitis B	120,000	417,000
Trichomoniasis	5 million	Not available
Bacterial vaginosis	Not available	Not available

Source: DSTD (2000).

Besides the asymptomatic nature of some STDs, another problem associated with understanding and tracking STD trends relates to how they are tabulated and reported. STD statistics are generally presented as **rates.** There are two types of rates: (a) **incidence rates,** which measure new cases and assess the risk of the spread of new cases of disease, and (b) **prevalence rates,** which measure the prevailing number of old and new cases and are a good barometer on the full impact of the condition as a public health problem. Acute infections that can be cured with antibiotics, such as syphilis, gonorrhea, and chlamydia, are typically reported and analyzed using incidence rates. Chronic diseases that can be treated but not cured such as HIV/AIDS, genital herpes, and human papilloma virus (HPV) are often reported and analyzed using prevalence rates. Table 15.1 shows the incidence and prevalence rates of commons STDs.

Epidemiological Synergy

Wasserheit (1992) coined the term **epidemiological synergy** to refer to the effects of infection with one STD on the transmission and development of complications of another. Generally this works two ways:

- Infection with one STD provides an entry point where other STD pathogens can invade.
- Infection with one form of STD could weaken the body's immune system, making exposure to another infection more risky.

An example of the former is the synergistic effect between genital ulcer diseases such as chancroid, genital herpes, and syphilis and increased susceptibility to HIV infection. The ulcerative lesions caused by chancroid, genital herpes, and syphilis literally provide an entry point for HIV.

Someone who has a genital ulcer and has sex with a person who is infected with HIV is more likely to become infected as a result. The epidemic of syphilis among men who have sex with men (MSM) in six major U.S. cities (discussed later) illustrates this phenomenon. Twenty to 73 percent of these men had coexisting HIV infection (MMWR [Morbidity and Mortality Weekly Report], 2002b).

Rates Statistics calculated by dividing the number of cases of disease by the population at risk of infection

Incidence rates Rates of new infection used to measure the likelihood of becoming infected

Prevalence rates Rates of prevailing infection used to measure the extent of the overall threat faced by the public

Epidemiological synergy The distribution of disease caused by the effects of infection with more than one condition

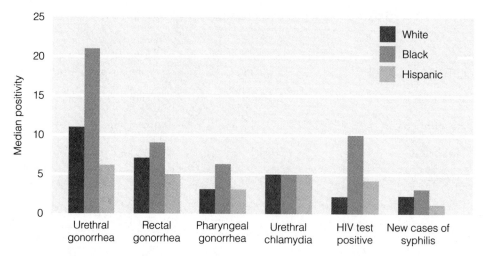

Figure 15.1 *Men Who Have Sex with Men* Health officials are alarmed at the dramatic rise in the numbers of cases of STDs among select groups of men who have sex with other men.
Source: DSTD (2002).

Genital ulcer disease may increase the risk of transmission per exposure 10 to 50 times in male-to-female transmission, and 50 to 300 times in female-to-male exposure (Hayes, Schulz, & Plummer, 1995). Figure 15.1 shows the high percentage of MSM attending public STD clinics who are infected with various STDs.

In comparison, consider infection with tuberculosis. Tuberculosis (TB), a communicable disease, has dropped 10-fold (from 53 to 5.6 cases per 100,000 people) since 1953. Although not a sexually transmitted disease, TB is an opportunistic infection among people with HIV and must be followed closely in this population (Division of TB Elimination [DTB], 2001). Infection with HIV weakens the immune system and the body's ability to resist exposure to new disease-causing organisms. A person who is HIV-positive and is exposed to tuberculosis is at greater risk for acquiring the infection than a person who is not HIV-positive (Finelli, Budd, & Spitalny, 1993). The coexistence of HIV with these other conditions also makes diagnosis, treatment, and follow-up much more difficult.

STD Transmission, Signs, and Symptoms

STDs can be grouped in several ways to study their transmission, symptoms, treatment, and prevention. Table 15.2 provides a summary of the transmission, symptoms, diagnosis, and treatment of the most common STDs.

One simple way to group STDs is by the nature of transmission. The main modes of STD transmission are as follows:

- Direct sexual contact (sexual contact with someone's STD symptoms, such as genital ulcers) or sexual contact with someone's infected semen, vaginal lubricant, blood, and other body fluids
- Maternal transfer (mother to fetus during pregnancy or childbirth)
- Sharing contaminated needles through injectable drug use

Minor STDs, such as crabs and scabies, can be passed through direct sexual contact with infected persons or, in rare cases, their contaminated bedding, items of clothing, and similar objects. Some STDs (such as HIV and hepatitis B) can be spread both by sexual contact and by injectable drug use.

Table 15.2 Common STDs, Their Source, Symptoms, Diagnosis, and Treatment

Name	Source	Signs and Symptoms	Diagnosis	Treatment
Chlamydia	Bacterium	Male: Watery discharge; pain when urinating Female: Usually asymptomatic; sometimes a similar discharge to men's; leading cause of pelvic inflammatory disease (PID)	Men: Culture of discharge from urethra Female: Cervical culture	Antibiotics other than penicillin
Gonorrhea (clap)	Bacterium	Male: Pus discharge from urethra; burning during urination Female: Usually asymptomatic; can lead to PID and sterility in both men and women	Male: Culture of discharge Female: Cervical culture	Antibiotics (ceftriaxone)
Genital herpes	Virus	Blisters in genital and rectal area	Presence of blisters and laboratory identification of virus in fluid of blister	Zovirax (acyclovir prescription)
Venereal warts	Virus (HPV)	Cauliflower-like growths in genital and rectal areas	Presence of lesions	Removal of lesions by laser surgery or chemicals
Syphilis	Bacterium (spirochete)	Primary: Chancre Secondary: Rash Latent: Asymptomatic Late: Irreversible damage to central nervous system, cardiovascular system	Blood test	Penicillin or other antibiotic
HIV/AIDS	Virus	Asymptomatic at first; opportunistic infections	Blood test, usually none in initial stages	AZT (now called ZDV; not a cure)
Chancroid	Bacterium (*Bacillus*)	Male: Painful irregular chancre on penis Female: Chancre on labia	Smear/stain and microscopic identification	Tetracycline
Pubic lice (crabs)	Metazoan	Intense itching of areas covered with pubic hair	Presence of lice and nits (eggs) on pubic hair	Prescription or over-the-counter shampoo

During sexual exposure to genital ulcers or other symptoms (such as genital warts), the uninfected person is exposed to infectious organisms that are present in the **serous fluid** of the lesions. During sexual contact, these pathogens are transmitted through the thrusting and grinding of sexual activity. The organisms are introduced into tiny breaks in the skin that commonly occur during sexual activity.

During sexual exposure to semen, vaginal lubricants, blood, and other body fluids, the infected partner passes the infection through unprotected vaginal or

Serous fluid A fluid that has the characteristics of serum

anal intercourse or oral sex. During sexual exposure to contaminated blood, STD organisms that live in the blood are passed between individuals as they exchange this body fluid. Blood is exchanged from person to person most commonly through (a) sexual contact with someone who has open lesions or ulcers that bleed during sex or (b) sexual contact that involves unlubricated anal intercourse and some vaginal intercourse.

STD micro-organisms can be passed by maternal transfer two ways:

- During pregnancy, STD micro-organisms in the mother's blood pass through the placenta and enter the bloodstream of the fetus.
- During labor and delivery, the newborn is exposed directly to disease-causing germs present in the birth canal.

Any type of shared injectable drug use is capable of transmitting blood-borne STDs. The transmission could be by an athlete shooting steroids and then passing the unsterilized needle to a friend to use, or it could be by a heroin addict doing the same. The risk is in the sharing, not the drug of choice.

In most cases, infestation with scabies and crabs occurs during sexual contact. A person whose genitals are infected with the lice pass on the crabs or scabies during sexual contact with an uninfected sex partner. Lice also are able to live on clothing and bedding and, in rare cases, can be spread via these inanimate objects.

Prevention and Risk Reduction

Personal health STD/HIV prevention programs focus largely on individual behavior as the basis for risk reduction. Many of these programs emphasize "safer sex" (using condoms consistently and correctly and verifying HIV status through testing) as the primary prevention approach. Others stress abstinence from sexual intercourse as the preferred preventive approach (Howard & McCabe, 1990).

Community health prevention programs emphasize public health interventions designed to stop the diseases from spreading. Examples of activities are political lobbying to establish needle exchange programs, increased funding of STD/HIV services (for example, to allow expanded hours), free and confidential treatment, and sociomarketing to promote condom distribution and family planning services.

The problem with compartmentalizing STD/HIV risks is that it fails to acknowledge that personal and community risks have a synergistic effect. We propose a new way to conceptualize the relationship between community and personal risks as pyramidal in nature, consisting of various public and personal factors that build upon each other. Figure 15.2 illustrates this Pyramid of Risk.

The foundation of the pyramid is made up of demographic variables that influence STD/HIV risk. These are generally beyond our individual control.

The next level of risk revolves around the sexual and medical history of ourselves or our partners. Because these risks are part of a person's past, they also cannot be changed. They are the history that each of us brings to any sexual encounter.

Sexual lifestyle The interaction between types and numbers of current sex partners

The third level of risk represents a person's current **sexual lifestyle,** the interaction between the types and numbers of current sex partners. The last level of risk is the one most educators focus on: personal sexual behavior. Most risk reduction pamphlets provide a laundry list of sexual behaviors that range from low risk to high risk. Although the four levels of factors influence STD/HIV risk independently, the interaction of levels can have a synergistic effect that can increase or reduce personal risk dramatically.

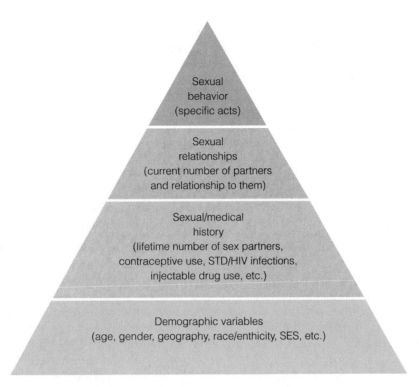

Figure 15.2 *A Pyramid of Risk for STDs* To assess one's true risk of acquiring STDs, demographic and sexual/medical history risks must be combined with behavioral and lifestyle factors.

Demographic Variables and the Distribution of STDs/HIV

Seven major demographic variables that contribute to STD/HIV risk are age, gender, sexual orientation, injecting drug user (IDU; the clustering of injectable drug users in communities), geography, socioeconomic status (SES), and race/ethnicity.

Age   There are more cases of STDs distributed throughout people aged 15 to 25 than in any other age group. Because more cases exist in this age group, the risk of acquiring an infection is greater if someone has sex with persons from this age category (versus the 55+ age group, in which STD rates are much lower). The risk is associated with the likelihood that someone will interact sexually with a member of this subpopulation.

Sexually active teenagers have the highest rates of infection with almost all STDs. Trends in gonorrhea infection illustrate this the best. Teenage girls had the highest risk of becoming infected. Rates for females in the 15- to 19-year-old age groups were 716 cases per 100,000 people. This was more than five times the national rate (about 132/100,000) (DSTD, 2001). Young women were approximately 20 times more likely to be infected with gonorrhea than females 30 years of age and older (Webster, Berman, & Greenspan, 1993; DSTD, 2000, 2001).

Other age-related STD considerations are as follows:

- The earlier the onset of intercourse (first time a person has sexual intercourse), the greater their potential exposure to different sex partners over their lifetime. There is an association between lifetime number of sex partners and increased risk of acquiring STDs.

- Individuals who initiate sexual activity earlier are more likely to have more sex partners over a lifetime (more than 25 percent of women initiating intercourse by age 15 had more than 10 lifetime sex partners, whereas only 6 percent of women initiating intercourse at age 20 or later had more than 10 sex partners).
- Adolescents and young adults are more likely than older adults to have multiple (sequential or concurrent) sexual partners.
- Adolescents and young adults are more likely than older adults to engage in unprotected sexual intercourse.
- The partners of adolescents and young adults are more likely to be at higher risk for having an STD than the partners of older adults.
- The transformation zone in women (the end of the cervix, where cervical tissue meets vaginal tissue) is most exposed during adolescence, and this tissue is most susceptible to STD infection in general and viral infection (cancer-causing) in particular (DSTD, 2000; Quinn & Cates, 1993; Alan Guttmacher Institute, 1991).

Data from the 2001 National Youth Risk Behavior Survey indicate new positive trends in sexual behavior among adolescents. Analysis of data from 1991 to 2001 shows a decrease in the overall percentage of high school students who have ever had sexual intercourse and who had multiple sex partners. Additionally, the study showed that condom use among students who were sexually active increased during that time period.

Unfortunately, reported condom use has leveled off since 1999. The lone disturbing finding of the study was an increased use, among sexually active teenagers, of alcohol or drugs before their last reported episode of sexual intercourse (MMWR, 2002e).

Gender   The risk for STDs/HIV is different for men and women. Biological gender is a risk factor related to the genetic, anatomical, and physiological differences between men and women (Kennedy, Scarlett, Duer, & Chu, 1995). Women face a greater risk than men for both acquiring a sexually transmitted disease and developing complications for several reasons:

- Heterosexual women are receptive sexually—vaginally, orally, and anally. This greatly increases their risks for initial infection by exposing a greater surface area of mucosal tissue (Quinn & Cates, 1993). Once infected with most STDs, heterosexual women tend to be asymptomatic more often than heterosexual men. Most heterosexual men notice initial symptoms of infection, whereas about half of women are asymptomatic (Morse, Moreland, & Thompson, 1990).
- Because of the asymptomatic nature of STDs in women, more women than men do not seek treatment during the initial stages of infection. This delayed access to treatment results in progression of the disease and a greater likelihood of developing complications. For example, about 15 percent of women develop complications associated with gonorrhea or chlamydia versus less than 1 percent of men (Morse et al., 1990).
- Menstruation plays a role in facilitating the movement of pathogens from the lower reproductive tract (below the cervix) to the upper parts, facilitating the development of complications. Women face the added risk of passing on their infection to their developing fetus during pregnancy or newborn through childbirth (Smeltzer & Whipple, 1991). The likelihood of transmitting infections such as syphilis or HIV is greatly reduced if mothers attend routine prenatal screening and receive treatment.

Sexual Orientation   Risks for STDs are affected by a person's sexual orientation. The risks that heterosexual women face accrue as a result of their anatomy and physiology, which facilitate exposure to disease agents. Sexual exposure results in infection without symptoms, and menstruation facilitates infection.

case study 15.2

Jim

Jim, 24, single, is white.

Jim was a student in Dr. Blonna's human sexuality class. Jim came to see him after class about some concerns regarding STDs.

You've got to help me. I made a mistake, and I'm superparanoid about what's going to happen to me. I was coming back to school last Friday night late, and I was cruising through Paterson [a large city adjacent to the town where the college campus is located]. I don't know what got into me, but I picked up a hitchhiker on Broadway and gave her a ride to the end of Paterson. She was really hot and offered to give me a blow job to thank me.

I said yes, and she went down on me in the parking lot where she lived. I don't know how to describe how I felt afterward—part ashamed, part stupid, part afraid. I'm so worried that I got AIDS from her.

On Monday in class, you talked about demographic risks, and the whole thing got me freaked. My girlfriend wanted to have sex last night, and I used a condom with her. She freaked out. She's on the pill, and we never use condoms. I broke down and had to tell her what I did. Am I going to die of AIDS?

Critical Thinking

What other sexual options did Jim have following his ride with the hitchhiker?

Use your Virtual Workbook to explore your answer to this question at **http://health.wadsworth.com/blonna1**.

Gay and bisexual men have some of the risks that heterosexual women do. They are receptive sexually and tend to have asymptomatic infections. This facilitates the development and spread of disease. In addition, certain diseases, such as HIV and hepatitis B, exist in **endemic** levels in the gay community. These diseases are incurable and capable of causing death (American Medical Association [AMA], 1996; Alter & Margolis, 1990).

Endemic A 20 percent level of ongoing infection within a specific population

Heterosexual men are at less risk than heterosexual women and gay men for a variety of reasons. First, their symptoms tend to be more obvious because these men usually are the insertive sexual partners and develop external symptoms. Early detection facilitates seeking prompt treatment and reducing complications. As an example, fewer than 1 percent of all heterosexual men infected with gonorrhea develop complications such as **epididymitis** (Morse et al., 1990). Also, female-to-male transmission of STDs is more difficult because heterosexual men are not receptive sexually, and vaginal fluids are less likely to transmit infection than is contaminated semen (Eng & Butler, 1997).

Epididymitis Inflammation of the small oblong body that rests upon and beside the surface of the testes

Of the four groups, lesbian women have the lowest rates of infection. Lesbian women tend to have fewer sexual partners over the course of their lifetime, and they do not engage in vaginal or anal intercourse (Kennedy et al., 1995).

IDU   The risk for STD/HIV is becoming increasingly related to the prevalence of **IDUs** (injectable drug users) in a community. Drug use is associated with increased STD/HIV risk in two ways.

IDU The acronym for *injectable drug user*

- Psychoactive drugs impair users' ability to make good decisions regarding sexual behavior. Therefore, engaging in safer sex becomes less likely when a person is using psychoactive drugs. And good choice of partner(s) is impaired by psychoactive drug use.
- Injectable drug use often involves needle sharing between users. This facilitates the transmission of blood-borne infections such as HIV and hepatitis B if one of the users is infected.

The drugs most often involved are crack cocaine and injectable heroin. A vicious cycle of drug abuse, exchanging sex for money or other resources, unsafe sex, and infection with a variety of genital ulcer diseases has occurred since the mid-1980s. This cycle is intimately related to the resurgence of syphilis and other diseases in urban America. The effects are most notable among young, urban, black and Hispanic/Latino men and women.

Urban/Rural and Geographic Differences   STDs including HIV are disproportionately higher in urban areas than in rural or suburban locations (DSTD, 2002). "Core urban populations" may be a major contributing factor for higher STD rates in urban communities and disproportionately high personal risk, despite individual behavior (Garnett & Anderson, 1996). The rate of acquisition of gonorrhea, for instance, in core urban populations is as much as 300 times higher than in the rest of the population (Rice, Roberts, & Handsfield, 1991). With a high level of infection and prevalence of deadly diseases, any sexual activity (even so-called safer sex) between or with members of this population carries a higher degree of risk than the same behavior with non–core group people.

Social and Environmental Wellness

STDs used to be called "social diseases" because of the nature of sexual transmission. Social wellness is a major preventive strategy against STDs. Being in a mutually exclusive, monogamous, disease-free relationship is the best prevention against STDs. In the United States, the quality of one's social environment seems to be directly proportional to socioeconomic status (SES). As SES rises, most Americans seek out safer, healthier communities, and safe communities carry much lower risk for STDs. High-risk/low-wellness communities should be targeted for STD prevention and treatment services and programs.

Socioeconomic Status (SES)   To a large extent, STDs mimic other chronic diseases. SES can either facilitate or hinder access to preventive and interventive STD health care. People of lower SES tend to lack enabling factors related to prevention and treatment of STDs such as health care insurance and access to treatment services. Even though free public clinics are available, they may not be utilized promptly because poor people often lack access to transportation, don't have sick days if they are employed, or are unaware of the availability of free care (Donelan et al., 1996).

Also, people of lower SES often do not perceive themselves to be at great risk for STDs/HIV and tend not to respond to symptoms promptly or consistently practice preventive behavior (Ramos, Shain, & Johnson, 1995). Poverty and lower SES, too, contribute to higher levels of drug use—a major risk factor for STDs/HIV (Potterat, Rothenberg, Woodhouse, Muth, Pratts, & Fogle, 1985).

Race/Ethnicity   African Americans and Hispanics continue to have the highest rates of STD infection in the United States. Rates for almost all STDs are substantially higher for these groups than for whites. Risk for certain STDs like gonorrhea and syphilis are as much as 30 times higher for African Americans than for whites (DSTD, 2000). Part of that disparity is attributed to the higher use of public health clinics by African Americans than whites. Public clinics tend to have more complete reporting of STDs than private health care providers (DSTD, 2000).

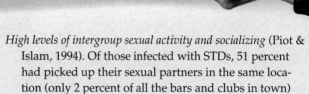

sex in society 15.1

Core Transmitters of STDs

STDs seem to be much more common in certain pockets of the population. These pockets occur mostly in urban areas among specific subpopulations of sexually active people called *core groups*. People in core groups (mostly urban African American and Latino lower-SES young men and women) have a disproportionate risk for acquiring STDs. The risk of transmission of STDs among a core group is 300 to 600 times greater than among the U.S. population in general. The following factors are related to transmission of STDs in the core population:

Endemic levels of infection (20 percent or more of the population infected) (Eng & Butler, 1997)

High concentrations of infected persons in small geographic areas (DSTD, 2000). Only 5.9 percent of census tracts accounted for 51 percent of cases of STDs, and an additional 9 adjacent census tracts accounted for 72 percent of cases and 74 percent of sexual contacts) (Garnett & Anderson, 1996).

High levels of intergroup sexual activity and socializing (Piot & Islam, 1994). Of those infected with STDs, 51 percent had picked up their sexual partners in the same location (only 2 percent of all the bars and clubs in town) (Webster et al., 1993).

High levels of repeat infections. Small percentages of infected individuals accounted for large percentages of multiple infections (Garnett & Anderson, 1996).

High levels of multiple STD infections (coexisting infection with gonorrhea and chlamydia; syphilis and HIV; HIV and chancroid) (Nakashima et al., 1996).

Longer than average duration of infectivity (because of a delay in seeking treatment) *and rate of asymptomatic infection among core group members* (Garnett & Anderson, 1996)

High levels of substance abuse and *higher levels of sex for drugs* than non–core group patients (Finelli et al., 1993)

Although disease rates in general are higher for blacks and Hispanics than whites, racial/ethnic differences are often markers for social class and poverty (Navarro, 1990). Poverty, especially that which affects the urban poor, is the true risk factor. The increased problem of STDs in minority populations in inner cities may stem in part from the unequal distribution of poverty, not race or ethnicity (Navarro, 1990). A greater proportion of blacks and Hispanics/Latinos live at or below poverty than whites. Socioeconomic differentials (often referred to as *class differentials*) are larger than race differentials in **morbidity.** When studies control for SES differentials, racial differences in disease distribution drop markedly. The problem of STDs in minority populations in inner cities is a result, in part, of the unequal distribution of SES (Navarro, 1990).

Morbidity The relative incidence of a disease

Sexual/Medical History

The next level of risk on the pyramid is sexual medical history. This is something we cannot control because it has occurred in the past. Yet, a person's sexual and medical history can greatly influence the present level of risk for STDs/HIV. The following are sexual/medical factors most associated with the current risk for STDs/HIV:

Lifetime number of sexual partners. In general, the greater the number, the higher the risk. Threshold levels of "safe" sexual activity have been identified (Dan, 1996). Once the threshold number of sexual partners is reached, the risk for disease increases exponentially.

Contraceptive use. Barrier contraceptive users have the lowest rates of infection. They are followed by other contraceptive users and nonusers, who have the highest risk (Rosenberg & Gollub, 1992).

Incidence The number of new cases of a disease during a specific time period

History of IDU. Persons with a history of IDU have an increased **incidence** of infection with blood-borne diseases, particularly HIV and hepatitis B (Alter & Margolis, 1990; Finelli et al., 1993).

Prior STD history. Persons who have been infected with STDs in the past are more likely to become infected again than those who have never been infected (Darrow, Barrett, McPhil, & Young, 1981).

Sexual Relationships

Sexual relationship refers to the connections between people rather then the specific behaviors in which they engage. In general, the risk for STDs/HIV decreases as sexual relationships move away from multiple, anonymous, sexual encounters toward monogamous (with uninfected partner), trusting partnerships. STD/HIV sexual relationship risks are specifically related to overall numbers of partners and the quality of the relationship (trust, understanding, and knowledge of one's partner). Figure 15.3 shows the continuum of risks for sexual relationships.

There are two dimensions of lifestyle of partner risk:

Familiarity risk. Familiarity risk is synonymous with *anonymity*. Laumann, Gagnon, Michael, and Michaels (1994) operationally defined the extent of familiarity along a continuum that measured how long the study subjects knew their partners before having sex with them. Their findings confirmed that the less familiar one is with the sex partner (the greater the anonymity), the greater is the risk. Anonymity is a risk factor because it influences the ability to make an informed choice about the risk for STD/HIV.

Exclusivity risk. Laumann et al. (1994) call the second variable *exclusivity*—the quality of the sexual relationship. Exclusivity, they believe, has to be examined for *both* partners. If one partner is monogamous but the other is not, the benefits of exclusivity are lost. Furthermore, if an uninfected person is monogamous with someone who has an STD, exclusivity can actually increase the risk by increasing the extent of exposure. For exclusivity to work, both partners have to be uninfected and monogamous. Subjects (and partners) who were not sexually exclusive were at increased risk for acquiring an STD (Lauman et al., 1994).

The highest risks were associated with the "interaction of risky partners" (lack of exclusivity and familiarity) and many partners. This sexual lifestyle, which combines multiple partners with anonymous sexual encounters, creates a deadly synergy that increases the risk exponentially (Lauman et al., 1994).

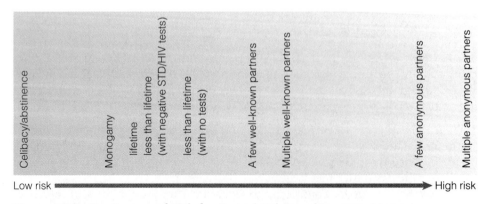

Figure 15.3 *Continuum of Risk for Sexual Relationships* STD risks increase as relationships become less familiar and exclusive.

case study 15.3

Lillie's Risk

Lillie, 43, divorced, is white.

Lillie is a continuing student who made these comments in class:

Thank you! Finally, someone has said what I believed all along: It's not just sexual behavior that's the risk. It's the behavior in the context of a relationship that determines risk. I was always so annoyed and insulted when sex educators told me that I should always insist that my partner wear a condom and that any woman who is sexually active is at equal risk of becoming infected. I always felt that as long as I had one uninfected partner, and the two of us were monogamous, I was at low risk.

It's funny because even though I'm not married, my boyfriend (of 3 years) is less of a threat to me than my husband used to be. My ex-husband was always cheating on me, and I was worried that even though I was monogamous, he'd bring something home to me.

I fully trust my current boyfriend. We've been monogamous (though unmarried) for 3 years, and I've never felt safer. We spent a lot of time building the trust and commitment in our relationship. I have great sex with him because I can fully relax and trust him, even though I've never gone down the list of things I need to know about his sexual past. We did talk about whether either of us ever had a viral STD, because viruses are forever.

Critical Thinking

Do you agree with Lillie's assessment of her STD risk? Why or why not?

Use your Virtual Workbook to explore your answers to these questions at **http://health.wadsworth.com/blonna1.**

Sexual Behavior

At the top of the Pyramid of Risk is sexual behavior. In general, as illustrated in Figure 15.4, the risks increase as behaviors incorporate unprotected insertion and ejaculation. The lower-risk behaviors are nonpenetrative and do not involve an exchange of bodily fluids. As we move along the continuum of risk, the behaviors reflect attempts to utilize barrier protection against infectious agents. The highest-risk behavior is receptive anal penetration including ejaculation, which consists of unprotected ejaculation of semen into the delicate, nonlubricated tissue of the rectum. This allows direct access of infectious STD/HIV agents to the bloodstream. Theoretically, as Figure 15.4 illustrates, the risk for STD/HIV is greater for the receptive partner of any sexual activity.

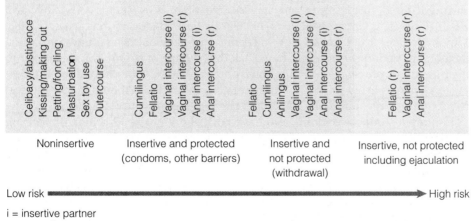

i = insertive partner
r = receptive partner

Figure 15.4 *A Continuum of Risk for Sexual Behaviors* STD risks increase as sexual activities become unprotected and receptive.

A Closer Look at Sexual Behaviors and STD Risk

Much remains to be known about the relative safety of various sexual behaviors. For instance, a wealth of literature documents the degree of protection condoms provide in preventing STDs. Little, however, has been written concerning the effects of nonpenetrative sexual activity and withdrawal. Some of these activities now are included in "safer sex" methods, instead of "safe sex" behaviors because of the lack of adequate documentation on their effectiveness.

The effects of some of the more bizarre techniques haven't been documented at all. Consider the recommendation of some safe sex educators of the use of dental dams and clear plastic food wraps to prevent the transmission of STDs through cunnilingus, fellatio, and vaginal intercourse. We do not advocate these measures because they are untested and not intended for those purposes. No evidence is available to suggest that they work. In fact, the American Dental Association issued a disclaimer concerning using dental dams (square pieces of latex designed to be used over the mouths of dental patients) for any circumstances other than dental hygiene. Clear plastic food wraps are an even more vivid example of safe sex gone mad. The notion of covering one's genitalia with plastic wrap and then having intercourse or oral sex would be comical if the potential results weren't so dangerous.

For those who choose to have sexual intercourse, barrier methods provide the best protection. For those who do not want to have intercourse, a variety of nonpenetrative sexual activities offer close to 100 percent effectiveness against STDs.

Condoms   If worn properly and used consistently, condoms (both male and female) help protect the wearer against some STD infection by preventing direct contact between the penis and cervical, vaginal, rectal, or pharyngeal secretions or lesions. They also protect against exposure to penile lesions, discharges, and infected semen. Proper use for preventing STDs requires putting them on prior to any sexual contact, and they must remain intact throughout sexual activity.

Condoms are more effective against sexually transmitted infections such as gonorrhea, chlamydia, trichomoniasis, and HIV, which are transmitted by fluids from mucosal surfaces and from semen (and therefore captured or blocked by the condom) than STDs transmitted by skin-to-skin contact such as HPV, herpes simplex virus (HSV), syphilis, and chancroid. The organisms of the latter diseases and others live in outcrops of blisters, warts, and lesions that could exist in areas that condoms do not protect (MMWR, 2002f). In laboratory studies, male latex condoms have been shown to block the larger bacterial pathogens (gonorrhea and chlamydia) and, to a lesser extent, smaller viral organisms (such as HIV, HSV, and HPV) (Grimes & Cates, 1990; Conant, Hardy, Sernatinger, Spicer, & Levy, 1986; Minuk, Bohme, & Bowen, 1986). Similar findings have not been found for natural membrane condoms. Although they block the passage of sperm and are similar in their ability to prevent pregnancy, their pores are large enough to allow the passage of some STD organisms. Natural membrane condoms should not be the first choice for the prevention of STDs unless one is allergic to latex (MMWR, 2002f).

In human studies, condoms also have been shown to be effective in reducing the risks for contracting STDs. Studies from all over the world, with diverse populations of users, have consistently documented that condoms reduce the risks for spreading STDs. Research as far back as the 1940s studied the use of condoms by troops in World War II and the Korean and Vietnam conflicts. In all three conflicts, soldiers and seamen using condoms had significantly lower rates of infection than their peers who did not use condoms (Hart, 1974).

More recent studies of college men, men and women attending STD clinics, sex workers in Kenya and Zaire, and many others document that condoms provide some protection against a host of STDs (Darrow, 1989; Cameron et al., 1991; Mann

My Most Persuasive Reasons
to Wait to Have Sex

Although there are many great reasons to have sexual intercourse, there are also some really good reasons to wait. One of the best ways to avoid an STD is to limit your sexual partners. This activity will help you practice being assertive about why you want to wait to have sex.

This will be more fun if you can find a friend to role-play this with you. It will be even more fun if you find a friend of the opposite sex. Tell your friend that you would like for him or her to act out the following scenario with you. You are playing the parts of a couple who disagree when to become sexually active. One partner is ready to become sexually intimate, but the other partner wants to stay monogamous and to wait at least 4 months to be tested for HIV/AIDS and STDs before becoming intimate. Your friend will play the role of trying to persuade you to have sex, and your role is to give your friend all of the good reasons that you two should wait. Once you have finished, decide who was the most persuasive and discuss other good arguments you could have used. The more we practice assertively telling a partner what we need, the more likely we are to do it in our "real" relationships.

et al., 1987). Although use of condoms does not provide 100 percent protection against STDs, the studies we have mentioned have reduced risk by 50 to 80 percent in actual users (Cates & Stone, 1992).

Women-Centered Barriers Although the male condom is the most reliable form of barrier protection against STDs/HIV, studies show that the women who stand to benefit the most do not use them consistently and correctly. The least consistent users of the male condom are adolescent women, women with a history of STD infection, and lower-SES women (who generally have less power and equality in their sexual relationships with men and have less negotiating skill) (Rosenberg & Gollub, 1992). This problem could be dramatically lessened, if not eliminated, if more women were to use female barriers consistently and correctly.

Clinical studies of the effectiveness of female condoms in preventing STDs are very limited. Laboratory studies have demonstrated the effectiveness of the female condom in blocking viruses. Female condoms are recommended for use when male condoms cannot be used properly (MMWR, 2002f).

In both laboratory and STD clinic studies, the following rates of effectiveness were reported for the sponge, diaphragm, and spermicides:

- An overall reduced STD infection rate among barrier users compared to nonbarrier users
- Lower STD infection rates (87 percent lower) for women using barriers and attending health maintenance organizations (HMOs) than nonusers
- Lower STD infection rates (61 percent lower than nonusers) for women attending STD clinics who used barriers
- Up to 70 percent effectiveness against gonorrhea when using barriers
- Up to 40 percent effectiveness against chlamydia when using barriers (Rosenberg & Golub, 1992)

Furthermore, in a study of 5,681 STD patients on the effectiveness of various contraceptive methods against STDs, not only was there a lower rate of infection among barrier users, but the lowest rates of infection were among sponge and diaphragm users. These rates were stable across all types of subjects, forms of sexual behavior, and STDs (Rosenberg & Gollub, 1992).

Even though condoms have a higher rate of theoretical effectiveness against STDs, the women who need them the most use them less consistently and correctly. Woman-centered barriers, though theoretically less effective against STDs, provided greater actual effectiveness for women who used them instead of the male condom.

Nonpenetrative Sexual Behaviors   The effectiveness of nonpenetrative sexual activity in preventing STDs is relatively undocumented. Effectiveness in preventing STDs is generalized from the hypothesized ability of these methods to prevent unintended pregnancy by preventing the deposit of live sperm into the vagina. Because these methods exclude penetration and ejaculation, their ability to prevent pregnancy is very high (theoretically close to 100 percent).

Methods such as masturbation, use of sex toys, and even oral-genital sexual contact in preventing the transmission of STDs have not been scientifically studied and documented. Do these methods offer the same protection against STDs?

healthy sex hints 15.1

Reducing the Risk for STDs: Some Basic Guidelines

Although no universal solutions will work equally well for everyone, here are a few guidelines for reducing your risk for acquiring an STD.

1. *Become comfortable with your own sexuality.* Learn as much as you can about your sexuality. This will make you more accepting of who you are and what you need. You will be less likely to give in to doing something risky if you know and respect yourself. This includes choosing to abstain if that's what you desire.

2. *Check yourself for signs and symptoms of STDs.* This goes hand in hand with item 1. If you are comfortable with your body and your sexuality, you will be more aware of changes that signify possible STD infection. If you or your partner has the sores, rashes, discharges, itching, or pain associated with STDs, avoid sex.

3. *Develop a repertoire of low-risk sexual outlets.* Learn how to enjoy a low-risk sexual outlet. It's perfectly OK to say no to unprotected intercourse and yes to masturbation or massage.

4. *Work on your communication skills.* Practice how to initiate a dialogue about STD risk reduction. You'll need to find out a lot about your partner to assess and reduce your personal risk. The only way to do this is to be able to talk openly about your sexual lifestyle. Practice now.

5. *Understand your demographic risks.* Find out about the area in which you live. You can get information about the level of STDs in your community from your local and state health departments.

6. *Know your partner's sexual/medical history.* Take time and care to find out the things you need to know about your partner, or develop the level of trust in the relationship that will allow you to make some judgments about your risk. In the meantime, if you choose to have sex with your partner, use condoms and non-intercourse options to reduce your risk.

7. *If you are at risk, seek regular checkups.* If you have a very high-risk profile, go in for an STD checkup every 3 months. If you are in a lower risk category, go in at least twice a year. Most states have a list of free public clinics in your area.

8. *If you are not in a mutually monogamous, disease-free relationship, protect yourself.* Do not rely on your partner to look out for your health. All forms of sexual activity carry some degree of risk for spreading STDs. Gauge the level of risk you are willing to assume.

9. *Strive to be in a mutually satisfying, disease-free relationship with one person.* If both you and your sex partner are monogamous and disease-free, you will not be at risk for STDs. Two mutually exclusive, uninfected partners can enjoy sex without fear of infection.

No one knows for sure. When theorizing about their ability to prevent STDs, one can say that, because they do not involve penetration and ejaculation, they must offer a high level of protection against STDs as well. We are not as totally convinced of this hypothesis as some other safer sex educators are.

The major difference in the ability of these activities to prevent STDs would be the presence or absence of genital symptoms that potentially could spread pathogens even in the absence of penile penetration and ejaculation. Also, STD organisms, in rare instances, could be passed from genital ulcers to the eyes via contaminated fingers. For instance, if a person who had genital lesions associated with herpes were to engage in mutual masturbation with his or her partner, and then rubbed the eyes, the herpes virus could be spread to this site.

These facts are why we present sexual behaviors on a continuum of risk from low to high. No behavior except celibacy is completely risk-free. Viewing sexual activity in this way will allow you to examine the risk of specific behaviors in the context of other sexual activities. You also must evaluate any behavior within the context of the relationship you have with your partner. The less you know about your partner, the more risky any behavior becomes.

Using the Pyramid to Reduce Risks

The pyramid model presented earlier in the chapter shows that the risk for STDs/HIV combines personal lifestyle and behavior, past sexual history, and demographic factors. Focusing on just one set of factors and ignoring the others

healthy sex hints 15.2

Are You Really Sleeping with Your Partner's Partners?

Probably the most overused myth associated with sexual lifestyle is the notion that when you "sleep with someone, you sleep with everyone they have ever had sex with." We're sure you all have heard this at one point or another during your lives. Here are seven reasons why we disagree with this message:

1. For the most part, it is an antisex, fear-based message. It targets guilt and a sense of helplessness. None of these are part of healthy sexuality.
2. It uses incorrect terminology. You will rarely get any STDs (except maybe crabs or scabies) by merely *sleeping* with someone. You must engage in some kind of sexual activity with the person to acquire an STD.
3. You do not "have sex" with anyone but the *person* you actually come in physical contact with. Any explanation other than this is nonsense (actually, it's a metaphor to induce fear).
4. Most nonviral STDs are cured when a person receives treatment. If your partner had a nonviral STD and was properly treated, the infection stopped there.

5. If your partner's partner was infected with an STD but did not pass it on to your partner, it *cannot infect you* under any circumstances.
6. Even viral STDs such as genital herpes can be controlled with treatment. *You* are not at risk for your partner's partner who had a viral STD unless this person infected your lover, who then passes the infection on to you.
7. Being exposed to your partner's antibodies to past sex partners is *not the same* as being exposed to disease-producing germs (although research shows that people can develop antibodies in response to being exposed to human semen, this is not the same thing as *being infected* with a disease).

Based on the data we just presented, do you still think you are sleeping with everyone your partner has slept with when you have sex with him or her?

sex in society 15.2

Interactions Among Geographic Differences, Sexual Behavior, and Disease Infectivity

Pinkerton, Chesson, and Layde (2002) found that the risk of acquiring STDs varies significantly according to the interaction of four major risk factors: (a) disease infectivity (the ease with which a disease is transmitted through penile-vaginal intercourse), (b) the level of infection within a community, (c) the number of different sex partners, and (d) the number of unprotected sex acts (consistent condom use).

Pinkerton et al. (2002) found that in geographic areas with high morbidity of very infectious diseases such as gonorrhea and chlamydia, the best way to reduce risk was to decrease the overall number of sexual partners. This was found to be more protective than the overall number of protected sex acts. In other words, by decreasing the overall number of different sex partners, one decreased their risk more than by using condoms consistently with multiple sex partners. Because highly infectious diseases are relatively easy to acquire with even one sexual exposure, lowering the number of potential exposures (by decreasing the overall number of partners) was found to be the best way to reduce risk.

In contrast, in geographic areas with high morbidity of less infectious diseases such as HIV, the best way to reduce risk was to increase the number of protected sex acts. Having fewer partners was less protective than using condoms with each sex act.

Because HIV is more difficult to spread through penile-vaginal intercourse than gonorrhea and chlamydia, being exposed to a single episode of intercourse with different partners (most of whom might be uninfected) might pose less of a risk of infection with HIV than being consistently exposed to a single, infected partner. Consistent exposure to a single infectious partner therefore required more consistent condom use (decreasing the overall number of unprotected sex acts).

The same dynamic can hold true for sexual/medical history. If the sex partner has a high-risk past (used injectable drugs and might be HIV-positive, for instance), the other partner's personal behavior might be much different from that of someone whose partner has no history of infection. If the personal history includes a risk such as prior infection with gonococcal pelvic inflammatory disease (PID), for instance, a woman might take extra precautions against becoming infected with gonorrhea again as it could increase the risk for developing PID again. Each individual has to develop a personal plan for STD risk reduction based on his or her (and the partner's) pyramid. Plans will vary according to the individuals involved. Although reducing risks this way takes a little more thought, it also respects individuality.

isn't enough. Though a person can never dismiss personal behavior as crucial to the success of prevention activities, other factors affect personal risk despite the most exemplary personal behavior.

For example, in certain core areas, individuals have 300 times more risk for acquiring infection simply by virtue of community risk factors (Potterat et al., 1985). Even if you are rather conservative in your behavior, if you live and interact sexually in such an area, engaging in any sexual activity carries a higher risk of becoming infected and engaging in risky sexual behavior may be life-threatening. This demographic influence might make risk reduction measures much different from someone who lives in a lower-risk area.

Diagnosis, Treatment, and Epidemiology of Various STDs

Epidemiological Dealing with incidence, distribution, and control, as in STDs

The following sections take a more detailed look at several STDs. Specifically, we'll consider how they are diagnosed and treated and, more generally, look at **epidemiological** issues around each one.

Syphillis

Diagnosis Syphilis is a blood-borne STD caused by infection with *Treponema pallidum*, a corkscrew-shaped bacterium. A **spirochete** type of bacteria, the *T. pallidum* is easily killed by penicillin and other broad-spectrum antibiotics. It is unique among STD organisms because its corkscrew shape and motility facilitate its entry into the bloodstream.

After exposure to the bacterium, it enters the body through breaks in the skin or by penetrating intact skin, and from there passes into the bloodstream. Once in the bloodstream, it can move freely throughout the body. The usual incubation period for syphilis is 3 to 4 weeks, but it can be as short as 10 days or as long as 90 days.

After the incubation period, a **chancre** appears at the spot where the organism entered. The primary chancre is painless and disappears within 1 to 5 weeks without treatment. Often it is internal (inside the vagina, mouth, or rectum). Because of this, many people who become infected with syphilis don't realize it. An infected person's blood test will detect antibodies to the syphilis spirochete a short time after the primary chancre appears. Fluid from chancres can also be used to diagnose early syphilis. A specimen of the fluid can be examined under a darkfield microscope. If infected, the specimen should be teeming with spirochetes, moving in their typical corkscrew motion.

About 6 weeks later a generalized rash appears. The rash varies from being highly noticeable, covering the entire trunk, to a mild eruption on the hands or feet. As with the chancre, the rash disappears without treatment after 2 to 6 weeks.

In about 25 percent of the cases, a second rash appears and also goes away without treatment. At this point, those who are infected enter the latency period, during which time they are infected but have no symptoms. They are capable of transmitting the infection only by donating blood or by a mother passing the infection across the placenta to a developing fetus, resulting in **congenital syphilis**.

All blood in the United States is tested for syphilis, and no cases of disease have been detected this way in decades. Because the symptoms of syphilis can be so mild and varied, it has been dubbed the "great imitator." It can mimic a variety of dermatological conditions and often is mistaken for these less serious infections. In adults, un-

Syphilis An STD caused by the spirochete bacterium *Treponema pallidum*

Spirochete A mobile, flexible, corkscrew-shaped bacterium of the genus *Spirocheta*, one type of which causes syphilis

Chancre A painless, indurated primary lesion of early syphilis

Congenital syphilis The disease acquired by the fetus in the womb and present at birth

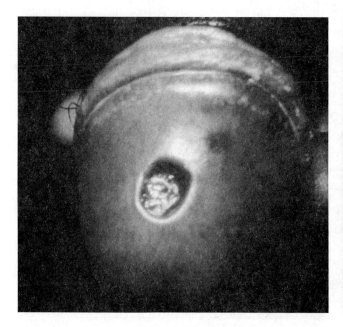
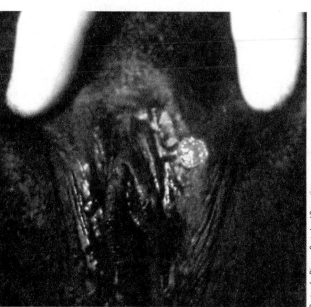

The typical chancre of primary syphilis is round with raised edges and painless; it is often internal and goes unobserved.

Centers for Disease Control and Prevention

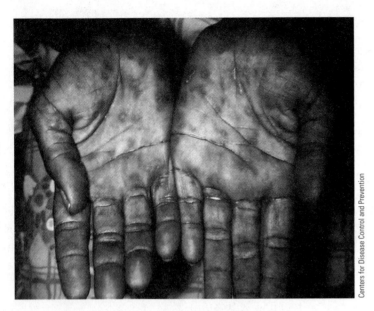

Centers for Disease Control and Prevention

The typical rash associated with secondary syphilis is bilateral (on both hands or feet instead of just one), discolored, and raised.

treated syphilis takes several years to develop into a serious illness. Because the spirochetes are traveling throughout the body, they can infect any organ or body system and cause major damage.

In the United States, untreated syphilis going undetected for the decades required to develop life-threatening illness is unusual. Most Americans have a blood test for syphilis (for example, for work, marriage, induction into the Armed Forces) at some point in their adult life. This also explains why disenfranchised people who live in poverty and are not in the mainstream are more likely to have undetected syphilis.

Treatment   Treatment of syphilis is relatively straightforward. Injections of penicillin are sufficient to treat most early cases of syphilis. One shot is administered to those who have been infected for less than 1 year. Those having infections more than 1 year are given three injections, each spaced 1 week apart. For individuals who are allergic to penicillin, Doxycycline or tetracycline, taken for a minimum of 14 days, is recommended for the treatment of early syphilis (MMWR, 2002f).

Epidemiology   The incidence of syphilis declined by a dramatic 99 percent from the 1940s to the present, primarily because of (a) the availability and widespread use of penicillin therapy and (b) the public health strategy of aggressive follow-up of sex partners. Public health officials prioritized syphilis control and insisted that all infected persons be interviewed and counseled about their disease. Their sex partners were followed up and given preventive treatment (penicillin unless allergic) for the disease (Dunn & Rolfs, 1991).

The largest recent decline has been in gay men of all ages from 1983 to 1986, partly because of their adoption of safer sex behaviors. From 1986 to 1990, in an epidemic of syphilis throughout the United States, rates increased from 12 cases per 100,000 to 20 per 100,000 (St. Louis & Wasserheit, 1998; Webster & Rolfs, 1993). This represented the highest level in the United States in 40 years.

Figure 15.5 *Primary and Secondary Syphilis Rates by Gender* Primary and secondary syphilis rates for men and women have steadily declined.

Source: DSTD (2002).

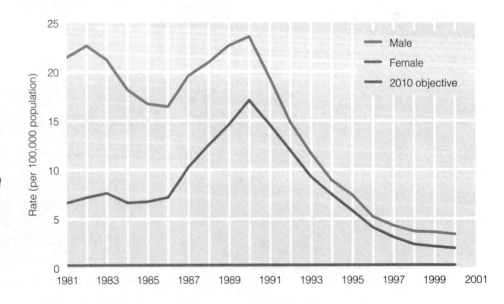

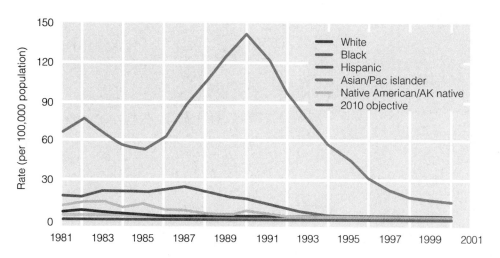

Figure 15.6 *Primary and Secondary Syphilis Rates by Race/Ethnicity* The decline in new cases of syphilis is consistent among all racial and ethnic groups.
Source: DSTD (2002).

Since that time however, syphilis rates have been dropping, reaching an all-time low. In 1999, 79 percent of over 3,000 counties in the United States reported no cases of early syphilis (DSTD 1999, 2001). Figures 15.5 and 15.6 show primary and secondary syphilis rates.

One disturbing contradiction to this trend has been the occurrence of several "miniepidemics" of syphilis within urban populations of men who have sex with men (MSM) in major metropolitan areas across the United States. Since 1977, syphilis outbreaks among MSM have occurred in New York City, Seattle, Chicago, San Francisco, Los Angeles, and Chicago (MMWR, 1999, 2002b; Rutherford, 2002; Bertrami, 2002). These men also demonstrated an increased risk for multiple STDs (Ciesielski, Flynn, & McLean, 2002).

The occurrence of these miniepidemics is generally accepted as secondary evidence of a relaxation of safe sex behavior of MSM in these areas. Many of these men suffer from what experts call "AIDS burnout," the relapsing back to unsafe sexual activity due to years and years of exposure to prevention messages and compliance with safe sex behaviors. This is prompting public health officials and members of the gay community to launch new safe sex campaigns to call attention to this new threat posed by the resurgence of syphilis within their communities (Rutherford, 2002; Bertrami, 2002).

Congenital Syphilis

The epidemic of early syphilis in the 1980s resulted in a dramatic increase in congenital syphilis cases and rates. Reported cases of congenital syphilis increased from 158 in 1983 to 7,219 cases in 1990 (from 4.3 to 174.7 cases per 100,000) (Zenker, 1991). A partial explanation for the dramatic rise in congenital syphilis was the adoption of a new case definition from the CDC. Under this new definition, a *case* is defined as any infant whose mother was determined to be untreated or inadequately treated for syphilis, regardless of the presence/absence of symptoms in the baby. This epidemic hit young, urban, African American and Hispanic people the hardest.

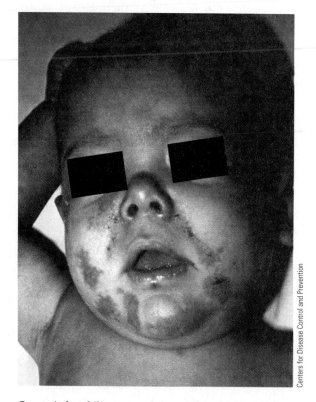

Centers for Disease Control and Prevention

Congenital syphilis occurs when an infected pregnant woman passes the infection to her developing fetus in utero.

Figure 15.7 *Congenital Syphilis Rates* Congenital syphilis rates have declined significantly but are still above the targets sets by Healthy People 2010.
Source: DSTD (2002).

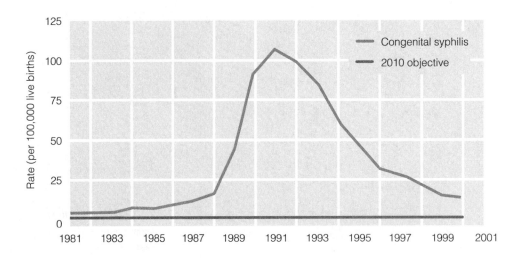

Since 1990, the decline in early syphilis has led to a corresponding decrease in congenital syphilis rates (see Figure 15.7). From 1990 through 2000, the average yearly decrease in congenital syphilis was 220 percent (compared to 21 percent for early syphilis). The current rate of 13.4 cases per 100,000 women is the lowest in a decade (DSTD, 2001).

The risks of congenital syphilis were greatest among young, lower-SES, drug-abusing mothers (Cates & Stone, 1992; Zenker, 1991; Nakashima et al., 1996). These young women are much less likely than their older, more affluent, and better-educated peers to seek and obtain adequate prenatal care. Many of these pregnant women fail to have the recommended three trimester visits with an obstetrician. A requirement of routine prenatal care is a blood test for syphilis. Most adult women with health insurance get this test early in their pregnancies. If it is positive, they can be treated. Treatment of the mother almost always results in treatment of her developing fetus.

Chancroid

Chancroid An STD named for the irregular and painful genital lesions it produces, caused by the bacterium *Haemophilus ducreyi*

Diagnosis **Chancroid** is often confused with syphilis because both present with an initial genital ulcer as the primary symptom. The ulcers associated with chancroid, however, are irregular in shape and painful (versus symmetrical and painless for syphilis).

The typical incubation period is 4 to 10 days, after which the ulcer appears. After their initial appearance, the ulcers progress to become beefy, granular, painful erosions. The ulcers are accompanied by painful, swollen, lymph glands in the groin.

Like syphilis, chancroid is diagnosed through the presence (or history) of symptoms and the results of a blood test. It is often diagnosed in part, ruling out infection with syphilis. A negative test for syphilis focuses the diagnosis on looking for antibodies to the causative organism, *Haemophilus ducreyi*, or isolating it in a biological culture.

Centers for Disease Control and Prevention

Unlike syphilis, the ulcers of chancroid are irregular in shape and painful.

Treatment Chancroid is easily treated with antibiotics taken either orally or through an intramuscular injection.

sex in society 15.3

The Tuskegee Study: It Couldn't Happen Here—or Could It?

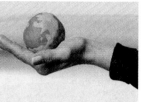

In 1932, the U.S. Public Health Service (USPHS) embarked on one of the most tragic experiments ever conducted by a government on its own people. From 1932 to 1970, in Macon County, Alabama, the USPHS conducted a study under the guidance of the Tuskegee Institute (which, ironically, is one of the nation's most prestigious black academic institutions) on the history of syphilis in blacks.

Syphilis, it was hypothesized, progressed differently in blacks than whites. The study originally was intended to be a short-term investigation (6 to 9 months' duration) but evolved into a 40-year project that followed the subjects well beyond the initial stages of their disease through latency into complications and ultimately to their deaths. Much of what we know about the disease, how it spreads, its complications, and how it attacks the body and kills comes from the Tuskegee Study.

The study followed 600 black subjects (399 infected men and 201 uninfected controls) for 40 years. Treatment was withheld intentionally from these men, even after they were diagnosed with serious, life-threatening complications of the disease. None of them benefited from penicillin as the effective treatment of choice in 1951. The USPHS devised elaborate plans to keep track of these men (and to continue to withhold treatment) even after they moved from Alabama to other states.

In 1966, Peter Buxtun, an investigator for the USPHS, brought the matter before the then-director of the Division of Venereal Diseases, Peter Brown. Given the moral climate and racial turmoil of the 1960s and the immorality of such an experiment, Buxtun pleaded that something be done. A special committee was impaneled within the USPHS to discuss the study. The committee ruled in favor of continuing the study to its natural end point.

Buxtun's pleas went unheeded, and the experiment continued. Not until Buxtun leaked his story to an Associated Press writer and it broke on the front pages of the *Washington Post* in 1972 was something done. In 1973, a special subcommittee of the U.S. Congress, chaired by Edward Kennedy (D-MA) began to investigate the matter. The committee found the USPHS culpable, the study was terminated, and special regulations concerning conducting government experiments were drawn up. These regulations now serve as guidelines for handling human subjects in any government-financed study. Surviving participants of the Tuskegee Study and their heirs filed a $1.8 billion class action lawsuit. The government settled the suit out of court for $10 million.

How all of this was allowed to happen—the circumstances behind the massive cover-up and the racial bigotry that may have poisoned a legitimate scientific quest for knowledge and understanding—are all chronicled in the work of James Jones's 1993 book *Bad Blood: The Tuskegee Study—A Tragedy of Race and Medicine.*

Epidemiology   Although chancroid is not common in the United States and other developed countries, it is endemic in some Third World countries and is considered a cofactor in the explosion of HIV infection in these nations. In the United States, the incidence of chancroid peaked in 1947 with 10,000 cases nationwide and steadily declined until 1981.

From 1981 to 1987, morbidity increased slightly, with eight distinct outbreaks scattered around the country. These outbreaks all had the following commonalities:

The introduction of infected individuals from outside areas (including merchant seamen and recent immigrants)
Predominance in black and Hispanic males
Linkage to prostitution (Hayes et al., 1995; Cameron et al., 1991; Morse et al., 1990)

Since 1987, chancroid morbidity has decreased steadily. The current level of infection is the lowest in 20 years, with just 78 cases reported in the United States. Of the 12 states reporting infections in 2001, three (New York, South Carolina, and Texas) were responsible for over 70 percent of all cases (DSTD, 2002).

HIV/AIDS

AIDS represents the end stage of **HIV.** Figure 15.8 traces the natural progression of HIV infection. As you can see, AIDS can develop within 2 years of exposure but typically takes longer. HIV infection is caused by person-to-person transmission of the human immunodeficiency virus. The most common modes of transmission are (a) sexual contact (vaginal or anal intercourse are most efficient), (b) sharing contaminated needles (through injecting drug use), and (c) maternal-to-fetal transfer. Once the virus has been transmitted, it enters the bloodstream, where it incubates from 8 weeks to 6 months, when it will show positive on a blood test.

Diagnosis A person who elects to take a blood test for HIV is given a screening test, called the *ELISA* (enzyme-linked immunosorbent assay), which detects the presence of antibodies to the HIV. If this test is negative, the person is counseled to come back for a second ELISA in a few months, to make sure the maximum incubation period has elapsed. If a person tests positive on the initial ELISA, he or she is given a second test, called the *Western blot,* to confirm infection. If this test comes back positive, the person is diagnosed as having HIV infection.

There are two new tests marketed by OraSure Technologies. OraSure, an oral screening using a swab, tests saliva for HIV antibodies. OraQuick tests blood from a fingerstick sample and provides results in 20 minutes. For either test, a positive result is followed up by a Western blot test.

HIV infection is essentially a disorder of the immune system. The virus weakens the body's immune system, making the person susceptible to other infections and chronic diseases. These are called **opportunistic infections** because they take advantage of the body's weakened state to attack and cause disease. When people with a fully functioning immune system come in contact with opportunistic organisms, they normally repel them.

People with HIV cannot fight off opportunistic infections and eventually die from them. Most people with HIV infection are completely free of symptoms for more than 10 years. Others deteriorate rapidly and develop symptoms and AIDS within 2 to 4 years.

Early symptoms of HIV infection stem from infections that begin to invade the body because of its weakened immune status. When the immune system begins to fail, the following symptoms begin to occur: fatigue, diarrhea, fever, night sweats, skin rashes, sudden weight loss, dry cough, swollen lymph nodes, and vaginal yeast infection. These symptoms can be present for weeks, months, or even years without opportunistic infections taking hold.

With treatment, many people with HIV can prevent these symptoms from ever occurring. And aggressive treatment can return symptomatic individuals to a symptom-free state. Although the medication doesn't kill the virus, it slows or stops viral replication and thereby boosts **immunocompetence.** If an opportunistic infection does take hold, the person moves from being infected with HIV to being diagnosed as having AIDS. In 1993, the CDC broadened the definition of AIDS to include 26 opportunistic infections. Infection with any one of these combined with being HIV-positive leads to a diagnosis of AIDS.

Treatment HIV/AIDS treatment is not a cure, because viruses have no cure. The multitude of new antiviral drugs and combination drug treatment regimens do not kill all of the HIV, as antibiotics kill bacteria. Antiviral therapy prevents or slows the unchecked replication and growth of HIV, helping the infected person's immune system keep the virus in check. This prevents the person from contracting opportunistic infections. Other treatments focus on killing the opportunistic infections that take hold.

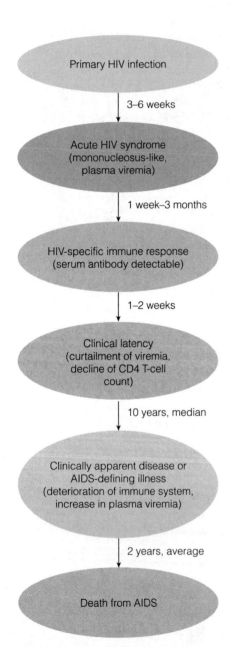

Figure 15.8 *The Natural History of HIV* It may take several years for a person infected with HIV to develop AIDS.

Prior to 1995, most HIV antiviral treatment revolved around drugs that inhibited the activity of reverse transcriptase, an enzyme that HIV requires to transform its RNA (ribonucleic acid) genetic material into DNA (deoxyribonucleic acid)—the first step in viral replication. These drugs prevented the spread of HIV to new cells but did little to stop viral replication in cells that were infected already.

In 1995, the FDA approved a new group of antiviral drugs called **protease inhibitors.** These drugs act against an enzyme, HIV protease, whose function is to break down and reassemble the proteins that infectious viral particles require. When protease is inhibited in infected cells, a noninfectious virus results.

Current treatment regimens called *highly active antiretroviral therapy* (HAART) combine the older reverse transcriptase drugs with the newer protease inhibitors to attack the virus in two ways. HAART is effective, first, in halting the spread of the virus and, second, in reducing viral loads (the amount of HIV RNA in plasma, a direct measure of disease progression) (Division of HIV/AIDS [DHIV/AIDS], 2002b; Ungvarski, 1997).

These advances in treatment have enabled persons infected with HIV to live longer and also have changed the face of the AIDS epidemic. As people live longer with HIV, fewer people develop AIDS and die as a result of HIV infection. In a sense, HIV becomes more of a chronic disease. Nowhere is this more apparent than in the declining death rate for AIDS.

An interesting note regarding HAART relates to its effectiveness in improving the quality of life of people with AIDS. HAART is responsible for increasing not only the life span of AIDS patients but also their daily activity level. Patients often have enough energy and feel well enough to resume most of their daily activities (including sexual activity). This increased level of sexual activity among people with AIDS, coupled with a desensitization to prevention messages, has been implicated in the recent increase in syphilis among MSM in major metropolitan areas in the United States discussed earlier in the chapter (MMWR, 2002b).

Epidemiology Tracking HIV and AIDS is complicated by the fact that while AIDS is a reportable disease by law in all states, HIV reporting is not mandated. HIV incidence and prevalence are usually estimated from extrapolating data from selected serologic testing sites. HIV seropositivity data found at these sites is generalized to the United States population as a whole to estimate the extent of the problem in society. Because AIDS reporting is mandatory, AIDS morbidity and **mortality** data are used to track the condition (DHIV/AIDS, 2002b).

> **Opportunistic infection** An infection that is able to develop as a result of the body's weakened immune status
>
> **Immunocompetence** The level of efficiency of the immune system
>
> **Protease inhibitors** A group of antiviral drugs used to prevent replication of HIV-infected cells
>
> **Mortality** The number of deaths during a specific time period

healthy sex hints 15.3
Should You Take the AIDS Test?

The question about whether to get tested for HIV has concerned many individuals. Where HIV infection and AIDS are concerned, clouds of fear, suspicion, and misunderstanding still loom large in many communities. Fears of being ostracized by family and friends, being kicked out of school, or losing a job have kept many people who suspect exposure to HIV from being tested. In some cases, people simply cannot face the possibility of a positive test and do not want to know.

If you are considering having a screening test for HIV, keep these tips in mind:

- Take your test anonymously in an alternative-site facility where you will be given a number and your name will not be used (some facilities do confidential, not anonymous, testing).

- Make sure the testing site does counseling before and after the test.

- Many college health centers offer HIV testing. Students can also get tested through Planned Parenthood, health departments, and other facilities specifically designed for HIV/STD testing.

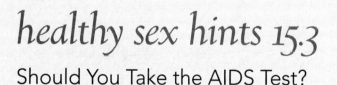

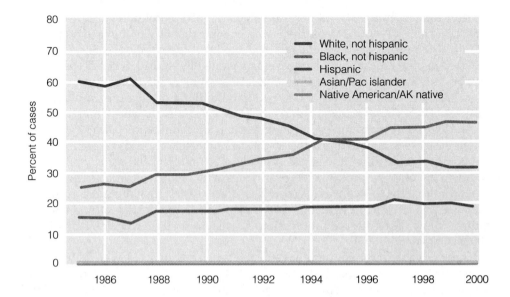

Figure 15.9 *AIDS Cases by Race/Ethnicity* AIDS cases are not equally distributed among all racial/ethnic groups.
Source: DHIV/AIDS (2002a).

As of December 31, 2002, 816,149 persons had been diagnosed with AIDS in the United States. Of the total, there were 666,026 cases in males and 141,048 cases in females. Of those, 57 percent (467,910) have died (DHIV/AIDS, 2002b). Of the prevailing cases, 50,352 (6 percent) were reported during 1981–1987, 203,217 (25 percent) during 1988–1992, 387,517 (47 percent) during 1992–1997, and the remaining 175,063 (22 percent) have been diagnosed since then (MMWR 1991, 1995a; DHIV/AIDS, 2002b).

Three major trends have occurred regarding HIV and AIDS in the past decade:

- Overall AIDS morbidity is down.
- Overall AIDS mortality is down.
- Overall HIV morbidity is down.

Since 1996, there has been a dramatic decline in the number of cases of AIDS. Morbidity declined among all risk groups from 1996 to 1998 but increased slightly from 1998 to 2001 among persons exposed through heterosexual contact (DHIV/AIDS, 2002a). From 1998 to 1999, AIDS incidence leveled

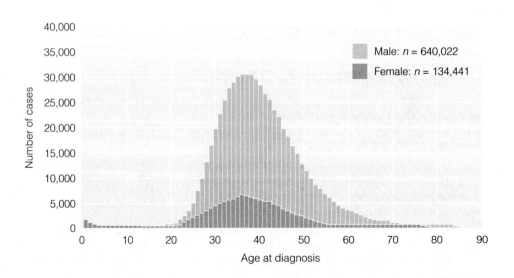

Figure 15.10 *AIDS Cases by Gender* The number of cases of AIDS has dropped dramatically for both men and women.
Source: DHIV/AIDS (2002).

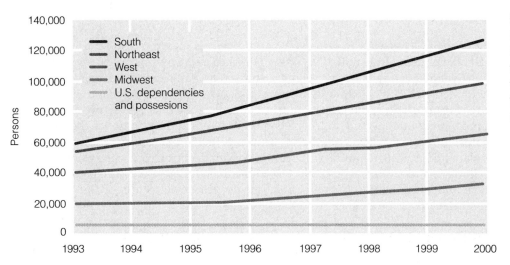

Figure 15.11 *Estimated Number of Persons Living with AIDS* People with AIDS are living longer thanks to more effective treatment regimens.
Source: DHIV/AIDS (2002).

off at around 41,000 cases, and there has been little change in the level of infection since then. AIDS prevalence is estimated at 362,827 persons (see Figures 15.9 and 15.10).

Regionally, AIDS morbidity has mimicked syphilis with all regions except the southern region experiencing a decrease in new cases (see Figure 15.11). AIDS remains a continuing problem of major public health significance, with most new cases occurring among MSM and injectable drug users (Karon, Fleming, Steketee, & DeCock, 2001; DHIV/AIDS, 2002b; MMWR, 2002c).

The number of AIDS deaths also sharply declined in 1996 and has continued to drop every year since then (Figure 15.12). The decline in AIDS deaths is consistent across all regions and all risk groups (DHIV/AIDS, 2002a). This decrease can be attributed mostly to the success of the newest generation of AIDS medications (MMWR, 1995b, 1995c, 1995d). The lowered AIDS death rate has resulted in more people with AIDS surviving the disease than at any time in the past. Lowering the death rate resulted in a slight increase in the prevalence of the condition as more existing cases add into the new cases each year.

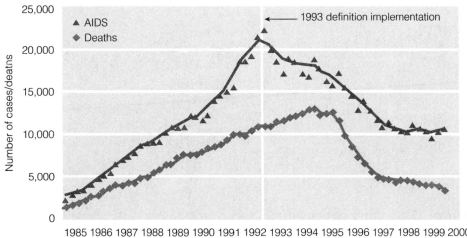

Figure 15.12 *Overall Incidence of AIDS Morbidity and Mortality* Both the number of AIDS cases and the number of AIDS deaths have declined markedly.
Source: DHIV/AIDS (2002).

Hepatitis B Virus (HBV)

Hepatitis B virus (HBV) A disease caused by contact with infected blood; often associated with unprotected sex with multiple partners

Carriers Individuals who have a given disease and are capable of passing it on but have no apparent symptoms

Diagnosis Hepatitis B virus (HBV) infection is another blood-borne disease capable of being transmitted sexually. HBV is a serious viral disease that attacks the liver and can cause extreme illness and even death. To most people, infection with hepatitis B is not clinically apparent. Between 10 and 68 percent of all cases are chronic **carriers;** the infected individuals have the disease and are capable of spreading it but have no noticeable symptoms. When they do notice their symptoms, they usually have jaundice, dark urine, fever, malaise, and moderate liver enlargement with tenderness. Diagnosis is made through a combination of a clinical examination and a blood test indicating the presence of hepatitis B surface antigen (HBsAG). Chronic infection can lead to cirrhosis of the liver and liver cancer.

Treatment HBV infection has no cure because, like HIV, it is caused by a virus. Treatment consists of boosting the strength of the immune system to help the body keep the virus in check. A vaccine for HBV has been available since 1981. At first, the vaccine was recommended for use by those whose work caused them to come in contact with potentially contaminated blood (such as health care workers and those living with persons infected with HBV). It is now recognized that many other persons are potentially at risk through drug-related behavior and sexual activity with infected persons and should consider becoming vaccinated (MMWR, 2002f).

Epidemiology An estimated 5 percent of the U.S. population is infected with HBV, with an estimated 200,000 new infections occurring annually. Of those 200,000 cases, 120,000 are thought to have been acquired through sexual activity with an infected partner. Of those, it is estimated that about 25,000 have acute infection acquired sexually (DSTD, 2000).

The risks associated with HBV infection are gender, age, sexual orientation, IDU status, and race/ethnicity (Figures 15.13 and 15.14). Men have a slightly higher incidence of HBV than women. Part of this is attributed to a higher risk among gay men. Eighteen percent of all HBV cases are among gay men. Hetero-

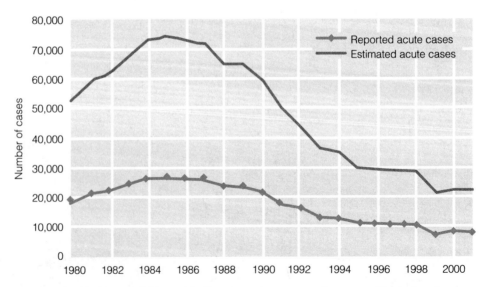

Figure 15.13 *Cases of Hepatitis B* Cases of hepatitis B have steadily declined since the mid-1980s.
Source: NCID (2003).

sexuals (especially those with a history of STDs and multiple sex partners) accounted for 40 percent of all infections. Persons involved with IDU activities accounted for 15 percent of all cases. Health care workers accounted for 2 percent of all cases, and household contact with a person infected with HBV accounted for 3 percent of the cases (National Center for Infectious Disease [NCID], 2003).

Genital Herpes Infection

Diagnosis   **Genital herpes** infection is caused by exposure to the herpes simplex virus type 1 (HSV 1) or herpes simplex virus type 2 (HSV 2) through sexual contact. HSV 1 initially was associated with oral infection and HSV 2 with genital infection. Over the past 25 years, however, the increased popularity of oral sex has led to an almost equal probability of contracting either form from the genital area. A 2- to 12-day incubation period follows transmission of the virus.

The initial symptoms (also known as the primary outbreak) start as discrete grouped **vesicles.** After a short time (a few hours to a few days), the vesicles break open, merge with each other, and form painful ulcers, which drain and crust over. The entire first episode takes 15 to 20 days. Often, a systemic, flulike syndrome accompanies the primary outbreak. The symptoms of this syndrome, known as the **prodrome,** include aches, fever, and malaise.

Recurring outbreaks occur in most sufferers on an average of five to eight times per year and last approximately 10 days per episode. Recurrences often are preceded by the same prodromal syndrome that accompanies the primary episode. The frequency and severity of recurring episodes diminish with time. Genital herpes in adults tends to be a self-limiting, albeit painful, STD. It is a much more serious condition among newborns (infected as they pass through the birth canal) and those whose immune systems are compromised because of HIV infection (MMWR, 2002f; Fleming et al., 1997).

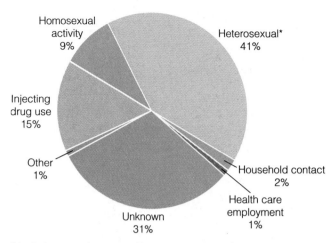

* Includes sexual contact with acute cases, carriers, and multiple partners

Figure 15.14 *Risk Factors for Hepatitis B* The majority of cases of hepatitis B are acquired through injector drug use and sexual activity.

Source: NCID (2003).

Genital herpes An infection caused by exposure to the herpes simplex virus type 1 or type 2 through sexual contact

Vesicles Fluid-filled blisters

Prodrome A systemic, flulike syndrome that accompanies genital herpes infection

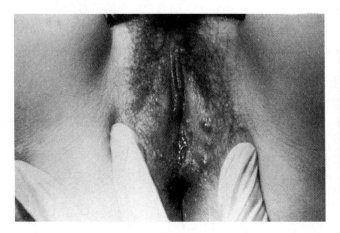

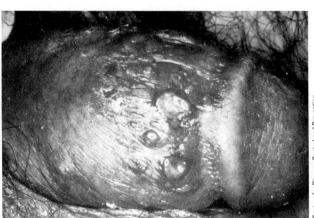

The primary symptoms of herpes are fluid-filled vesicles that break open to form painful, highly infectious ulcers.

Centers for Disease Control and Prevention

case study 15.4

Susan, an HSV Sufferer

Susan, 23, single, is white.

Susan was a woman one of the authors met while conducting a self-help group for persons suffering with genital herpes. Susan had just found out that the ulcerative genital infection she had was caused by HSV. She came to the group to learn how to manage her disease.

I was shocked when my doctor told me I had herpes. I couldn't figure out how I got it, since I've been sexually involved with just my boyfriend for the past 6 months and he doesn't have any symptoms.

The doctor explained that my present boyfriend might not even have given it to me. [The doctor] explained that since I had several other sex partners since beginning to have intercourse at 19 years old, any of those guys could have given it to me. He said I might not have had any initial symptoms or might have missed them because they were so mild.

Now, because I've been stressed out—a new job, graduate school, getting engaged, moving into a house—the herpes is coming back. He suggested that I come here and learn about how to cope with it if I keep getting recurrences. I'm so stressed, but I know this is also the worst thing for me if I want to help my body keep it under control. Please help me!

Critical Thinking

What makes the potential transmission of a past viral condition such as herpes different from a past bacterial infection such as gonorrhea?

Use your Virtual Workbook to explore your answer to this question at **http://health.wadsworth.com/blonna1.**

Treatment Genital HSV infection has no cure. Advances in antiviral therapies, such as acyclovir, have made drugs available that shorten the duration of outbreaks and reduce the number and likelihood of recurrent episodes (Morse et al., 1990). Systemic antiviral drugs such as acyclovir can be used as daily suppressive therapy (suppress the likelihood of an outbreak); however, these drugs do not have lasting effects once discontinued (MMWR, 2002f). As with the other viral STDs, most treatment regimens focus on slowing the replication of the virus and boosting the immune system. Treatment also includes techniques to speed drying and healing of the vesicles and blisters associated with the infection.

Epidemiology Initial consultations with private physicians for genital herpes increased from fewer than 25,000 in 1996 to about 175,000 in 1997 (see Figure 15.15). A similar increase in office visits (from 18,000 to 176,000)—a more accurate index of morbidity—was also noted.

Figure 15.15 *Genital Herpes Consultations*
The number of visits to physicians for genital herpes has increased significantly over the past 40 years.
Source: DSTD (2002b).

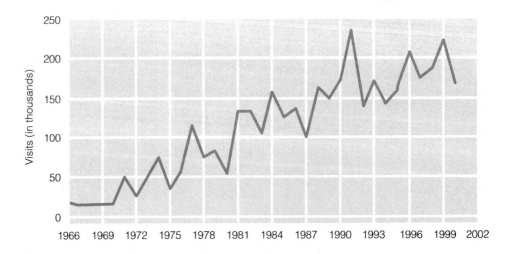

The prevalence of HSV remained relatively stable through the 1990s, with an estimated 45 million people in the United States infected with the virus (DSTD, 2000). The majority of those infected do not have clinical disease. In a broad-based national study, fewer than 10 percent of those who tested positive with the virus knew they were infected (Fleming et al., 1997). Women are at a greater risk than men for acquiring the infection. It is suggested that this is due to the greater efficiency of male to female transmission (DSTD, 2002).

Genital Warts (HPV)

Diagnosis **Genital warts,** also known as venereal warts, are caused by infection with the **human papilloma virus (HPV).** There are at least 46 known varieties of HPV. Of these, at least 12 types of the virus are associated with genital infection. The virus is spread through direct contact with an infected person's genital warts during sexual contact.

The average incubation period for genital warts is 3 months from the time of exposure. The initial warts can be isolated or appear in clusters on the genitals and perianal area. The warts vary in size from 1/8 inch to considerably larger, and in some cases growths become so large that they cause deformity of genital structures. Growths can **autoinnoculate** adjoining tissue. These "kissing lesions" are often found on the labia or under the foreskin of uncircumcised men. Infection with warts is not painful, but continued growth can cause a painful obstruction of the vaginal, anal, or urethral opening.

Estimates of infection with no symptoms vary from 10 to 45 percent of infected individuals (Cates, 1991). Most HPV infections are temporary, and symptoms resolve by the body's immune response. Although studies have shown that most cases of HPV are undetectable after 2 years, reactivation of the virus can occur (DSTD, 2002; Ho, Bierman, Beardsley, Chang, & Burk, 1998).

Genital warts An STD caused by the HPV or human papilloma virus

Human papilloma virus (HPV) A condition spread through direct contact with an infected person's genital warts during sexual contact

Autoinnoculate To self-inflict the spread of disease from one body part to another

healthy sex hints 15.4
Self-Help for People with Genital Herpes

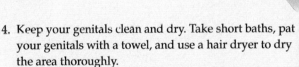

Most people with genital herpes are able to manage their infections and prevent spreading their infection to others. The following tips will help you do just that.

1. If you are taking acyclovir or other herpes medication on a maintenance schedule and it helps reduce recurring episodes of infection, continue taking the medicine as prescribed.
2. At the first hint of prodromal symptoms, consider yourself infectious and capable of spreading your infection. During this time, abstain from intercourse, engage in nongenital sexual pleasuring, or use condoms.
3. Treat any outbreak as you would the flu (another viral infection), with bed rest and over-the-counter pain relievers.
4. Keep your genitals clean and dry. Take short baths, pat your genitals with a towel, and use a hair dryer to dry the area thoroughly.
5. Avoid pantyhose, tight underwear, and binding clothes until the blisters crust over and dry up. If you can, take a day or two off during the worst symptoms, stay in bed, and avoid wearing clothes.
6. Do not cover the blisters with petroleum jelly or other cream that blocks air from drying the area.
7. Minimize stress, as it delays healing.

The genital warts associated with HPV infection can get large enough to block the openings of the urethra, vagina or anus.

Cervical interepithelial neoplasms (CIN) Tumors or growths within the cervical membrane tissues

The major concern associated with HPV is the increased risk for cancer. Cervical infection with HPV is associated with at least 80 percent of all cervical cancer cases (Schiffman, 1992; Woodman et al., 2001). Women with HPV infection of the cervix are 10 times more likely to develop cervical cancer than women without the infection (Schiffman, 1992). As many as 10 percent of women with cervical HPV infections will develop **cervical interepithelial neoplasms (CINs)** within 1 year. HPV types 16, 18, and 31 have been found in all types of genital cancers. HPV 16 is responsible for more than half of all cases of cervical cancer. Four HPV types, 16, 18, 31, and 45, account for 80 percent of all cervical cancer associated with HPV (Ciaran et al., 2003; DSTD, 2000).

Treatment   No medication is available to cure a person of HPV infection, because this is another viral condition. Various forms of treatment, however, are used to remove warts from the skin's surface. Warts do not disappear by themselves. They are removed by applying medications to the warts that dry them out. If this treatment doesn't work, the warts are removed surgically by laser excision, through freezing, or by burning them off.

Epidemiology   An estimated 20 million Americans are infected with HPV. Each year approximately 5.5 million new people are infected in the United States (Ciaran et al., 2003; DSTD, 2000). Recent estimates, based on studies of diverse populations ranging from adolescent high school girls and female students attending college health centers to STD clinic patients, indicate that approximately 1 percent of all Americans are infected with HPV (Moscicki et al., 2000; DSTD 2000).

Women and individuals in the 20- to 24-year-old age bracket constitute the bulk of the visits (see Figure 15.16). Routine testing of women for HPV in four locations yielded the following infectivity percentages:

9 percent of women seeking routine Pap smears at ob/gyn facilities across the United States tested positive;

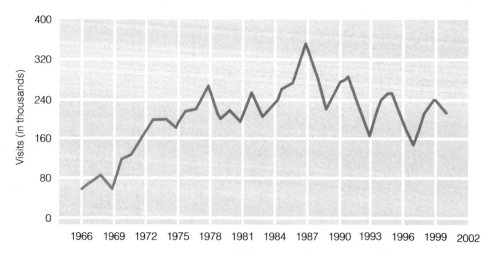

Figure 15.16 *Genital Warts Consultations* The number of visits to physicians for genital warts has leveled off somewhat over the past decade but still remain very high.
Source: DSTD (2002).

between 9 percent and 45 percent of women attending health services in a university health center had positive test results;

23 percent of women attending family planning clinics were positive;

82 percent of street prostitutes in a select study had the virus (Quinn & Cates, 1993).

Moscicki et al. (2000) found that over 50 percent of adolescent girls who were HIV-positive and over 30 percent of those who were HIV-negative tested positive for HPV. HPV may become an even more serious problem among HIV-infected persons than other groups. These individuals have a greater susceptibility to pre-cancerous lesions on the cervix (among heterosexual women) and anus (among gay men) than their non-HIV-infected peers. In one HIV study of gay men, HPV infection was found in 60 percent of those who were HIV-negative and almost 100 percent of those who were HIV-positive (DSTD, 2000).

Chlamydia

Diagnosis   Chlamydia is a sexually transmitted disease caused by the *Chlamydia trachomatis* organism. It is transmitted through contact with infected semen or cervical mucus. It also can be passed through oral contact (usually fellatio) with infected mucus patches in the throat.

During sexual contact, the organisms are passed by person-to-person contact with the infected ejaculate or mucus. Incubation is from 1 to 30 days. The initial symptoms of chlamydia in men are a scanty, clear to milky-white discharge from the penis, and burning upon urination. Some women notice a scanty, clear to milky-white discharge and irritation of the vulva. Seventy-five percent of women and 50 percent of men usually have no symptoms for chlamydia. As previously mentioned, this is why screening sexually active women (and their sex partners) for chlamydia in a variety of health care facilities that serve them is the basis for the government's prevention program for the disease.

Chlamydia trachomatis The most prevalent sexually transmitted bacterial pathogen, causing the STD chlamydia

healthy sex hints 15.5
NAATs: Tests for Chlamydia

A recent advance in chlamydia and gonorrhea testing is the nucleic acid amplification tests (NAATs). These tests detect the presence of chlamydia through DNA testing. They actually identify nucleic acid sequences that are specific to chlamydia. Unlike smear or culture tests, NAATs do not require viable organisms to diagnose the disease. The specimens are easily obtained through urine samples. Patients do not need to be symptomatic to obtain specimens, and samples can be collected anywhere urine collection can be performed. The beauty of NAATs is that it reduces dependence on invasive tests and allows public health programs to expand testing into locations such as schools where other means of testing were unacceptable.

A recent study in a Philadelphia school-based clinic setting demonstrated a yield of more than 20 percent among students tested (Bertrami, 2002).

Another advantage of NAATs is their ability to test for gonorrhea infection at the same time using the same specimen. The same Philadelphia study found that almost half of students infected with chlamydia had coexistent gonorrhea infection. These gonorrhea infections would often go undetected with traditional tests that only checked for chlamydia. The ability to test for both infections simultaneously using an easy-to-obtain urine specimen represents a major breakthrough in STD testing and a major tool in the prevention of gonorrhea and chlamydia (MMWR, 2002d).

PID The acronym for *pelvic inflammatory disease*, a generic term that can apply to any STD that produces the characteristic symptoms of infection

In the 1960s and 1970s, chlamydia infection was believed to be a relatively minor problem. Men with the infection were often referred to as having "nonspecific urethritis" and were not counseled extensively regarding the necessity to have their sexual partners examined. Chlamydia, however, was discovered to be a major source of **PID** (pelvic inflammatory disease). Up to 20 percent of all women with *C. trachomatis* infection will develop PID. PID can result in chronic pain, ectopic pregnancy, and sterility, and in rare instances it is fatal. More than half of all PID is caused by *C. trachomatis.* Infection in men rarely leads to major complications. Less than 1 percent of men infected with *C. trachomatis* develop epididymitis (Morse et al., 1990).

Treatment   Chlamydia infection is relatively easy to treat. Azithromycin (1 gram, taken orally in a single dose) or doxycycline (100 milligrams, taken orally twice a day for 7 days) are the two recommended treatments. The organism is destroyed by a number of antibiotics and alternative treatments (MMWR, 2002f).

Epidemiology   *Chlamydia trachomatis* is the most prevalent sexually transmitted bacterial pathogen in the United States. In 2000, 702,093 cases of chlamydia were reported to the Centers for Disease control from 50 states and the District of Columbia (DSTD, 2001). The chlamydia rate for 2000 was 257.5 cases per 100,000 persons. This represents an increase of 2.3 percent from the rate of 251.6 in 1999. The reported number of chlamydia infections was approximately double the 358,995 reported cases of gonorrhea (DSTD, 2001).

Between 1987 and 2000, the chlamydia rate in the United States increased from 50.8 to 257.5 cases per 100,000 persons (DSTD, 2001). Most experts agree that the continuing increase in reported cases of chlamydia is due to increased screening for this infection and also the development and use of more sensitive screening tests (DSTD, 2001). Figure 15.17 shows the rapid climb in rates during the years 1987–2000.

Although the current estimated incidence is about 3 million cases annually (down from estimates of 4 to 5 million), chlamydia rates continue to rise and represent a serious disease threat because of the asymptomatic nature of infection (Webster et al., 1993). Seventy-five percent of women and 50 percent of men usu-

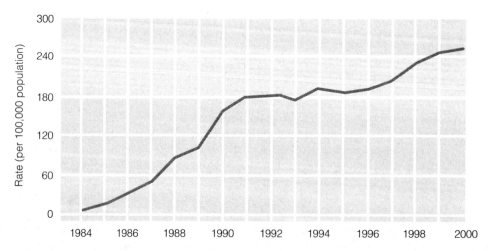

Figure 15.17 *Chlamydia Morbidity* The number of new cases of chlamydia infection continues to rise every year.
Source: DSTD (2002).

ally have no symptoms for chlamydia. This is why screening sexually active women (and their sex partners) for chlamydia in a variety of health care facilities that serve them is the basis for the government's prevention program for the disease. Most public STD and family planning clinics routinely screen all gonorrhea patients for infection with chlamydia trachomatis, since roughly 50 percent of all gonorrhea patients have coexistent infection with chlamydia (Cates et al, 1999).

Reported chlamydia rates in women are much higher because screening programs have typically been directed mostly at women. Most cases of nongonococcal urethritis infection (NGU) are attributed to *C. trachomatis*. Chlamydia exists at endemic levels in young women. More than 40 percent of all cases of chlamydia are among 15- to 19-year-olds. In studies of adolescents, approximately 10 percent of all girls and 5 percent of all boys tested positive for the infection (DSTD, 2000). Chlamydia rates by race/ethnicity show a slightly lower rate for whites than for all other racial/ethnic groups. As with many STDs, rates are highest in the South than in other regions (DSTD, 2002; Karon et al., 2001; Guaschino & DeSeta, 2000).

Gonorrhea

Diagnosis **Gonorrhea** is similar to *C. trachomatis* clinically. Following sexual exposure, the organism incubates from 1 to 30 days. Most people who develop symptoms notice them within 1 to 3 days. The initial symptoms are the same as those associated with chlamydia. Discharge and burning upon urination are the most common symptoms in men. The difference is in the severity of symptoms. Gonorrhea symptoms usually are more severe—heavy discharge, yellowish-green in color, and severe burning. The symptoms usually are enough to cause men with the infection to seek treatment. Up to 20 percent of men have no symptoms. About 50 percent of women infected with gonorrhea are asymptomatic, and a small percentage will notice a discharge or have irritation of the vulva.

In women, gonorrhea often results in complications, the most common of which is PID (pelvic inflammatory disease)—occurring in approximately 15 percent of all women with untreated gonorrhea. These women, as with those who develop PID from chlamydia, have an increased risk for chronic pain, ectopic pregnancy, sterility, and even death. Less than 1 percent of men with untreated gonorrhea develop disseminated gonococcal infection and/or epididymitis (Morse et al., 1990). Like chlamydia, gonorrhea is easy to treat.

Gonorrhea A sexually transmitted disease caused by the bacteria *Neisseria gonorrheae*

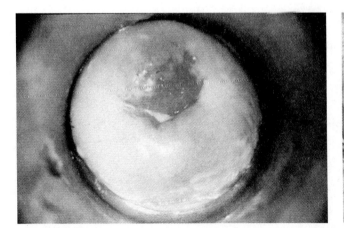
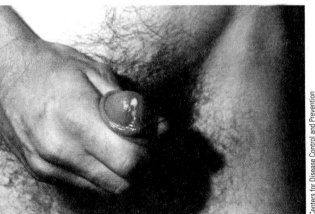

Gonorrhea infection typically produces a profuse, thick, yellow-green discharge, but it can also mimic the milder symptoms of chlamydia. Infection in the cervix, throat, or rectum is often asymptomatic.

Centers for Disease Control and Prevention

Intellectual and Emotional Wellness

High-level intellectual wellness is the cornerstone of effective prevention of STDs. Knowing the risks and how to reduce them is critical to preventing STDs. This knowledge includes information about personal behavior and also about lifestyles and demographic risks. Intellectual wellness also fosters enhanced decision making. Reducing the risks for STD is all about personal choice. Because STDs are sexually transmitted, their prevention and control are more than just a medical matter. STDs involve our most intimate emotions. Knowing about prevention and seeking treatment are one thing. Working through the anxiety, fear, and guilt, and a host of other emotions that interfere with clear thinking about STDs is another thing. Emotional health can help us deal with the emotions that can cloud rational thinking.

Treatment   Recent increases in drug-resistant strains of gonorrhea, particularly those acquired in Asia or the Pacific, including Hawaii, have prompted a change in the recommended treatment for gonorrhea. Single-dose regimens taken either orally or intramuscularly (via a shot) of the following drugs are the recommended treatment: Cefiximine (oral), Ceftriaxone (intramuscularly), Ofloxacin (oral), and Levofloxacin. Because infection with chlamydia often coexists asymptomatically with gonorrhea, the CDC recommends that all persons with gonorrhea who have not had a test to rule out chlamydia be treated for both infections at the time of their gonorrhea diagnosis (MMWR, 2002f).

Epidemiology   Gonorrhea is one of the most common STDs, with more than 350,000 cases reported annually (DSTD, 2002). Because it can be easily diagnosed clinically in a physician's office, public health officials estimate that gonorrhea might be underreported by as much as 50 percent (DSTD, 2000). Between 1975 and 1997 (see Figure 15.18), gonorrhea rates decreased by 72 percent nationally (DSTD, 2002). Of that decline, 22 percent was between 1986 and 1989 and credited largely to safer-sex behaviors by white gay men (Fox, Del Rio, & Holmes, 2001). One of the Healthy People 2010 health status objectives for the nation, reducing gonorrhea rates to 225 cases per 100,000 people, was based on a projection of the continued decline in gonorrhea rates (U.S. Department of Health and Human Services [USDHHS], 2002).

Figure 15.18 *Gonorrhea Rates* Gonorrhea rates seem to have leveled off but still exceed targets set by Healthy People 2010.

Note: The Healthy People 2010 (HP2010) objective for gonorrhea is 19.0 cases per 100,000 population.

Source: DSTD (2002).

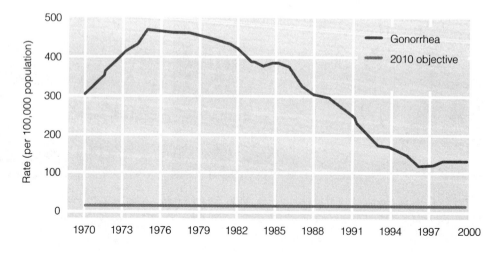

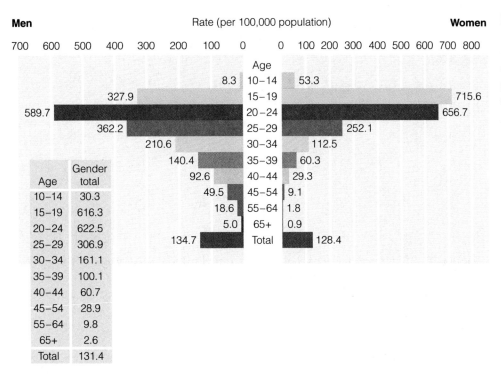

Figure 15.19 *Gonorrhea Rates by Age and Gender* Gonorrhea is endemic among some populations of young men and women.
Source: DSTD (2002).

Since 1997, however, gonorrhea morbidity has been on the rise. Gonorrhea rates have risen 9 percent since 1999 (DSTD, 2002). Experts fear that the 9 percent overall rise in morbidity might actually mask a more serious increase in gonorrhea rates among men who have sex with men. A national program that tracks drug-resistant gonorrhea in 26 major cities across the United States reported that during the period 1994–1999, the proportion of gonorrhea cases among MSM more than doubled, from 6 to 13 percent. In San Francisco, the rate of rectal gonorrhea among men infected with the disease increased from 21 cases per 100,000 to 38 cases per 100,000 for 1994–1997.

These data could indicate a reversal in the adoption of safer-sex practices among this population that spearheaded the dramatic decline in cases a decade ago. It also is an ominous warning of possible changes in HIV morbidity if safe-sex practices among this high-risk group change (DSTD, 2001). Even more alarming is the increase in drug-resistant gonorrhea reported in Hawaii and several clusters within the continental United States (DSTD, 2001).

Figure 15.19 illustrates gonorrhea rates by age and gender. Gonorrhea rates continue to be highest in the 15- to 19- and 20- to 24-year-old age groups for both men and women. The highest rates continue to be among young girls between 15 and 19 years old. Rates among adolescents increased by 13 percent from 1997 to 1999. Rates for these women (regardless of race/ethnicity) are approximately double those of men at this age. Rates for men and women in the 20- to 24-year-old age group are more closely aligned. Rates have increased in all racial/ethnic groups since 1997. The southern states continue to have the highest rates among all regions in the United States (DSTD, 2002).

Nongonococcal Urethritis (NGU)

Diagnosis **Nongonococcal urethritis (NGU)** is diagnosed when *Neisseria gonorrhea* is ruled out as the causative agent of discharge and burning in a male. In most cases, a negative lab test for gonorrhea and the presence of symptoms is

Nongonococcal urethritis (NGU) An infection in the urethra of males, usually caused by chlamydia bacteria

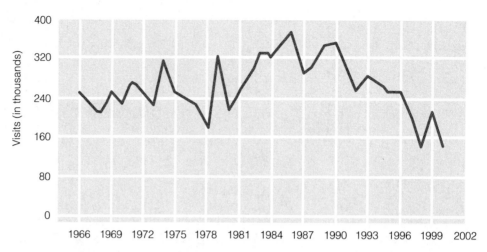

Figure 15.20 *Nongonococcal Urethritis Consultations* The number of visits to private physicians for NGU has dropped in the past decade.
Source: DSTD (2002).

enough to diagnose NGU. NGU is also a surrogate measure of chlamydia in men, as more than half of all cases of NGU are attributable to *C. trachomatis*. In some cases, a test for *C. trachomatis* is done.

Treatment NGU presents the same symptoms as chlamydia infection in men and is treated using the same treatment schedule recommended for chlamydia.

Epidemiology Figure 15.20 illustrates visits to physicians' offices for NGU. Visits to physicians for NGU peaked in 1990 and, except for a slight increase in 1999, declined steadily throughout the decade (DSTD, 2002). Annual incidence of NGU is estimated at approximately 3 million cases annually in the United States (DSTD, 2000).

Pubic Lice

Pubic lice *Phthirius pubis;* small insects (metazoan) that infest the host's pubic hair

Diagnosis Infection with **pubic lice,** commonly called *crabs,* is caused by infestation of *Phthirius pubis.* The lice are transmitted during sexual contact from the infested pubic hair of one person to the other. In rarer instances, the lice are transmitted from contaminated bedding, clothing, and towels that people share. Female lice lay eggs, called *nits,* which attach to the shaft of the pubic hair of the exposed individual. The incubation period for lice is between 24 and 48 hours, at which time the eggs hatch and another batch of lice spread throughout the pubic hair.

Symptoms of pubic lice are (a) visual confirmation of the lice, (b) intense itching of the pubic and perianal area, (c) skin irritation, and (d) secondary sores and erosions from scratching. Although infestation rarely leads to complications, persons with pubic lice sometimes develop secondary infections from their intense scratching.

Treatment Treatment of lice consists of special shampoos that kill the lice on the skin and hair. The shampoos are applied to the affected areas, allowed to sit for up to 10 minutes, and rinsed off thoroughly. Bedding, clothing, and other contaminated articles must be washed and dried thoroughly under hot settings or dry-cleaned. Fumigation of the person's house is not necessary (MMWR, 2002f).

Scabies

Diagnosis   Like crabs, **scabies** is caused by infestation with a mite. This mite, *Sarcoptes scabies*, is transmitted in the same way as pubic lice. Symptoms are similar with one notable exception: *S. scabies* actually burrows under the skin of an infected person and feeds on cellular matter. Diagnosis usually consists of identifying the mite's burrows under the skin.

Treatment   Because of the burrowing of the mites involved in scabies, treatment involves applying a lotion (similar to the shampoos used in pubic lice) that is left on the skin for 8 to 14 hours before being washed off. More than one application of the lotion may be required (MMWR, 2002f).

Scabies A condition caused by the *Sarcoptes scabiei* parasite, which burrows under the skin and lays eggs

Your responses to the Personal Assessment, Thought Questions, and Test Yourself! quiz questions can be logged online in your Virtual Workbook at **http://health.wadsworth.com/blonna1.**

Personal Assessment

15.1 American College Health Association Risk Assessment Form

Many factors must be considered in assessing your health and fitness. Among these are (a) your risk of acquiring or transmitting any sexually transmitted disease (STD) and (b) your use of psychoactive chemicals in connection with sexual activity, a practice that can increase your risk of acquiring an STD. STDs considered here include, but are not limited to, gonorrhea; syphilis; genital herpes; genital warts; chlamydia; hepatitis B; giardiasis; and infection with HIV, the virus that causes AIDS.

The first two questions are biographical in nature and are not part of the risk assessment score. They are intended to guide your provider in making the best possible appraisal of your health. The remaining 11 are the scored behavioral risk assessment. Please be honest in responding to the questions—we assure you that this document will be handled with the utmost confidentiality by you and your health care provider only. Please feel free to discuss the results with your provider. You may retain the survey for your own reference. *In any event, it will not be placed in your medical record.*

There are 11 questions listed below. Please check the one single answer that best describes your preferences or activities.

A. How long have you been sexually active? _____

B. Your most recent consistent sexual partner experience

   male _____ female _____ both male and female _____

1. How many sexual partners *per month* in the last year?
   3 _____ 5 or more
   2 _____ 2–4
   1 _____ 0–1

2. How many partners *per month* in the year previous?
   3 _____ 5 or more
   2 _____ 2–4
   1 _____ 0–1

3. The kinds of sexual contacts I have are
   3 _____ one-time or anonymous "tricks," "one night stands," groups, or prostitutes
   2 _____ multiple times with two or more partners
   1 _____ exclusively with one partner

4. I have sexual encounters or contacts most frequently
   3 _____ in baths, bookstores, parties, "massage parlors," "spas," public restrooms, autos
   1 _____ in my or my partner's home

5. The frequency with which I use drugs or alcohol to enhance my sexual encounters:
   3 _____ frequently
   2 _____ occasionally
   1 _____ rarely/never

   Please circle drug used: "poppers" (amyl or butyl nitrates), alcohol, marijuana, hallucinogens (LSD, mushrooms), "angel dust" (PCP), amphetamines, barbiturates, Quaaludes, ecstasy, eve, cocaine, crack, or (please fill in others)

6. I have injected myself with one or more of the above drugs in the past 5 years.
   4 _____ yes
   1 _____ no

7. I have sexual encounters most frequently in
   3 _____ New York, Los Angeles, San Francisco, Miami, Washington, Dallas, Houston, Newark, Atlanta
   2 _____ other large urban areas (Boston, Philadelphia, St. Louis, Seattle, San Diego, etc.)
   1 _____ small cities, towns, rural areas

8. Those kinds of sexual activities I practice most frequently are (please circle specific activities)
   4 _____ vaginal or anal intercourse without a condom, oral-anal contact (rimming), direct fecal or urine contact (scat or water sports), or manual anal contact (fisting)
   3 _____ "protected" vaginal or anal intercourse (use of condoms and spermicides)
   2 _____ oral-genital contact (fellatio or cunnilingus)
   1 _____ masturbation, massage, body rubbing, kissing

9. My current sexual partner and I have discussed our previous sexual behavior and experiences with each other.
   4 _____ No
   1 _____ Yes

10. I negotiate with sexual partners for safer sexual practices.
    4 _____ No
    2 _____ Sometimes
    1 _____ Yes

11. I ask potential sexual partners about their use of drugs and steroids, especially their use of needles.
    4 _____ No
    2 _____ Sometimes
    1 _____ Yes

Add up the numbers from each question (1–11) and see the key below to determine your level of risk.

My score is _____.

If you answered "1" (the last option) for question 8, deduct 3 points.

Total Adjusted Score: _____

Key:

17 or more: You appear to be at high risk for developing STDs, including HIV infection, and for possibly developing dependence on psychoactive substances. You should visit your health care provider immediately to discuss your risk of these dangers.

12–16 points: You appear to be at moderate risk for developing either an STD or chemical dependence and are encouraged to lower your overall risk by altering the behaviors that resulted in high scores on some of the questions. See your health care provider for any questions or concerns you may have regarding your risk.

11 points: You are at low risk for problems and are encouraged to continue your healthy behavior. Please feel free to contact your health care provider at any time for updated information regarding safer sex, AIDS, or any other issues.

This scoring system was designed to (a) increase your awareness of STDs and the risk factors associated with acquiring or transmitting STDs, (b) stimulate self-evaluation of your health and your sexual lifestyle, and (c) encourage your taking responsibility for your health and the health of your sexual contacts. **This questionnaire is yours to keep and review. It will not go into your medical record even if you bring it to your health care provider.**

Source: Reprinted from the special report, "AIDS on the College Campus" (no longer in print), by Leland G. Wessell, M.D., M.P.H., with permission from the American College Health Association, PO Box 28937, Baltimore, MD 20840-8937.

Thought Questions

1. What are the various modes of transmission associated with STDs/HIV?

2. What are four major trends associated with STDs over the past two decades?

3. What is the underlying premise of the Pyramid of Risk for STDs?

4. How are demographic variables related to the risk for STD/HIV?

5. What are five important things to know about a potential sex partner's sexual history as related to STD/HIV risk?

6. How do sexual lifestyles and sexual behavior work together to increase or decrease risk?

7. What are the major signs and symptoms of STDs in men and women?

8. Why do gay men and heterosexual women have a similar risk profile?

Test Yourself!

1. Which group is not experiencing an increase in STD morbidity and mortality?
   a. Urban, heterosexual, African Americans
   b. Rural homosexual men
   c. Hispanic adolescents
   d. Female partners of HIV-infected intravenous drug users

2. *Epidemiological synergy* refers to
   a. the proliferation of STDs that cause damage to the epidermis.
   b. a synergestic effect caused by two different germs.
   c. the increased risk for acquiring an STD if already infected with one.
   d. a pattern of rampant disease spread through populations.

3. The Pyramid of Risk for STDs assumes that
   a. there are four levels of STD risk; some can be changed, some cannot.
   b. disease risk is like a pyramid or iceberg.
   c. those at the top of the risk pyramid have the greatest chance of becoming infected.
   d. there are five levels of risk that correspond to demographics.

4. Which best characterizes the risk associated with sexual lifestyle and sexual behaviors?
   a. They are two separate risk categories that do not relate to each other.
   b. The lower your STD lifestyle risk, the less attention you need to pay to specific sexual behaviors.
   c. The higher your STD lifestyle risk, the less attention you need to pay to specific sexual behaviors.
   d. Sexual medical history does not impact sexual lifestyle risk.

5. Which of the following is *not* an STD risk associated with one's sexual medical history?
   a. Number of lifetime sexual partners
   b. History of contraceptive use
   c. Immunization status
   d. Age of onset of sexual intercourse

6. The belief that "when you sleep with someone, you sleep with everyone they have slept with" is inaccurate because
   a. it is a simplistic metaphor.
   b. your partner's sex partners had sex with him or her, not you.
   c. being exposed to antibodies that your partner produced in relation to their sex partners is not the same thing as having sex with those people.
   d. all of the above

7. Which of the following is *not* a viral STD?
   a. Syphilis
   b. HIV
   c. HPV
   d. Genital herpes

8. Why do gay men and heterosexual women share a similar STD risk profile?
   a. They both are sexually attracted to heterosexual men who carry most STDs.
   b. They are insertive sexually.
   c. They are receptive sexually.
   d. Their primary sex partners are men.

9. Which of the following is most responsible for the pattern of decreasing AIDS mortality?
   a. The sexual behavior of HIV high-risk groups has changed.
   b. Cocktail AIDS drugs are used.
   c. Less virulent strains of HIV now predominate.
   d. Most people with AIDS have already died.

10. Which STD is making a comeback in selected major U.S. cities after being on the verge of extinction in the past 5 years?
    a. Smallpox
    b. Syphilis
    c. Scabies
    d. Chancroid

Media Menu

You can link to the following online tools by visiting
http://health.wadsworth.com/blonna1.

Face to Face Video

Debbie shares her experience of living with AIDS.

Film

HIV/AIDS Client Support

 InfoTrac Activity

Levine, H. (2001, August). Should you come clean about your sexual history? *Cosmopolitan, 231*(2), 146–150.

 Web Resources

The Division of STD Prevention

www.cdc.gov/nchstp/dstd/dstdp.html

The Division of STD Prevention, at the Centers for Disease Control and Prevention, provides national leadership through research, policy development, and support of effective services to prevent STDs (including HIV infection) and their complications such as enhanced HIV transmission, infertility, adverse outcomes of pregnancy, and reproductive tract cancer.

The Division of HIV/AIDS Prevention

www.cdc.gov/hiv/dhap.htm

CDC's HIV mission is to prevent HIV infection and reduce the incidence of HIV-related illness and death, in collaboration with community, state, national, and international partners.

University of Pittsburgh Student Health Services

www.studhlth.pitt.edu/about.html

A site that provides a variety of information that encourages healthy lifestyles, including an online self-assessment for STD risk.

American Social Health Association (ASHA)

www.ashastd.org

A nonprofit organization dedicated to stopping sexually transmitted diseases and their consequences. The site offers excellent links and information to other ASHA programs. It provides STD information, facts and questions, sexual health glossary, and support groups sections.

Gay Men's Health Crisis

www.gmhc.org/

A nonprofit organization providing support services to men, women, children, and their families with AIDS in the New York City area, as well as education and advocacy nationwide.

Herpes Resource Center (HRC)

www.ashastd.org/herpes/hrc.html

Accurate information about herpes simplex virus infections. This site offers a wide selection of good herpes links. HRC provides questions and answers, how to tell your partner, when to tell your partner, and issues of herpes and pregnancy.

References

Alan Guttmacher Institute. (1991). *Sex and America's teenagers.* New York: Author.

Alter, M., & Margolis, H. (1990). The emergence of hepatitis B as a sexually transmitted disease. *Medical Clinics of North America, 6,* 1529–1541.

American Medical Association, Council on Scientific Affairs. (1996). Health care needs of gay men and lesbians in the United States. *Journal of American Medical Association, 257,* 1354–1359.

Bertrami, R. (2002, November). *Chlamydia screening in the Philadelphia public schools.* Paper presented at the annual Meeting of the American Public Health Association, Philadelphia.

Cameron, D. W., et al. (1991). Condom use prevents genital ulcers in women working as prostitutes: Influences of human immunodeficiency virus infection. *Sexually Transmitted Diseases, 18,* 188–194.

Cates, W., et al. (1999). Estimates of the incidence and prevalence of sexually transmitted diseases in the United States. *Sexually Transmitted Diseases, 26*(Supplement): S2–S7.

Cates, W., & Stone, K. M. (1992). Family planning, sexually transmitted diseases and contraceptive choice: A literature update—Part I. *Family Planning Perspectives, 24*(2), 75–84.

Ciaran, B. J., Woodman, S. C., Rollason, T. P., Winter, H., Bailey, A., Yates, M., & Young, L. S. (2003, January 4). Human papillomavirus type 18 and rapidly progressing cervical intraepithelial neoplasia: Mechanisms of disease. *The Lancet, 361*(9351), 40.

Ciesielski, C. A., Flynn, J., & McLean, C. (2002, October). *B1B—Sexually transmitted diseases, HIV testing, and HIV risk behaviors among men who have sex with men seeking care at Howard Brown Health Center.* Paper presented at Annual DSTD Meeting.

Conant, M., Hardy, D., Sernatinger, J., Spicer, D., & Levy, J. (1986). Condoms prevent transmission of AIDS-associated retrovirus. *Journal of the American Medical Association, 255,* 1706.

Dan, B. D. (1996). Sex and the singles whirl: The quantum dynamics of hepatitis B. *Journal of the American Medical Association, 256*(10), 1344.

Darrow, W. W. (1989). Condom use and use-effectiveness in high-risk populations. *Sexually Transmitted Diseases, 16,* 157–162.

Darrow, W. W., Barrett, D., McPhil, K. J., & Young, A. (1981). The gay report on sexually transmitted diseases. *American Journal of Public Health, 71*(9), 1004–1011.

Division of HIV/AIDS, Division of STD Prevention. (2002a). Cumulative AIDS cases through 12/02 [Online]. Available: www.cdc.gov/hiv/stats.htm#cumaids.

Division of HIV/AIDS, Division of STD Prevention. (2002b). *Surveillance report, 2001: Year-end edition, 12/01.* Atlanta: Public Health Service.

Division of STD Prevention, Centers for Disease Control and Prevention. (1999). *The national plan to eliminate syphilis from the United States.* Atlanta: Public Health Service.

Division of STD Prevention, Centers for Disease Control and Prevention. (2000). *Tracking the hidden epidemics: Trends in STDs in the United States 2000.* Atlanta: Public Health Service.

Division of STD Prevention, Centers for Disease Control and Prevention. (2001). *Sexually transmitted disease surveillance report 2000.* Atlanta: Public Health Service.

Division of STD Prevention, Centers for Disease Control and Prevention. (2002). *Sexually transmitted disease surveillance report 2001.* Atlanta: Public Health Service.

Division of TB Elimination, Centers for Disease Control. (2001.) *Surveillance report: Executive summary.* Atlanta: Public Health Service.

Donelan, K., Blendon, R. J., Hill, C. A., et al. (1996). Whatever happened to the health insurance crisis in the United States? Voices from a national survey. *Journal of the American Medical Association, 276,* 1346–1350.

Dunn, R. A., & Rolfs, R. T. (1991). The resurgence of syphilis in the United States. *Current Opinions in Infectious Diseases, 4,* 3–11.

Eng, T. R., & Butler, W. T. (Eds.). (1997). *The hidden epidemic: Confronting STDs.* Washington, DC: Academy Press, Institute of Medicine.

Finelli, L., Budd, J., & Spitalny, K. (1993). Early syphilis: Relationships to sex, drugs, and changes in high-risk behavior from 1987–1990. *Sexually Transmitted Diseases, 2,* 89–95.

Fleming, D. T., McQuillan, G. M., Johnson, R. E., Nahmias, A. J., Aral, S. O., Lee, F. K., & St. Louis, M. E. (1997). Herpes simplex virus type 2 in the United States, 1976 to 1994. *New England Journal of Medicine, 337,* 1105–1111.

Fox, K. K., Del Rio, C., & Holmes, K. K. (2001). Gonorrhea in the HIV era: A reversal in trends among men who have sex with men. *American Journal of Public Health, 91,* 907–914.

Garnett, G. P., & Anderson, R. M. (1996). Core-group transmission of STDs. *Sexually Transmitted Diseases, 20*(4), 181–191.

Grimes, D. A., & Cates, W. (1990). Family planning and sexually transmitted diseases. In K. K. Holmes, P. A. Mardh, P. F. Sparling, P. Wiesner, W. Cates, S. M. Lemon, & W. E. Stamm (Eds.), *Sexually transmitted diseases* (2nd ed., pp. 1087–1094). New York: McGraw-Hill.

Guaschino, S., & DeSeta, F. (2000). Update on *Chlamydia trachomatis* [review]. *Annals of the New York Academy of Science, 900,* 293–300.

Hart, G. (1974). Factors influencing venereal infection in a war environment. *British Journal of Venereal Disease, 50,* 68–72.

Hayes, R. J., Schulz, K. F., & Plummer, F. A. (1995). The cofactor effect of genital ulcers on the per-exposure risk of HIV transmission in sub-Sahara Africa. *Journal of Tropical and Medical Hygiene, 98,* 1–8.

Ho, G. Y. F., Bierman, R., Beardsley, L., Chang, C. J., & Burk, R. D. (1998). Natural history of cervicovaginal papilloma virus infection in young women. *New England Journal of Medicine, 338,* 423–428.

Howard, M., & McCabe, J. B. (1990). Helping teenagers postpone sexual involvement. *Family Planning Perspectives, 22,* 21–26.

Karon, J. M., Fleming, P. L., Steketee, R. W., & DeCock, K. M. (2001). HIV in the United States at the turn of the century: An epidemic in transition. *American Journal of Public Health, 91*(7), 1060–1068.

Kennedy, M. B., Scarlett, M. I., Duer, A. C., & Chu, S. Y. (1995). Assessing HIV risk among women who have sex with women: Scientific and communication issues. *Journal of the American Medical Women's Association, 50,* 103–107.

Laumann, E. O., Gagnon, J. H., Michael, R. Y., & Michaels, S. (1994). *The social organization of sexuality: Sexual practices in the United States.* Chicago: University of Chicago Press.

Mann, J., Quinn, T., et al. (1987). Condom use and HIV infection among prostitutes in Zaire [letter]. *New England Journal of Medicine, 316,* 345.

Minuk, G., Bohme, G., & Bowen, T. (1986). Condoms and hepatitis B virus infection. *Annals of Internal Medicine, 104,* 584.

MMWR. (1991). The HIV/AIDS epidemic: The first 10 years. *Mortality and Morbidity Weekly Report, 40,* 22.

MMWR. (1995a, November 24). First 500,000 cases of AIDS—United States. *Mortality and Morbidity Weekly Report, 44.*

MMWR. (1995b, July 14). HIV: Preventing the spread of opportunistic infections. *Mortality and Morbidity Weekly Report, 44.*

MMWR. (1995c, July 7). Preventing HIV infection in women and children. *Mortality and Morbidity Weekly Report.*

MMWR. (1995d, June 2). Update: Trends in AIDS among men who have sex with men—United States, 1989–94. *Morbidity and Mortality Weekly Report, 44.*

MMWR. (1999). Resurgent bacterial sexually transmitted disease among men who have sex with men—King County, Washington, 1997–1999. *Morbidity and Mortality Weekly Report, 48,* 773–777.

MMWR. (2002a). Gonorrhea—United States, 1998. *Morbidity and Mortality Weekly Report, 49,* 538–542.

MMWR. (2002b, September 27). Primary and secondary syphilis among men who have sex with men, NYC 2001. *Morbidity and Mortality Weekly Report, 51*(38), 853–856.

MMWR. (2002c, August 17). Provisional cases of selected notifiable disease. *Morbidity and Mortality Weekly Report, 51,* 746–754.

MMWR. (2002d, October 18). Screening tests to detect chlamydia and gonorrhea infections. *Morbidity and Mortality Weekly Report, 51* (RR-15).

MMWR (2002e, September 27). Trends in sexual risk behaviors among high school students—United States, 1991–2001. *Morbidity and Mortality Weekly Report, 51*(38), 853–856.

MMWR. (2002f, May). 2002: Sexually transmitted disease: Treatment guidelines. *Mortality and Morbidity Weekly Report, 51* (RR-6).

Morse, S., Moreland, A., & Thompson, S. (1990). *Sexually transmitted diseases.* New York: Gower Medical.

Moscicki, A. B., Ellenberg, J. H., Vermund, S. H., Hooland, C. A., Darragh, T., Crowley-Nowick, P. A., et al. (2000, February). Prevalence of and risks for cervical human papillomavirus infection and squamous intraepithelial lesions in adolescent girls. *Archives of Pediatrics & Adolescent Medicine, 154*(2), 127.

Nakashima, A. K., Rolfs, R. T., Flock, M. L., et al. (1996). Epidemiology of syphilis in the United States, 1941–1993. *Sexually Transmitted Diseases, 23*(1), 16–23.

National Center for Infectious Disease. (2003). Hepatitis surveillance 1980–2001 [Online]. Available: www.cdc.gov/ncidod/diseases/hepatitis/resource/dz_burden02.htm.

Navarro, N. (1990). Race or class: Mortality differentials in the United States. *Lancet, 336,* 1238–1240.

Pinkerton, S. T., Chesson, H. W., & Layde, P. M. (2002, September). NIMH prevention trial group: Utility of behavioral changes as markers of STD risk reduction in sexually transmitted disease/HIV prevention trials. *Journal of AIDS, 31*(1), 71–79.

Piot, P., & Islam, M. Q. (1994). Sexually transmitted diseases in the 1990s: Global epidemiology and the challenges for control. *Sexually Transmitted Diseases, 21* (Supplement 2), 7–13.

Potterat, R., Rothenberg, R., Woodhouse, D. E., Muth, J. B., Pratts, C. I., & Fogle, J. S. (1985). Gonorrhea as a social disease. *Sexually Transmitted Diseases, 1,* 25–32.

Quinn, T., & Cates, W. (1993). Epidemiology of STDs in the 1990s. In T. Quinn (Ed.), *Sexually transmitted diseases.* New York: Raven.

Ramos, R., Shain, R. N., & Johnson, L. (1995). Men I mess with don't have anything to do with AIDS: Using ethnotheory to understand sexual risk perception. *Sociology Quarterly, 36,* 483–505.

Rice, R. J., Roberts, P. L., & Handsfield, H. H. (1991). Sociodemographic distribution of gonorrhea incidence: Implications for prevention and behavioral research. *American Journal of Public Health, 10,* 1253–1257.

Rosenberg, M. J., & Gollub, E. L. (1992). Commentary: Methods women can use that may prevent sexually transmitted disease, including HIV. *American Journal of Public Health, 82*(11), 1473–1478.

Rutherford, J. (2002, November). *Rise in syphilis among select groups of men who have sex with men.* Paper presented at the annual Meeting of the American Public Health Association, Philadelphia.

Schiffman, N. H. (1992). Recent progress in defining the epidemiology of human papillomavirus infection and cervical neoplasia. *Journal of National Cancer Institute, 84,* 394–398.

Smeltzer, S., & Whipple, B. (1991). Women & HIV. *Journal of Nursing, 4,* 249–256.

St. Louis, M. E., & Wasserheit, J. N. (1998). Elimination of syphilis in the United States. *Science, 281,* 353–354.

Ungvarski, P. J. (1997). Update on HIV infection. *American Journal of Nursing, 97*(1), 44–51.

U.S. Department of Health and Human Services. (2000, November). *Healthy People 2010: Understanding and improving health* (2nd ed.). Washington, DC: U.S. Government Printing Office.

Wasserheit, J. (1992). Epidemiological synergy. *Sexually Transmitted Diseases, 2,* 61–77.

Webster, L. A., Berman, S. M., & Greenspan, M. (1993), Surveillance for gonorrhea and primary and secondary syphilis among adolescents United States, 1981–1991. *Mortality and Morbidity Weekly Report, 42*(SS-3), 1–10.

Webster, L. A., & Rolfs, R. T. (1993). Surveillance for primary and secondary syphilis, United States, 1991. *Mortality and Morbidity Weekly Report, 42*(SS–3), 13–18.

Woodman, C. B., Collins, S., Winter, H., Barley, A., Ellis, J., Prior, P., et al. (2001). Natural history of cervical human papillomavirus infection in young women: A longitudinal cohort study. *Lancet, 357*(9271), 1831–1836.

Zenker, P. (1991). New case definition for congenital syphilis. *STDs, 1,* 44–45.

chapter *sixteen*

Sexual Coercion

Student Learning Objectives

After reading this chapter, students will be able to

- Define *sexual coercion* and *sexual victimization* and the three forms highlighted in this chapter: harassment, rape, and child sexual abuse.

- Explain and give examples of the three conditions that constitute sexual harassment.

- Describe the dynamic of power over subordinates in determining sexual harassment.

- Define *rape,* and differentiate it from other forms of sexual aggression.

- Describe the typical pattern of rape by a stranger, and develop a personal plan to reduce the risk for this form of rape.

- Define *acquaintance rape* and identify the risks.

- Develop a personal plan for reducing the risk for date rape.

- Describe the risks associated with the major "date rape" drugs.

- Assess the impact of alcohol abuse in coercive sex.

- Describe the characteristics of rapists.

- Evaluate common myths associated with rape and rapists.

- Describe the preconditions of child sexual abuse.

- Evaluate ways to reduce the risks for child sexual abuse.

Test your understanding of these objectives by taking the end-of-chapter quiz, available online at ***http://health.wadsworth.com/blonna1.***

activity teaser: *What is the message in the music? Learn more in the Personal Exploration Activity on page 537.*

case study 16.1

Marc: Learning That No Means No

Marc, 23, identifies as Italian American.

Critical Thinking

Assuming that both Marc and the third woman were really interested in *some form* of sexual encounter, how could this scene have ended differently?

Use your Virtual Workbook to explore your answer to this question at **http://health.wadsworth.com/blonna1.**

Marc, a senior, was a student in one of Dr. Blonna's human sexuality classes. He submitted a written assignment about how he learned the difference between yes and no.

I'm embarrassed to write this, but I think the story needs to be told. I grew up learning that when a woman said no, she really meant yes. My brother and his friends explained it to me by saying that women do this so they can remain ladies but still get laid. It made sense to me then, even though I now realize this kind of thinking is crazy.

I didn't encounter this with the first two women I had sex with. They both willingly went along. I went out with my second girlfriend for almost 2 years. When we broke up, I had to start dating again and didn't get anywhere with the first two girls I went out with. They didn't even let me get to first base.

The third woman was very sexy. I met her at a frat party, and she was hot. We danced a little and had a couple of beers, and then she wanted to leave. I walked her back to her room, and she invited me up. Her roommates had gone home for the weekend, and we started making out on the couch. She was so sexy, and I thought she really wanted to have sex. She let me feel her breasts and put my hand in her pants, but every time I tried to unzip her jeans, she pulled away and said no. I figured she was just teasing and really wanted me to continue, so I kept pushing the limit.

After about 20 minutes of this, she suddenly pushed me off of her and literally dumped me on the floor. She screamed at me, "Look, I told you no five times! I don't want to fuck you. Now get out before I call the campus cops!"

I was shocked and very upset. I really didn't want to rape her, just push her until she gave in. I felt embarrassed and wanted to explain how I felt, but she told me if I didn't leave immediately, she'd call the police. I ran out of there zipping up as I left. I've seen her on campus, but she won't even look at me. I learned that no really means no!

As we have seen in the case of Marc, there is a fine line between pursuing sex assertively and sexual coercion. Marc learned firsthand that "No means no," or that line is crossed. **Sexual coercion** is any nonconsensual sexual behavior that occurs as a result of arguing, pleading, and cajoling, in addition to force. **Sexual victimization** occurs when a person is deprived of free choice and is forced to endure, observe, or comply with sexual acts. Coercive sex can take many forms. The commonality is the element of power and victimhood. In this chapter, we focus on three forms: rape (also called sexual assault), sexual harassment, and child sexual abuse. We will start our examination with a look at rape.

Rape

The dictionary definition of **rape** is "sexual intercourse without the consent of the man/woman and effected by force, duress, intimidation or deception as to the nature of the act" (Benton, 1996). The word *rape* comes from the Latin term *rapere*, which means to steal, seize, or carry away. Rape has been a common theme in literature, art, and popular culture throughout history.

Chilling examples of rape occur regularly in cartoons, comic strips, and other "children's entertainment." The caveman, replete with club and knuckles dragging the earth, is out and about to find a mate. When he spies the female he desires, he hits her with the club, knocks her out, and drags her away by her long hair (presumably to make her his wife).

Sexual coercion Any nonconsensual sexual behavior that occurs as the result of arguing, pleading, and cajoling and includes, but is not limited to, force

Sexual victimization Depriving a person of free choice and forcing him or her to endure, observe, or comply with sexual acts

Rape Illicit sexual intercourse without consent

More than 95 percent of rapes are committed by men against women or other men. Although 9 of 10 rapists are men, this does not mean that all men rape, nor are all men potential rapists. If you were to take a sample of 100 rapists, more than 90 would be men. If you were to take a random sample of 100 men, fewer than 10 would be rapists or potential rapists. The statistic does mean, however, that most of the rapes are committed by a small percentage of men who achieve power over women and other men by forced sexual aggression.

Rape is a form **sexual aggression,** a broader term that encompasses all forms of nonconsensual physical sexual activity against men, women, children, and gay people as victims (Cate & Lloyd, 1992). It includes fondling, oral sex, and anal sex, as well as vaginal intercourse. *Sexual coercion*, the broadest term, covers all nonconsensual sexual behavior that results from arguing, pleading, and cajoling, in addition to force.

The term *victim* is gradually being replaced by words such as *target* and *survivor*, in some contexts. This language avoids further degradation of the person who was raped. The new terminology connotes the encouragement for survivors to reclaim control over their lives.

In most states, to be considered rape, the target's body (usually the vagina) has to be penetrated. Forced oral sex and the insertion of fingers and other objects into the vagina, anus, or mouth don't automatically qualify as rape. Although these sexually aggressive acts are still illegal and can result in prosecution, they are tried as less serious offenses than is rape. Rape includes acquaintance rape (also known as date rape), stranger rape, marital rape, gang rape, and statutory rape. A last category of rape, male rape, usually is committed by men against other men but does occur, rarely, with women as the perpetrators.

Sexual aggression Any form of forced sexual contact, including but not limited to intercourse, without the person's consent

Physical Wellness

Men who engage in coercive sex often use their physical strength to intimidate, threaten, and/or overpower their victims. High-level physical wellness may empower women and help prevent becoming victims of coercive sex. Activities such as lifting weights to develop strength and practicing self-defense skills can help women repel would-be attackers. Feeling physically stronger and more prepared to fight might also send nonverbal messages to would-be attackers. Perpetrators are less likely to target women who appear strong, self-assured, and able to defend themselves.

Here are some common myths associated with rape:

Myth: Rape is a sexual act, not a violent one.

Fact: Although the rapist achieves sexual gratification through his actions, the rape is first and foremost an act of violence. If sexual release were all that a rapist desires, he could achieve that by finding a willing partner, masturbating, or paying a prostitute for sex. The rapist seeks to dominate his victim, to exert power, and to humiliate by using threat and violence. In contrast, sex is a consensual act of pleasure, not a violent act of power.

Myth: Women secretly want to be raped.

Fact: Even though many men and women have rape fantasies, there is a world of difference between using fantasy to become sexually aroused and actually desiring to be assaulted, forced to submit to another's sexual onslaught, and humiliated or beaten in the process. In a fantasy, you control the situation, orchestrate the script, and create the happy ending. In a rape, someone assaults you and controls you. Women do *not* want to be raped.

Myth: A woman can't be raped if she really doesn't want to be.

Fact: The logic of this myth revolves around the difficulty surrounding inserting a penis into a vagina that is thrashing to and fro. Men who rape use force to hurt women, to injure them to the point of submission. They have been known to break a woman's hip to stop it from moving. Rape is not about two lovers playfully teasing each other into submission. Rape is about force, domination, and pain.

Myth: Women ask for it by the way they act and dress.

Fact: Women don't dress provocatively to invite rapists. The idea of a woman wanting to attract a man and initiate a sexual liaison by acting in a sexy way is much different from the notion of a woman dressing in revealing clothing because she wants to be raped. If a woman intentionally acts and dresses provocatively to attract a man, that style doesn't give any man the right to rape her.

Myth: *No* really means *yes*.

Fact: Where does the notion that *no* means *yes* come from? Is it a rationalization, made up by men, to justify their domination and overpower women into submission? Or is it a leftover piece of baggage from the Victorian era, reminding women that ladies are not supposed to enjoy sex? In that line of thinking, because a lady can't ask for sex, she has to say no even though she means yes. That way she can have it both ways: maintain her status as a lady and still have sex ("He did it to me"). Wherever this belief came from, it's time to stop it and realize that *no* means *no*. When in doubt, don't continue.

Myth: Rape is justifiable under certain circumstances.

Fact: Rape is never justifiable. No one—husband, lover, boyfriend, father, or any man—ever has the right to force sex on anyone.

Myth: Most rapists are crazy.

Fact: Most rapists are not crazy. They are similar to the average man except for three distinguishing characteristics: (a) They are hostile toward women and have a harder time handling it, (b) they have more traditional beliefs about gender roles, and (c) they are more willing to use force to achieve their ends.

Myth: Women are responsible for preventing rape.

Fact: *Everyone* is responsible for preventing rape.

Posttraumatic Rape Syndrome

An estimated 70 percent of adults in the United States have experienced a traumatic event at least once in their lives, and up to 20 percent of these people go on to develop **posttraumatic stress disorder (PTSD).** PTSD can occur in either victims or witnesses of traumatic events ranging from natural disasters to rape (American Psychiatric Association [APA], 2000). The three main diagnostic criteria for PTSD are (a) reexperiencing the event through dreams, flashbacks, and other means; (b) persistent avoidance of stimuli associated with the event; and (c) persistent symptoms ranging from difficulty falling asleep to irritability and outbursts of anger (APA, 2000).

An estimated 1 out of 10 women will get PTSD at some time in their lives. Women are about twice as likely as men to develop PTSD. This incidence may be due to the fact that women tend to experience interpersonal violence (such as domestic violence, rape, or abuse) more often than men. The estimated risk for developing PTSD for people who have experienced various traumatic events is as follows: rape, 49 percent; severe beating or physical assault, 31.9 percent; other sexual assault, 23.7 percent; serious accident or injury (for example, a car or train accident), 16.8 percent; shooting or stabbing, 15.4 percent; sudden, unexpected death of a family member or friend, 14.3 percent; child's life-threatening illness, 10.4 percent; witness to a killing or serious injury, 7.3 percent.

Posttraumatic stress disorder (PTSD) A syndrome developing after exposure to an extremely traumatic event. Symptoms include anxiety, sleeplessness, eating disorders, depression, and hyperactive nervous system activity.

Burgess and Holmstrom (1974) coined the term *rape trauma syndrome* (RTS) to identify a cluster of emotional responses to the extreme stress experienced by victims of rape. RTS has two phases. The first is the acute (initial) phase, which usually lasts anywhere from a few days to a few weeks after the attack. The next phase is the reorganization phase, which usually lasts anywhere from a few weeks to several days after the attack.

Acquaintance rape, also known as *date rape,* is a form of rape defined as forced sexual intercourse by a dating partner. Many experts consider acquaintance rape to be the most common and least reported of all forms of rape (Cate & Lloyd, 1992). Previous research has shown that college campuses, contrary to public opinion, are not safe havens from sexual coercion. College women are at a greater risk for rape and other forms of sexual assault than women in the general population or in a comparable age group (Fisher, Koss, Gidycz, & Wisnewski, 1987). This is due in part to the nature of the college environment where large concentrations of young women come into contact with young men in a variety of public and private settings at various times on and off their college campuses. Fisher, Cullen, and Turner (2000), in a national study of 4,446 college women, found that almost 3 percent (2.8 percent) of study participants experienced a completed or attempted rape during the academic year. They estimate that women at a college that has 10,000 female students could experience more than 350 rapes a year.

Acquaintance rape Forced intercourse by a person, other than a spouse, whom the victim knows

healthy sex hints 16.1

What to Do If You Are Raped or Sexually Assaulted

What to Do If You Have Been Raped

1. Go to a safe place away from your attacker.
   - Your first concern is your personal safety.
2. Call a friend, family member, or someone else you trust, and ask her or him to stay with you.
3. Go to a hospital emergency department immediately.
   - Preserve all physical evidence of the assault. Do not shower, bathe, douche, brush your teeth, or change your clothes before you go to the hospital.
   - Hospital staff will provide medical care for sexual assault victims.
   - Even if you think that you do not have any physical injuries, you should still have a medical examination and discuss with a health care provider the risk of exposure to sexually transmitted diseases and the possibility of pregnancy resulting from the sexual assault.
4. If you want to report the assault, call your local police department from the hospital.
   - The police department will have trained rape crisis personnel to help you.

- Reporting the crime can help you regain a sense of personal power and control and can also help ensure the safety of other potential victims.
5. If you suspect that you may have been given a rape drug, ask the hospital or clinic where you receive medical care to take a urine sample.
   - The urine sample should be preserved as evidence.
   - Rape drugs, such as Rohypnol and GHB, are more likely to be detected in urine than in blood.
6. Write down as much as you can remember about the circumstances of the assault, including a description of the assailant.
7. Talk with a counselor who is trained to assist rape victims about the emotional and physical impacts of the assault.
   - It will be difficult, but it is important to talk with someone who understands the trauma of rape and knows how to help.

Source: American Academy of Family Physicians (2003).

The Sexual Victimization of College Women

Fischer et al.'s (2000) study, "The National College Women Sexual Victimization Study (NCWSV)," was chartered by the National Institute of Justice, the research arm of the United States Bureau of Justice Statistics. The study is noteworthy for several reasons relating to design, sampling, and questioning methodology.

The NCWSV was designed to overcome the shortcomings of previous studies that attempted to estimate the incidence of sexual victimization of college women. Previous studies were flawed by small sample sizes, nonrandom sampling techniques, delimitating types of sexual victimization studied, and confusing labeling of both the types of sexual victimization under study and the details of the specific incidents reported by subjects.

The study was designed as a telephone survey of 4,446 female college students. Each subject was interviewed over the phone by a trained female interviewer. The study greatly expanded the types of sexual victimization (incidents) under study, including (a) completed rape, (b) attempted rape, (c) completed sexual coercion, (d) attempted sexual coercion, (e) completed sexual contact with force or threat of force, (f) attempted sexual contact with force or threat of force, (g) completed sexual contact without force, (h) attempted sexual contact without force, (i) threat of rape, (j) threat of contact with force or threat of force, (k) threat of penetration with force, and (l) threat of contact with force. These terms are defined in Table 16.1.

The sample for the NCWSV was composed of undergraduate and graduate women attending 2- or 4-year institutions across the United States during the fall 1996 semester. The sample was stratified to include students from all sized institutions (1,000–2,499; 2,500–4,999; 5,000–19,999; and 20,000 or more) and locations (urban, suburban, and rural). Schools were randomly chosen from a probability proportional to total female enrollment. Subjects were then randomly chosen from the institutions picked for the study (Fisher et al., 2000).

A key methodological issue that is credited for the study's success was its use of a two-tiered questioning approach. Subjects were initially queried with a set of "screening" questions that identified whether the subject had experienced a sexual victimization event.

Screening questions were very graphic in their depiction of the potential sexual victimization events. For instance, the first screening question was "Since school began in fall 1996, has anyone made you have sexual intercourse by using force or threatening to harm you or someone close to you? Just so there is no mistake, by *intercourse* I mean putting a penis in your vagina." No previous sexual victimization surveys used such specific screening questions that, in a sense, operationally defined the event under study. Such specific wording left little doubt for subjects regarding the nature of the question being asked and contributed to higher response rates.

If a woman answered yes to the screening question, the interviewer asked a series of "incident report" questions that described in detail the nature of the event. Incident report questions covered all aspects of the event, ranging from the relationship of the perpetrator to the subject, the environment in which the event occurred, whether the victim used force to repel the perpetrator, and additional details.

Key Findings of the NCWSV As previously mentioned, the most startling finding of the study was the overall high incidence of sexual victimization and attempted sexual victimization among college women. Overall, 2.8 percent of the sample had experienced either a completed rape (1.7 percent) or an attempted rape (1.1 percent). This accounts for a rape victimization rate of 27.7 rapes per 1,000 female students (Fisher et al., 2000). The actual rate of the overall incidence

Table 16.1 Descriptions of Types of Victimizations

Type of Victimization	Definition
Completed rape	Unwanted completed penetration by force or the threat of force. Penetration includes penile-vaginal, mouth on your genitals, mouth on someone else's genitals, penile-anal, digital-vaginal, digital-anal, object-vaginal, and object-anal.
Attempted rape	Unwanted attempted penetration by force or the threat of force. Penetration includes penile-vaginal, mouth on your genitals, mouth on someone else's genitals, penile-anal, digital-vaginal, digital-anal, object-vaginal, and object-anal.
Completed sexual coercion	Unwanted completed penetration with the threat of non-physical punishment, promise of reward, or pestering/verbal pressure. Penetration includes penile-vaginal, mouth on your genitals, mouth on someone else's genitals, penile-anal, digital-vaginal, digital-anal, object-vaginal, and object-anal.
Attempted sexual coercion	Unwanted attempted penetration with the threat of non-physical punishment, promise of reward, or pestering/verbal pressure. Penetration includes penile-vaginal, mouth on your genitals, mouth on someone else's genitals, penile-anal, digital-vaginal, digital-anal, object-vaginal, and object-anal.
Completed sexual contact with force or threat of force	Unwanted completed sexual contact (not penetration) with force or the threat of force. Sexual contact includes touching, grabbing or fondling of breasts, buttocks, or genitals, either under or over your clothes; kissing, licking, or sucking; or some other form of unwanted sexual contact.
Completed sexual contact without force	Any type of unwanted completed sexual contact (not penetration) with the threat of nonphysical punishment, promise of reward, or pestering/verbal pressure. Sexual contact includes touching, grabbing or fondling of breasts, buttocks, or genitals, either under or over your clothes; kissing, licking, or sucking; or some other form of unwanted sexual contact.
Attempted sexual contact with force or threat of force	Unwanted attempted sexual contact (not penetration) with force or the threat of force. Sexual contact includes touching, grabbing or fondling of breasts, buttocks, or genitals, either under or over your clothes; kissing, licking, or sucking; or some other form of unwanted sexual contact.
Attempted sexual contact without force	Unwanted attempted sexual contact (not penetration) with the threat of nonphysical punishment, promise or reward, or pestering/verbal pressure. Sexual contact includes touching, grabbing or fondling of breasts, buttocks, or genitals, either under or over your clothes; kissing, licking, or sucking; or some other form of unwanted sexual contact.

(continued)

Table 16.1 Descriptions of Types of Victimizations *(continued)*

Type of Victimization	Definition
Threat of rape	Threat of unwanted penetration with force and threat of force. Penetration includes penile-vaginal, mouth on your genitals, mouth on someone else's genitals, penile-anal, digital-vaginal, digital-anal, object-vaginal, and object-anal.
Threat of contact with force or threat of force	Threat of unwanted sexual contact with force and threat of force. Sexual contact includes touching, grabbing or fondling of breasts, buttocks, or genitals, either under or over your clothes; kissing, licking, or sucking; or some other form of unwanted sexual contact.
Threat of penetration without force	Threat of unwanted penetration with the threat of non-physical punishment, promise of reward, or pestering/verbal pressure. Penetration includes penile-vaginal, mouth on your genitals, mouth on someone else's genitals, penile-anal, digital-vaginal, digital-anal, object-vaginal, and object-anal.
Threat of contact without force	Threat of unwanted sexual contact with the threat of non-physical punishment, promise or reward, or pestering/verbal pressure. Sexual contact includes touching, grabbing or fondling of breasts, buttocks, or genitals, either under or over your clothes; kissing, licking, or sucking; or some other form of unwanted sexual contact.

Source: Fisher, Cullen, and Turner (2000, p. 8).

of rape was actually 35.3 rapes per 1,000 women. This is due to the fact that some women in the study were actually raped or had experienced attempted rape more than one time during the 7-month study period. The 35.3/1,000 rate is what projects out to an estimated 350 rapes per year among 10,000 college women in any given university (Fisher et al., 2000).

Another disturbing finding of the study was the small percentage of women who actually defined their victimization as rape (even though they said yes when asked whether someone had "by force or threat put their penis into your vagina"). Fisher et al. (2000) explain that this reluctance may be due to reasons such as feeling embarrassed, not clearly understanding the legal definition of rape, or being reluctant to label someone they are intimate with and who victimized them as a rapist (Fisher et al., 2000).

A third finding of the study was the overall incidence of other forms of sexual victimization. As Table 16.2 shows, when other forms of sexual victimization were studied, the rates varied from 9.5 to 66.4 cases per 1,000 women. The types of sexual victimization ranged from threats of rape and sexual contact to completed sexual coercion.

Figure 16.1 shows that the overall percentage of women who were sexually victimized in the study exceeded 15 percent (Fisher et al., 2000).

A fourth finding of the study was the relationship of the perpetrator to the victim. For both completed and attempted rape, 9 out of 10 women knew the perpetrator. The relationships most often cited were a boyfriend, ex-boyfriend, classmate, friend, acquaintance, or coworker. College professors were not cited in any of the completed or attempted rapes (Fisher et al., 2000).

Table 16.2 Rates of Sexual Victimization

Type of Victimization	Victims			Incidents	
	Number of Victims in Sample	Percentage of Sample	Rate per 1,000 Female Students	Number of Incidents	Rate per 1,000 Female Students
Completed or attempted					
Completed sexual coercion	74	1.7	16.6	107	24.1
Attempted sexual coercion	60	1.3	13.5	114	25.6
Completed sexual contact with force or threat of force	85	1.9	19.1	130	29.2
Completed sexual contact without force	80	1.8	18.0	132	29.7
Attempted sexual contact with force or threat of force	89	2.0	20.0	166	37.6
Attempted sexual contact without force	133	3.0	29.9	295	66.4
Threats					
Threat of rape	14	0.31	3.2	42	9.5
Threat of contact with force or threat of force	8	0.18	1.8	50	11.3
Threat of penetration without force	10	0.22	2.3	50	11.3
Threat of contact without force	15	0.34	3.4	75	16.9
Total	568			1,161	

Source: Fisher et al. (2000, p. 16).

The vast majority of the rapes occurred after midnight and on campus in the victim's residence, in other living quarters on campus, or at a fraternity house. Risk factors positively associated with rape were (a) frequently drinking to get drunk, (b) being unmarried, (c) having a history of a previous sexual assault, and (d) living on campus. The vast majority of women reported that they did not suffer physical or emotional injuries as a result of the completed or attempted rape. About one in five reported being injured (20 percent). The percentages for other forms of sexual victimization were lower, ranking from 0 percent (completed sexual contact without force) to 17 percent (threatened rape) (Fisher et al., 2000).

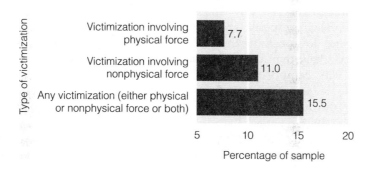

Figure 16.1 *Percentage of Women Sexually Victimized*

Source: Fisher et al. (2000, p. 17).

Environmental Wellness

High-level environmental wellness implies safety, security, and respect. A safe home environment includes appropriate parenting, setting boundaries for behavior, and getting help with emotional problems. A neighborhood that offers high-level environmental wellness is well lit and policed, and it has neighbors looking out for one another. The schools are safe and do not tolerate sexual harassment and discrimination. The community has safe playgrounds and parks that are well patrolled and not inviting for sex offenders. A college that offers high-level environmental wellness is a microcosm of any community. It has policies and procedures in place for dealing with harassment and discrimination and offers safety and protection. Its students don't fear walking to their cars after class or attending social functions. In addition, enforcement is swift, fair, and equal for all on campus.

Drinking and Date Rape

Many college students use alcohol and other drugs to "fit in," cope with college stressors, and reduce inhibitions related to dating and sex. Unfortunately, alcohol consumption is often linked to sexual coercion and other forms of violence. The National Advisory Council on Alcohol Abuse and Alcoholism's Report on College Drinking estimates that more than 70,000 students are the victims of alcohol-related sexual victimization (sexual assault and rape) (Task Force, 2002).

Often, this alcohol is consumed in large quantities for the express purpose of getting drunk. Weschler, Davenport, Dowdell, Moeykens, and Castillo (1994) coined the term **binge drinking** to describe such a pattern of alcohol consumption. Binge drinking is operationally defined as "having five or more drinks in a row, at least once during the previous 2 week period" (Weschler et al., 1994, p. 1673). The greatest predictors of binge drinking were living in a fraternity or sorority house, engaging in drinking games, and living a "party-centered" lifestyle (Weschler et al., 1994).

Bingeing on alcohol often becomes part of the social fabric of the college experience. Weschler et al. (1994) studied the binge drinking behavior of more than 17,000 students on 140 four-year college campuses across the United States. About one in six (16 percent) of all the respondents were nondrinkers (15 percent of the men, 16 percent of the women). About two in five (41 percent) were drinkers but did not binge. Almost half (44 percent) of all the students were binge drinkers. About one in five (19 percent) were frequent binge drinkers (17 percent of the women and 23 percent of the men). These students had three or more binge drinking episodes within the past 2 weeks.

Weschler and colleagues found binge drinking to be associated with unplanned and unsafe sexual activity, physical and sexual assault, other criminal violations, physical injury, interpersonal problems, and poor academic performance. Binge drinkers were more likely than nonbinge drinkers and abstainers to engage in unplanned sexual activity, not use protection when having sex, get hurt or injured, damage property, argue with friends, miss classes, get behind in schoolwork, and do something they later regretted. Frequent binge drinkers were 10 times more likely than bingers to have unplanned and unprotected sex, get into trouble with campus police, and get injured or damage property. When asked to evaluate the seriousness of their bingeing and its repercussions, less than 1 percent of the binge drinkers designated themselves as problem drinkers (Weschler et al., 1994).

In a follow-up study, Weschler, Eun, Kuo, Sebring, Nelson, and Lee (2002) found that 1 percent of students living in residence halls or fraternity and sorority

Binge drinking Having four or more drinks at one sitting

houses were victims of alcohol-related sexual assault and/or rape. About 20 percent of students experienced alcohol-related threats and and/or attempted sexual contacts.

Despite the overall decline in drinking among all adults in the United States over the past two decades, drinking on college campuses fails to show a corresponding dropoff. Drinking by college students often revolves around its social nature. College women perceive drinking as a way of being around others and seeking the acceptance of peers (Gleason, 1994). Alcohol is consumed more for social than for personal reasons (Montgomery, Benedicto, & Hammerke, 1993). Students reported using alcohol more for the purpose of meeting members of the other sex than for personal reasons, although alcohol did make them feel better about themselves.

Drinking behavior that elsewhere would be characterized as alcohol abuse is often socially acceptable and even desirable behavior on certain college campuses (Weschler et al., 1994). "Party schools" foster reputations and environments in which binge drinking is part of the fabric of college life. Conversely, institutions that do not have alcohol outlets within 1 mile of campus and colleges that prohibit alcohol use for everyone (even those older than 21 years of age) have lower rates of alcohol bingeing.

Other Date Rape Drugs

Many other drugs, used alone or in consort with alcohol have been implicated in sexual victimization. Marijuana, cocaine, gamma hydroxybutyrate (GHB), benzodiazepines, ketamine, barbiturates, chloral hydrate, methaqualone, heroin, morphine, LSD, and other hallucinogens have all been used to facilitate rape (Higher Education Center, 2003). When combined with alcohol (which they often are), many of these drugs cause reduction of inhibitions, weakness, memory loss, and blackout. These incapacitating effects are used by sexual victimization perpetrators to take advantage of their targets (Higher Education Center, 2003).

Two drugs in particular, **Rohypnol** and GHB, have been dubbed "date rape drugs" because of their increased use and association with sexual assault and rape. Rohypnol was the key target in the Drug-Induced Rape Prevention and Punishment Act of 1996. This legislation was developed in response to the threat posed by Rohypnol. The act established harsher penalties for the use of even the smallest quantities of flunitrazepam (the chemical name of Rohypnol) for the purpose of facilitating a violent crime (U.S. Congress, 1996).

Rohypnol—also known as roofies, rophies, Mexican valium, ropies, and the "forget me" drug (to name a few)—is the trade name for flunitrazepam, a benzodiazepine. Benzodiazepines are depressant drugs. Rohypnol is similar to Valium in its effects on the body, only 10 times more powerful. The United Nations Commission on Narcotic Drugs has transferred Rohypnol from a Schedule IV to a Schedule III drug. Several states in the United States have already moved Rohypnol to Schedule I (Office of National Drug Control Policy [ONDCP], 2002b).

Rohypnol is a tasteless, odorless, clear drug available in powder form. It mixes easily in liquids and is virtually undetectable when mixed in alcoholic beverages (its preferred delivery by date rape perpetrators). When swallowed, it takes effect in 15 to 20 minutes, and its effects last for more than 12 hours. Users experience a slowing of psychomotor performance, muscle relaxation, sleepiness, and/or amnesia. Rohypnol leaves the body after 72 hours and is undetectable after that time (ONDCP, 2002b).

Rohypnol and GHB, available in liquid or pill form, are often mixed into the drinks of unsuspecting victims.

Rohypnol A depressant drug also known as the "date rape drug," because it causes loss of memory and makes women vulnerable to uninvited sexual intercourse

Jonathan Nourok/PhotoEdit, Inc.

GHB—also known as cherry meth, liquid X, organic Quaalude, and fantasy, to name a few—is similar in its nature and effects to Rohypnol. It is also a tasteless, odorless, clear, depressant drug. It is available in either powder or liquid form and easily mixes in alcoholic beverages, where it is undetectable. GHB is not produced legally in the United States. It is produced in clandestine laboratories. Users claim it can produce euphoric, hallucinogenic states and act as a growth hormone that stimulates muscle growth. Because of this latter claim, GHB is often marketed through the same channels (gyms, health clubs, rave clubs, and so forth) where anabolic steroids are sold (ONDCP, 2002a).

Both drugs have been implicated in date rape in the United States. Both drugs, besides having classic depressant drug characteristics (slowing central nervous system functioning), can cause memory loss and loss of consciousness. Because of this, women who have been assaulted and raped while under the influence of these drugs are unable to resist the perpetrator or recall any of the details concerning the incident. The assailant mixes the drug into the drink of the unsuspecting woman, allows it to take effect, takes advantage of her, and denies any knowledge of the event if the woman realizes or suspects what has happened. Because both drugs pass through the victim's system within 72 hours, she typically does not have the opportunity to get tested for the drugs (ONDCP 2002a, 2002b).

Stranger Rape

Stranger rape Forced intercourse by a person who is unknown to the target person

Stranger rape is rape by a person whom the target does not know. The overwhelming majority of rapes reported to the police and resulting in prosecution are stranger rapes. Although stranger rape can involve a premeditated assault with an anonymous assailant descending upon the victim totally without warning, statistics prove otherwise. Most cases of stranger rape seem to spring out of

healthy sex hints 16.2
Reducing Risks for Date Rape

The following are specific strategies for women to reduce their risks for date rape:

- Arrange for your first date to be in a public place or as part of a larger group.
- Arrange your own transportation, or go with your friends.
- In the earliest stages of the relationship, suggest paying for yourself. This will derail any notion that your date thinks you owe him something. It also will give you an opportunity to assess his views about women.
- Pay attention to your date's attitudes and behavior. Is he controlling? Does he want to make all of the decisions?
- Avoid using alcohol and other drugs if you don't want to become involved in intimate sexual activities.
- Do not accept *any* drinks from another person. Pour your own drink or only drink from sealed bottles.

- Don't send mixed messages or anything that can be perceived as "teasing." If kissing is acceptable but you don't want to go any farther, state this clearly: "I'd like to hug and kiss, but I don't want to let things go any farther than this."
- If things begin to get out of control, resist. Use more and more emphatic verbal resistance: "I said *no!*" If this doesn't work, use physical force: punch, slap, kick.
- Men are much more likely to believe you if you use physical force when you're saying no. Push him away, stand up, open the door, ask him to stop, or leave. If this doesn't work, say, "This is rape. I'm calling the police."
- Run away. If he persists, escape. Get away. Go to a public place, and call the police.

chance meetings that create the potential for assault. The assailant targets the victim in a park, a shopping mall parking lot, while driving in a car, and so on. The perpetrator initiates contact, appears friendly and "safe," and lulls the victim into relaxing her (usually the victim is female) guard, allowing the perpetrator to strike. The assailant maneuvers the target to one or the other of their cars or lures the victim into an alley, stairwell, or other remote location, then commits the rape.

Stranger rapes are more likely to involve guns, knives, and other weapons than other forms of rape (Rennison, 2001). Older persons are more likely to be

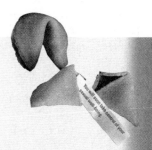

healthy sex hints 16.3
Reducing Risks for Stranger Rape

Personal Preparation

1. *Plan in advance.* Be aware of where you are, areas of possible trouble, and escape routes.
2. *Avoid dark and isolated areas.* Park in well-lit areas, as close to stores as possible. Avoid dark side streets, back roads, and the like, whenever possible. Jog and bicycle only in busy or public places.
3. *Arrange for an escort.* Have someone leave work, school, or an event with you and walk you to your car. Avoid empty stairwells and elevators unless you are accompanied by your escort.
4. *Use technology.* Carry an airhorn or whistle. If you can afford it, install automatic door locks and alarms in your car. Buy a cellular phone and carry it with you. Install your local police department number as a quick-dial memory number.
5. *Take a self-defense course.* Know how to defend yourself. A few simple techniques can make a difference.
6. *Remain vigilant.* Don't let your guard down. You are a potential victim any time you go anywhere by yourself.

What to Do If You Are Attacked

1. *Run away if you can.*
2. *Resist if you can.* Be as active and loud as possible: Scream, curse, yell, and cause a scene. If you have a whistle or horn, blow it.
3. *Fight back.* Kick, punch, bite, scratch, vomit, and spit. Use your keys, umbrellas, rolled-up newspapers, and books to jab for the eyes, throat, and face. There are no rules, and fighting back may reduce the abuse you might sustain without increasing your risk of injury. Carry keys in your hand as a weapon.
4. *Stall for time.* If you can't fight back, talk to your attacker—by name, if you know it. Express "empathy." Get him talking. Try to escape at the first distraction.

In the Car

1. *Always drive with your doors locked.*
2. *Lock your doors immediately after you park.*
3. *Approach your car with your keys in your hand* (have them sticking out like brass knuckles), and check the backseat to make sure no one is hiding there before you let yourself in.
4. *If you break down, do not leave the car.* Leave only to quickly tie a white rag to the antenna, then lock yourself in, and wait for the police. If someone other than the police arrives, ask this person to call the police or a local garage. Don't open the door.
5. *If your car is hit from behind, don't leave the car.* Put your flashers on and wait for the police to arrive.
6. *Buy a cellular phone, if you can afford it.* It will enable you to call the police immediately.

At Home

1. *Don't list your full name in the phone book, over the doorbell, or on the mailbox.*
2. *Install secure locks on all windows and doors.* Change locks if you lose your keys, move, or change your living situation (a roommate, husband, or boyfriend leaves).
3. *Install a peephole and safety chain and bar on your door.*
4. *Don't let people in your home unless you can verify who they are.* All service representatives (gas company, police, and so on) have identification. Request that they hold it in front of the peephole so you can see it. When in doubt, call the agency and verify who they are.
5. *Leave a light on near the entrance* when you know you will be returning home after dark.
6. *Organize or join a neighborhood watch program* for your block, building, or complex.
7. *Get a dog.* Perpetrators are less likely to attack you if you have a dog with you.

case study 16.2

Donna: A Saga of Spousal Abuse

Donna, 33, divorced, identifies as African American.

Donna is a continuing education student and the mother of two daughters, 10 and 11 years of age. She related her story to one of the authors in a diary detailing her sexual development.

My father was an alcoholic. I didn't realize it as a young child, but by the time I was a teenager, I understood why my dad had lost his driver's license a couple of times, had a hard time holding down a steady job, and was so angry all of the time. Of course, by then it was too late. I loved him so much and felt so guilty about admitting to myself that he was an alcoholic. I blamed myself a lot for his behavior. "Maybe it's my fault Daddy drinks so much," I thought. "Maybe if I was a better daughter, he'd be OK."

Often Dad's anger was directed at Mom. He'd come home drunk after stopping off for "a few beers" after work and just be itching for a fight. The least little thing Mom would do would set him off, and he'd smack her with the back of his hand. My sister and I would run for our lives and dive under our bed or lock ourselves in the closet until he'd pass out. We'd hear Mom getting hit but would be too afraid to do anything.

Afterward Mom would try to comfort us by saying that Daddy was really a "good man" and "cared" about her, but he just couldn't hold his liquor. She said that sometimes a woman has to stand by her man even when things weren't going well. I think about those words now, and I shudder.

Sometimes he'd turn on us if we tried to help Mom. He broke my arm once during one of these outbursts, and I had to go to the hospital to have a cast put on. To this day I can't believe that the hospital staff didn't know what was happening and intervene. Not only was my arm broken, but I had black-and-blue marks all over from where Dad hit me with his belt and his hand.

I ran away when I was 18. I guess it wasn't really running away since I was legally an adult, but to me it was because I wasn't leaving—I was escaping (at least I thought I was). I bounced around the country for a couple of years, in and out of jobs as well as relationships with men.

My first real love was a guy who reminded me a lot of my father. I guess I felt like a victim and was attracted to a guy who allowed me to be a victim. I needed to be punished to feel good, and he

Critical Thinking

How could Donna's early experiences with her mother and father have resulted in different choices she made in her life after she left home at 18?

Use your Virtual Workbook to explore your answer to this question at **http://health.wadsworth.com/blonna1.**

raped in their homes than in public places, and the assailant often gains access by overpowering them or by posing as a delivery person, utility representative, and the like (Muram, Miller, & Cutler, 1992). A relatively recent type of stranger rape involves targeting women who are driving by themselves. The perpetrators intentionally rear-end the cars of their potential victims, forcing them to pull off the road, where they are assaulted when they leave their car to investigate the accident. Often the rape is combined with stealing the woman's car.

Marital Rape

For many years, police were reluctant to investigate and prosecute marital rape. In a landmark case from 1978, Greta Rideout of Oregon filed charges against her husband for nonconsensual sex, bringing marital rape to national attention. Approximately 13 percent of married women have been raped by their husbands (Russel, 1990). In most cases, the husband used force (84 percent) or the threat of force (9 percent). The rape was an isolated incident for 31 percent of the victims. Another 31 percent reported being raped more than 20 times, and the rest fell somewhere in the middle (Russel, 1990).

was up to the task. He'd treat me like dirt, constantly tell me I wasn't pretty and was terrible in bed, couldn't do anything right, and on and on. He drank, just like my dad, and beat me just like my dad beat my mom.

Fate saved me from him, however. He was a real bad guy and was arrested for stealing a car and crashing it into a storefront. He was sent to jail for 5 years, and I wasn't into waiting around, so I took off and wound up in a neighboring state.

I met my husband shortly after arriving. I was working as a barmaid, and he came into the bar late one night. I was very attracted to him and wound up going home with him that night. I moved in after about a month and got pregnant with my first child about 6 months later. He liked to drink, but it didn't seem to affect him at first. He was a pretty good guy until times got tough.

After the baby was born, we got married and he lost his job the next week. He couldn't find another job and had to go on unemployment for 6 months. He couldn't handle this and began to take it out on me. I was pregnant with our second child at the time. He started really abusing me for my size (I gained a lot of weight) and began hitting me. I almost miscarried one night after he hit me and knocked me down. When he sobered up, he felt really bad and apologized. He told me he'd never do it again. He said he loved me.

I felt trapped and didn't know what to do. I was pregnant, had a 1-year-old baby, had no education, no real job skills, no money in the bank, and few real friends to turn to. I continued to live with him but began to fear for my safety and that of the kids. I started to try to think of a way out. Something deep within me didn't want to wind up like my mother. He must have sensed it because he got very controlling. He tried to limit my involvement with any friends, checked my mail, scrutinized the phone bills. The beatings were coming more often, and he began to hit the kids more and more.

Things finally came to a head one night. After a particularly savage fight, a neighbor called the police. When the police arrived, they saw what he had done to me and locked him up. My children and I were examined, and I pressed charges for domestic and child abuse. To make a long story short, the kids and I found refuge in a battered women's shelter, and he got 3 years in prison.

As soon as I was able, I filed divorce papers, went back to work, saved a few dollars, and left the state. I located my sister, also divorced with two kids, and we moved in together. We've both been working our way back slowly ever since—caring for each other and our kids, trying to put our lives back together. I'm in a support group for survivors of spousal abuse and have been dating a very nice man for about a year.

Perpetrators of marital rape share some of the same personality traits as other rapists—namely, anger, power, and sadism. Husbands who rape are also more likely to abuse their wives verbally, psychologically, and physically. More than 30 percent of wives who were raped also reported having been targets of physical abuse during their marriage (Frieze, 1983).

Verbal and psychological abuse often prove more damaging than physical abuse. The verbal and psychological abusers create an environment of endless criticism, suspicion, and torment. Abusers often undermine their mates' confidence and self-esteem through constant criticism of everything from the way they look to their level of competence in performing simple household tasks. Abusers are extremely jealous and turn even the most casual remark or involvement with another person into suspicions of flirting or having an affair. This constant flow of criticism, insults, and accusations is tormenting and can result in a host of psychological problems (Marano, 1996).

Survivors of marital rape suffer after-effects that are similar to those of women who have been sexually assaulted by someone they know (date rape). Because they know their assailants intimately and have an established history of trust, they feel especially betrayed, humiliated, and angry.

Statutory Rape

Statutory rape refers to sexual intercourse between a person older than the legal age of consent with a partner who is younger than the legal age of consent. The legal age of consent in the states varies from 12 to 21 years of age. Traditionally, most states' original legal wording of definitions of statutory rape defined perpetrators as males and victims as females. Revised definitions of statutory rape are more gender-neutral and describe adult perpetrators and victims under the legal age of consent.

The recent high-profile case of 34-year-old teacher Mary Kay Letourneau, convicted of the statutory rape of her 12-year-old student/lover, illustrates the importance of these revisions. Letourneau received national attention when the former elementary school teacher was convicted of having sex with (and becoming pregnant by) her former student. Even though the two claimed to be in love and the sex was consensual, the courts convicted her of statutory rape.

In statutory rape cases, consent of the underage partner has little bearing in the case. In the eyes of the law, people under the age of consent are not considered legally capable of making an informed decision concerning their sexual behavior.

Incidence of Rape

The true incidence of rape in the United States is unknown. There are two primary national sources of data regarding rape in the United States: the Federal Bureau of Investigation (FBI) Uniform Crime Reports and the Bureau of Justice's National Crime Victimization Survey.

The FBI collects crime reports sent in on a voluntary basis from the individual states. These crime reports confirm to operational definitions established as part of the FBI's Uniform Crime Reporting (UCR) system. The UCR is a nationwide program that includes over 17,000 city, county, and state law enforcement agencies. It reports crime data that represent about 92 percent of the population of the United States (Rantala & Edwards, 2000).

Traditionally, the UCR has labeled rape as forcible rape and defined it in the following way: "the carnal knowledge of a female forcibly and against her will. Rapes by force and attempts or assaults to rape regardless of the age of the victim are included. Statutory offenses (no force used—victim under the age of consent, are excluded)" (FBI, 2001). Sex crimes other than prostitution were reported under the category "sex offenses."

The UCR underwent major revisions starting in 1982, when the FBI decided to assess and upgrade its crime-reporting system. A new system, the National Incident-Based Reporting System (NIBRS), started phasing in at the end of 1987. NIBRS expanded the number of reportable offenses, revised and refined how these offenses were defined, and collected detailed information surrounding the incidents. Under NIBRS, the FBI not only continued to gather data on forcible rape and sex offenses but added new "group A" offenses: sex offenses—forcible and sex offenses—nonforcible. Currently, 4,192 law enforcement agencies (covering about 17 percent of the U.S. population) submit NIBRS data in addition to UCR crime reports (Rantala & Edwards, 2000).

The Bureau of Justice, National Crime Victimization Survey (NCVS), is a biannual telephone survey of over 89,000 people over the age of 12 conducted by the Census Bureau. It provides an estimate of the volume of violent and nonviolent crime in the United States. It differs from the UCR system because it is a survey and not a tabulation of actual crime reports filed by the police.

The Uniform Crime Reporting (UCR) Program and National Crime Victimization Survey (NCVS) were designed to complement each other. The UCR Program's primary objective is to provide a reliable set of criminal justice statistics for law enforcement administration, operation, and management, as well as to indicate fluctuations in the level of crime in America. The

NCVS was established to obtain and provide previously unavailable information about victims, offenders, and crime (including crime not reported to the police). While the two programs employ different methodologies, they measure a similar subset of serious crimes. (FBI, 2001)

Because studies that use reported incidents as their measure may greatly underestimate the true incidence of rape, independent researchers conduct survey research studies on smaller samples of women and extrapolate the findings to the population as a whole (similar to the NCWSV survey discussed previously). Often these independent studies define rape differently, use differing methodologies, and mix incidence and prevalence measures, making meaningful comparisons of their data almost impossible (Koss, 1996).

In 2001, the FBI's UCR program reported 90,491 cases of rape. This was slightly higher (0.3 percent) than the 90,178 cases reported in 2000 (FBI, 2001). The actual rate of rape was 32 per 100,000 women. This figure is down significantly from the 1992 rate of 70.3 rapes per 100,000 women reported a decade ago (FBI, 2001). The National Crime Victimization Survey reported an estimated 147,000 rapes (92,000 completed and 55,000 attempted) in 2000. This is down significantly from NCVS reports from 1999 of an estimated 201,000 rapes (141,000 completed and 60,000 attempted) (Rennison, 2001).

Although the actual numbers of cases in these two sets of data are greatly disparate, most experts (police and civilian) agree that the actual number of rapes is probably much higher than the reported or estimated numbers that usually show up in reports or in the press. Rape is one of the least reported of all crimes in the United States. Between 10 and 50 percent of all rapes may go unreported to the police (Williams, 1984). If we use the 2000 FBI reported cases as a baseline, that means that as many as 50,000 additional cases went unreported that year. Rape survivors are reluctant to report the crime for several reasons: fear of retaliation by the rapist; embarrassment or shame; fear of rejection by husband, boyfriend, or family; a desire to protect the rapist; and a lack of confidence in the judicial system (Koss, 1992).

In a study of 246 rape victims, the following six variables were found to be related to whether a victim reports a rape (Williams, 1984):

- The relationship between the victim and the rapist
- How the two came together
- Threat of force
- Use of force
- Extent of injury
- Use of medical treatment

Victims were more likely to report when the rapist was a stranger or acquaintance rather than a friend or relative, had broken into her house or had assaulted her in a public place (versus a party or other social situation), had threatened to use force (versus not threatening her), did use force (less likely to report if no actual force), had caused substantial injury (versus little physical harm), and had sought medical care for her injuries (versus not seeking medical care).

A close look at the variables related to a greater likelihood of reporting indicates that women are much more likely to report a rape when evidence of the attack was available. This could consist of observable or clinical evidence of injury and the need for medical attention, when the woman clearly was not at fault (forced entry or a public place, didn't know the perpetrator or didn't know him well), and she felt emotionally distant from the rapist.

The variables found to be unrelated to the reporting of a rape were the victim's age, race, employment, living situation, the rapist's age, race, number of rapists, and place of assault (Williams, 1984). Perhaps more rape victims would come forth if they didn't feel that they were responsible for providing the burden of proof that the crime occurred. This attitude in part stems from the myths associated with rape that persist despite years of efforts to clear up misconceptions about the crime by individuals and organizations concerned about rape.

sex in society 16.1

A Historical Look at Rape

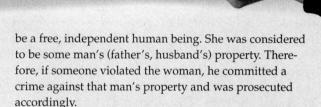

In *Against Our Will*, one of the most definitive works on the subject, author Susan Brownmiller (1975) described the evolution of our current attitudes toward rape and the laws against it. According to Brownmiller, rape has a long, sordid history. In antiquity, women were considered one of the spoils of war, objects to be taken and used in whatever way one wished. After a battle, the conquering army routinely rounded up all female survivors and had free rein to do what they wanted with them. Women who resisted were routinely slaughtered. Women who were spared were often sold off as slaves once their captors became bored with them.

Although rape seems to have been a part of all cultures, it has not always been considered a crime against a person. The earliest statutes against rape were laws related to property. Women were not considered persons. Instead, they were valued as property. They could provide labor and bear children—two important commodities in an agrarian economy dependent on the availability of workers.

Under Hammurabi's Code (a Babylonian law approximately 4,000 years old), a woman was not considered to be a free, independent human being. She was considered to be some man's (father's, husband's) property. Therefore, if someone violated the woman, he committed a crime against that man's property and was prosecuted accordingly.

Women also were categorized according to their marital status and virginity. Virgins were considered purer than nonvirgins in relation to sex-related crimes. The purest of all virgins were those engaged to be married. A man convicted of raping a betrothed virgin was put to death and his victim set free. A man convicted of raping a married woman also was put to death. His victim, however, also was put to death because she was considered a willing victim or accomplice in the crime. Presumably, the feeling was that she somehow led the rapist on or consented to the act.

The two early beliefs briefly described here about women and rape—that a woman is a man's property and that rape cannot occur unless a woman somehow consents—still exist and form the foundation of much of the legislation and belief systems that people share about rape.

Characteristics of Rapists

Most of what we know about men who rape comes from research conducted on convicted rapists. It is estimated that less than 10 percent of all rapists are convicted of this crime. FBI statistics in 1992 on convicted rapists, similar to those for perpetrators of other serious crimes, indicate that most are under 25 years of age, are from single-parent or foster parent homes, are marginally employed, have a low income, and have little formal education.

Because less than 10 percent of all rapists are ever convicted of their crimes, several researchers have studied populations of men who rape who have not been convicted or incarcerated. In one of the most comprehensive reviews of the literature, Cate and Lloyd (1992) identify seven characteristics of men who rape:

1. They are much more likely than their nonrapist peers to hold traditional beliefs about women and women's roles and female stereotypes. These beliefs range from nonsexual views concerning a woman's place (in the home) to sexual beliefs that men are the initiators during sex and that women want men to initiate.
2. They believe in rape-supportive myths—women secretly want to be overpowered during sex; they like it rough; *no* really means *yes*—and other stereotypical beliefs about women.
3. They use exploitative techniques such as coercing women into sex using alcohol and other drugs.

4. They accept the use of violence as a way to solve problems and dominate others.
5. They are more likely to vent their anger and express their need to dominate sexually rather than find other outlets for these feelings.
6. They devalue all that is feminine. They are hostile toward "feminine" personality attributes such as nurturance and collaboration and devalue traditional female pursuits such as child care and homemaking.
7. They are generally more sexually active than their peers who do not rape.

Malamuth, Sockloski, Koss, and Tanaka (1991) studied the sexual behavior of college men. Using a large, representative sample (their sexual histories were unknown) instead of convicted rapists, they found four characteristics of men who rape:

1. *Hostility toward women.* Men who rape have a deep-seated hostility toward women and feminine traits. They devalue traits such as nurturance and equality and value dominance, power, and aggression.
2. *Hostile home environment.* Men who rape grew up in households where violence, battering, sexual abuse, and hostility between family members were the norm.
3. *History of delinquency.* Men who rape associate with peers who are delinquent and reinforce the same hostile, aggressive behaviors that were modeled in their homes and that contributed to their own delinquency.
4. *Sexual **promiscuity**.* Contrary to the perception that men who rape are sexually deprived, rapists generally are more sexually active than nonrapists but report much higher levels of dissatisfaction with their sex lives than their nonraping peers.

Promiscuity Frequent and indiscriminate change in sexual partners

Malamuth et al.'s and Cate and Lloyd's work seems to confirm Sanday's (1987) findings concerning hostility toward women, stereotypical perceptions about women, and the devaluation of women and all things feminine as key attributes of rapists and societies that are "rape-prone."

healthy sex hints 16.4
Helping a Friend Who Has Been Raped

Even though trained rape crisis professionals are available in most communities, the first contact a survivor has is often a friend, roommate, or family member. If someone you care about has been raped, here are some tips to help you support her:

- *Accept her.* Be nonjudgmental about what happened. Tell her she is not to blame for the incident.
- *Listen.* Encourage her to tell you what happened. Listen actively and give her positive feedback.
- *Offer shelter and support.* Tell her you'll be there for her (and be sure you are). Offer her a safe haven until her

ordeal is over. Care for her needs (food, clothing, a shoulder to cry on).
- *Have empathy.* Tell her you're sorry for what happened but glad she's alive and her injuries aren't worse.
- *Encourage action.* Tell her it's important that she report what happened to the police and go to the hospital.
- *Accompany her to the police station and hospital.*
- *Keep your own feelings in check.* She will remain calmer if you do.

Characteristics of Targets

Any female can be the target of rape. The woman can be young or old, attractive or unattractive, dressed provocatively or conservatively. Most targets tend to be under 30 years of age and single. Age and marital status may have more to do with the likelihood that these women travel, shop, walk, and live alone rather than some other factor.

Women who are the targets of rape are no different from nontargets in terms of personality attributes, lifestyle, or behavior. Attempts to characterize targets as being different from other women only serves to blame the victim rather than understand that it is the men who rape through their own actions.

Sexual Harassment

Title VII of the Civil Rights Act of 1964 stipulates that it is an unlawful employment practice for a labor organization to exclude or to expel from its membership or otherwise to discriminate against any individual because of his or her race, color, religion, sex, or national origin. Sexual harassment has been deemed to be a form of discrimination based on sex.

The issue of sexual harassment leaped onto the television screens and front pages of the United States in 1992 with the much-publicized Clarence Thomas–Anita Hill sexual harassment hearings by the U.S. Congress, after President George H. Bush had nominated Thomas to the Supreme Court (see Sex in Society 16.2). Thomas had been Hill's boss at the Equal Employment Opportunity Commission (EEOC). Hill came forward at the time of Thomas's nomination with claims of sexual harassment.

These hearings brought sexual harassment out of the closet and forced people to examine this dark side of human sexual behavior. Since then, the number of sexual harassment complaints filed with the EEOC has increased from 6,000 in 1990 to 15,475 in 2001 (EEOC, 2003). Of the 15,475 charges filed, 7,309 were dropped due to no reasonable cause, 4,628 were closed administratively due to a variety of causes (inability to locate charging party, failure to respond to EEOC communications, and so forth), and 1,389 were withdrawn by the charging party because the claimant received desired benefits. Approximately 4,768 claims merited resolution, with 1,568 settled by the EEOC with the charging party receiving the desired benefits, and the rest being resolved in the charging party's favor through a variety of ways (EEOC, 2003).

U.S. Supreme Court rulings have made it easier to sue (and win) sexual harassment cases because victims no longer have to prove psychological harm, just that sexually inappropriate behavior took place (Kaufman, 1997).

According to the EEOC, sexual harassment consists of unwelcome sexual advances, requests for sexual favors, and other verbal or physical conduct of a sexual nature. These constitute **sexual harassment** when

(1) submission of such conduct is made explicitly, or implicitly a term or condition of an individual's employment or academic advancement, (2) submission or rejection of such conduct by an individual is used as the basis for academic or employment decisions affecting the individual, or (3) such conduct has the purpose or effect of unreasonably interfering with an individual's work or academic performance or creating an intimidating, hostile, or offensive working or educational environment. (EEOC, 2003)

Brad Markel/Liaison/GettyImages

The Thomas–Hill trial brought the subject of sexual harassment out of the closet and into millions of American living rooms, board rooms, and courtrooms.

sex in society 16.2

The Clarence Thomas–Anita Hill Hearings

The Thomas–Hill congressional hearings in 1992 had effects far beyond the matter of deciding whether Clarence Thomas should sit on the U.S. Supreme Court. As a result of these hearings, the issue of sexual harassment came to the fore and led to a whole new zeitgeist of how people are to conduct themselves in the workplace. The hearings were also noteworthy in that this event involved two prominent blacks—Thomas, a judge, and Hill, a law professor at the time of the hearings—with opposing political ideologies.

In her testimony, Hill described her position as an employee of Thomas at the Equal Employment Opportunity Commission (EEOC). She claimed that, beginning in 1982, Thomas had pressured her to go out on dates and that he had made lewd comments to her, including references to a pubic hair on a Coke can and the size of his penis. She stated that, because Thomas was well connected and could help advance her career, she was reluctant to speak out at the time. She produced three witnesses who testified to Hill's having told them that she was being harassed, though they did not recall Hill's having accused Thomas by name.

Hill's critics charged that she waited too long (10 years) to speak of the harassment and that she had agreed to testify to members of committee only under condition of anonymity. Her detractors took this as an indication that she made the charges only to try to derail Thomas's chances to gain a Supreme Court berth. They produced a number of witnesses who had worked for Thomas at the same time as Hill did, and these witnesses testified that they had observed no evidence of harassment and were not harassed themselves. Finally, Hill's critics questioned why she had followed Thomas to another job subsequent to the alleged harassment.

Thomas denounced the charges as completely untrue and a "high-tech lynching." In a close vote, he was confirmed to the Supreme Court. Irrespective of the outcome, the legacy of the hearings was far-reaching and has an enduring symbolic value. Major changes include the recognition of sexual harassment in the workplace, its definition, and enactment of legislation making sexual harassment easier to prove. Monetary awards and settlements also increased dramatically. In 1990, sexual harassment awards handled through the EEOC totaled $7.7 million; by 1996, settlements had reached $27 million.

Awakened by the prospects of costly lawsuits, the public and private sectors alike have gone on the defensive. Sexual harassment training is becoming common. Formal policies now are the rule rather than the exception in the workplace. More women (and men) are filing suit and supporting the victims of harassment. As a result of the Thomas–Hill hearings, public attitudes and actions regarding sexual harassment were irrevocably changed.

Sexual harassment has two facets:

- Unwanted sexual attention or advances
- A hostile environment (work or school) in which the person faces daily stress and oppression because of the unwanted sexual attention

Although the two often go together, they can exist independently.

Sexual harassment relates in part to how males are socialized. Men tend to interpret women's friendliness as a sign of sexual interest, as an invitation to pursue sexual involvement (Johnson, Stockdale, & Saal, 1991; Stockdale, 1993). Men and women perceive sexual harassment differently. Men are much less likely to perceive certain behaviors as harassing than women are (Jones & Remland, 1992). Thus, men have difficulty judging their behavior and its potential for harassment. The courts, too, have trouble determining whether certain actions cross the line between aggressive courting and sexual harassment.

Sexual harassment Unwelcome sexual advances, requests for sexual favors, and other verbal or physical conduct of a sexual nature in the workplace or educational setting

Environmental/Occupational Wellness

A work environment with high-level environmental wellness is a place where workers coexist without fear of abuse, discrimination, or harassment. Policies to guard against harassment and discrimination are in place and are enforced swiftly, fairly, and equally for all levels of workers. Healthy workplaces are environments where people pursue their occupations in a safe and supportive atmosphere. Sexual harassment exists in exactly the opposite environment—one that is hostile, where those in power use their positions to take advantage of others. Each person has the responsibility to report coworkers and bosses who abuse the work site and thus turn it into a hostile environment for everyone.

Conditions of Sexual Harassment

Sexual harassment has three attributes that transcend individual perception and set the context for any interaction between individuals:

- A power differential in the relationship
- Inappropriate approach
- Pressure after expression of disinterest

A hallmark of sexual harassment is the use and abuse of power to secure sexual favors. Power differentials exist in the workplace and the classroom based on roles and responsibilities. The boss, supervisor, and professor have power over workers and students by the nature of their roles and authority. A boss or supervisor is responsible for evaluating work performance, giving assignments, and the like. A professor evaluates papers, tests, and exams and ultimately assigns a grade to students in the class.

When someone holds power over another by virtue of a "superior" role, the subordinate person has a harder time refusing the advances. The subordinates fear reprisal—in a poor performance review, no raise, undesirable work assignments, even termination. In a school environment, the students fear a less objective review of their work and lower grades. Also, being approached in a respectful, inquiring way is vastly different from being approached in a harassing way.

Physical intimidation often plays a big part in creating a hostile environment.

Bruce Ayres/Getty Images

Linda and Beth: Sexual Harassment Victims

Linda, 27, married, identifies as Filipino; Beth, 33, single, is white.

Linda, a secretary for a medium-sized trucking company, is being harassed by her boss, John. He takes every opportunity to position himself around Linda to maximize the opportunity for physical contact. John leans over her desk, puts his arm around her chair, places himself in a doorway through which she must pass, and uses these opportunities to brush against Linda.

He has made comments about the size of her breasts, her shapely legs, and how he could really show her a good time in bed. Both John and Linda are married, and she has told him she is not interested in having an affair with him.

Beth is a driver for a local bus company, one of two women who drive for this company. The other 48 drivers are men. All drivers report to the local garage, where the buses are parked. The garage has two locker rooms, restrooms, a cafeteria, and administrative offices. Beth has complained to her supervisor (a man) that the work environment is not conducive to her well-being and may even be hostile. The male drivers are fond of soft- and hard-core pornography and have pinned-up pictures of naked women on the walls of the garage. They also leave these magazines out on the tables in the cafeteria.

Besides the print materials, the male drivers congregate in the cafeteria and tell sexually degrading jokes about women. They generally refer to women in derogatory terms when Beth is alone with them and when the other female driver is there. Although no one has made any direct advances toward her (she is living with her boyfriend and uninterested), she feels the work environment is hostile to women.

Both of these women are victims of sexual harassment—Linda, who is the victim of unwanted sexual advances from her boss, and Beth, who hasn't been personally confronted but is forced to work in a hostile environment created by her coworkers.

Critical Thinking

When does one worker's sexually open workplace become another's hostile environment?

Use your Virtual Workbook to explore your answer to this question at **http://health.wadsworth.com/blonna1.**

Finally, if the pursuing person stops the pursuit once the subordinate has expressed noninterest or displeasure, it's not harassment. Persistence and an attempt to pressure the other person into responding, however, are more likely to be considered harassment, especially if the first two criteria are also present.

Sexual Harassment Among Gay People

The original language of the Civil Rights Act of 1964 that governs the EEOC's handling of sexual harassment cases was directed at discrimination based on sex. It was never intended to provide similar protections based on sexual orientation. Quittner (2002) identifies several recent court cases where the plaintiffs filed sexual harassment charges with the EEOC against their employers for discrimination based on sexual orientation.

In all of the cases, convincing cases were made for portraying work sites that were indeed hostile environments and denial of promotions based on sexual orientation. In one case, a butler at a prestigious Las Vegas hotel was subjected to taunts, catcalls, physical assaults (grabbing his crotch, poking his genitals, and so forth), and threats. He became afraid to go to work and was eventually fired from the job. He filed a sexual harassment suit against the hotel. He lost his case, the courts citing that while the law clearly prohibits a gay man or woman from sexually harassing a heterosexual (that is, an opposite-sex) coworker, there were no protections for same-sex sexual harassment in the workplace.

Quittner (2002) cites another case of a male correctional officer in New York state being forced to leave his job after repeated incidents of verbal abuse from fellow heterosexual officers escalated into physical violence. The officer was denied by the District of New York federal court from suing his employer for same-sex sexual harassment. Such cases highlight the need for additional legislation to protect against harassment. In some states and cities, harassment based on sexual orientation is protected under broader antidiscrimination statutes.

Sexual Harassment Involving Children and Teens

One of the outcomes of the Thomas–Hill hearings and subsequent legislation is an attempt to define and prevent harassment at all levels. This has extended into all segments of society, including the elementary school.

Sexual Harassment in Elementary Schools Sexual harassment in the schools goes way beyond mere teasing. Although poking fun and teasing can be emotionally painful and stressful, they do not constitute sexual harassment. In childhood, teasing peers of the other sex is a developmentally appropriate form of gender validation and, if not carried to an extreme, actually can strengthen the bonds

healthy sex hints 16.5

Sexual Harassment: How to Fight Back

The following guidelines may be helpful in fighting back if you think you have been the victim of sexual harassment on campus or at work.

1. If the harassment includes rape or attempted rape, file criminal charges against the perpetrator.
2. If the act does not include rape or attempted rape, confront the person who is harassing you. Write a letter to the offender, and follow up with a meeting. Be as clear and specific about the offender's actions as possible.
   - Be specific about the incidents, times, and dates. A history and pattern of events are important. Most harassers are repeat offenders.
   - Describe exactly what happened, your feelings about the incidents, and how you reacted. Include a short statement indicating your desire for the harasser to stop.
   - Sign and date the letter, and make duplicate copies.
   - Send a copy to the perpetrator, and indicate that if the behavior doesn't stop immediately, you will press charges using the letter as evidence.
3. Seek support. Don't hide what happened.
   - Talk to coworkers, fellow students, and people identified with the issue. This may help put pressure on the offender to stop.
   - Contact a local support group, and talk to others who have experienced the same problem.
   - Relate your incidents to your significant other.
4. If the behavior doesn't stop, meet with the offender's supervisor. Discuss the incidents and give a copy of your letter to the supervisor.
   - In a work setting, this is the offender's immediate supervisor.
   - In a college setting, this person may be the department chairperson, the student center director, a member of the sexual harassment panel, or the dean of students.
5. Know your rights. Sexual harassment is against the law. You do not have to put up with it.
   - Obtain the company's/school's sexual harassment policy. Read it thoroughly, and make sure you follow its guidelines for handling your case.
   - Identify the administrative office and person responsible for handling sexual harassment violations in your workplace or school.

Although it may seem frightening, it's better to act quickly than to wait and see what happens. Harassers rarely stop their activities if they are not challenged.

Coercive Sex in the Media

personal exploration activity

We all know that it is immoral to push, coax, or force someone to have a sexual interaction when they do not want to be sexual. However, this type of behavior is fairly common in today's music. The music we listen to may influence the way we think and act, so it is important to recognize the messages we are receiving. This activity will help you start to critically analyze the impact of the music in your life.

For the next week, list all the songs you hear on a sheet of paper in two columns: sexually coercive lyrics and nonsexual or healthy sexual lyrics. To really analyze the songs, you will have to listen closely to the lyrics. If you cannot understand the words, try looking on the group's Web site for the lyrics. You may be quite surprised at the song's message when you see the actual words. At the end of the week, evaluate your choices of music. Is your favorite music reflecting a healthy, positive view of sexuality or a negative, destructive one? Are you willing to reduce or eliminate the songs that reinforce the idea that sex is to be gotten at all cost and replace these with songs that reflect a healthy, positive approach to sexuality?

little boys and girls have with their friends. Most of it is innocent and not discriminatory.

When the teasing is sexual in nature, it is a different matter. Uninvited sexual advances, lewd comments, ogling, and catcalls are different from simple put-downs ("Boys are better than girls," and vice versa) and nonsexual teasing. Even if they are not outright sexual acts directed at a child, they are capable of creating a climate of hostility that characterizes sexual harassment.

Often the focus of childhood teasing is sexual orientation. Children sometimes tease same- or opposite-sex peers with taunts of "queer," "homo," "fag," "lesbo," "dyke," and the like. Whether the perception is accurate or not, it creates a hostile environment for these children, making daily interactions with peers painful.

Several noteworthy court rulings have been made regarding sexual harassment by elementary school students (LeLand, 1996). In Lexington, North Carolina, in 1966, 6-year-old Jonathan Prevette was suspended for kissing a classmate in an incident that the court ruled was sexual harassment. In response, the boy's parents threatened to sue if their son was not reinstated and the policy changed. The school board reviewed the case and agreed that the incident wasn't sexual harassment and that the policy required retooling.

In another case, in New York, 7-year old De'Andre Dearinge was charged with sexual harassment for kissing a student against her will and pulling a button off her skirt. Again, the school board intervened and reinstated the child.

What both of these examples illustrate is the difficulty in determining whether specific incidents involving students constitute sexual harassment or represent something else. Obviously, singular, isolated incidents have to be evaluated differently from repeated acts that are more in keeping with creating a hostile climate and failing to stop when the other person expresses a desire to halt the sexual overtures or remarks.

Some child development authorities think that most 6- and 7-year-olds like the ones publicized in North Carolina and New York are too young to understand the concept of sexual harassment. Their behavior might be better labeled as a form of bullying in which they use power over another inappropriately. Some child development experts view this as a sort of testing the waters, and children (both perpetrator and victim) need to be educated about how to handle the situation rather than take it out of their hands. By having the proper authorities (such as school officials) step in, the victim relinquishes the ability to develop a repertoire of assertive behavior that could be used to fend off future would-be harassers (Leland, 1996).

case study 16.4

Bethany: A Proposition from Her Professor

Bethany, 23, lesbian, is white.

Bethany, a college senior, was having trouble with one of her classes and went to see her professor, a 35-year-old married man.

When I went to see him, I was a little surprised that he shut the door. It was after our late-afternoon class, and there wasn't anybody around in his department. He had this weird little smile on his face when he asked me to sit down. I sensed something was wrong and should have left then, but I didn't. When I sat down, his first remark was about how good I smelled. I smiled and thanked him but thought to myself that the comment was totally inappropriate.

I explained to him that I was there because I was worried about my grade for the semester. I had gotten a D on the last test and didn't want to lower my grade below a B–. He told me not to worry; he didn't like to see me so sad. Again I smiled but thought that this remark was also inappropriate. He said he'd take care of me, that I was one of his favorite students. With that, he slid his hand over the table and began rubbing my hand with his.

I was getting very uncomfortable by now and moved my hand away. He said, "Don't be so tense; let me rub your shoulders." He started to get up, but I stood up and said, "I don't think that's necessary. I must be going." He said, "Sit down. I thought you wanted to talk about your grade."

I sat back down, and he proceeded to explain to me that he'd had his eye on me all semester and was hoping I'd come to visit him. He explained that other female students in the past had worked out "special arrangements" to boost their grades. I asked him, "What kind of special arrangements?" He said, "Come on now, Beth, don't be so naive. You're a very sexy girl. We could have lots of fun together."

At this point, I was so flustered that I got up quickly and excused myself. I had to beat him to the door because he got up as if to block my exit, but I already had opened the door. He smiled and told me not to do anything foolish. I didn't tell anyone because I was afraid he'd flunk me. He kind of ignored me the rest of the semester but did wind up giving me a higher grade than I thought I earned.

Prosecutors would counter this defense by claiming that abuse of power is the first step in harassment. If a 6- or 7-year-old thinks he or she can kiss or pull a button off a skirt of a classmate, the next act might be more overtly sexual in nature. Also, by stepping in quickly, school officials are bringing the issue to the students' (and parents') awareness.

In response to these and a host of other lawsuits being filed around the country, the U.S. Department of Education's Office for Civil Rights issued a new policy entitled "Sexual Harassment Guidance: Harassment of Students by School Employees, Other Students, and Third Parties." The document attempts to bring standards for determining sexual harassment in line with the guidelines used for evaluating adult cases. The policy defines the same two types of sexual harassment used in adult rulings: quid pro quo (say, sexual favors for advancement) and hostile environment (Chmielewski, 1997).

Sexual Harassment in College

Over the past decade, many colleges have instituted sexual harassment policies, in response to concerns of students, faculty members, and administrators. Most sexual harassment in college is between male professors and female students. Although the reverse (female professor harassing a male student) or same-sex harassment can happen, both are much less common.

Between 15 and 50 percent of undergraduate and graduate-level college women report having been the victim of sexual harassment by a professor. Furthermore, between 10 and 20 percent of male undergraduates have been the victims of sexual harassment (Benson & Thomson, 1990). This behavior encompasses either unwanted sexual advances or the creation of a hostile environment. In a study at the University of California–Berkeley, approximately one-third of female students reported at least one incident of sexual harassment on campus (Benson & Thomson, 1990).

The NCWSV, although not designed to measure sexual harassment per se, found that approximately 11 percent of the 4,446 women studied had been sexually victimized (other than rape). These incidents included sexual coercion, sexual contact with or without force, threats of rape, sexual contact, and penetration. About 10 percent of the women had also been victimized in the past. Even more startling is the percentage of women who reported being stalked in the previous academic year. The NCWSV defined stalked as "repeatedly followed, watched, phoned, e-mailed, or communicated with in some way that seemed obsessive to you and made you afraid or concerned for your safety." Fully 13.1 percent of the women, using these criteria, reported being stalked in the previous academic year. Although none of these NCWSV data meet the classic criteria for sexual harassment, many would argue that this scenario could represent a hostile environment for some campus women (Fisher et al., 2000).

Child Sexual Abuse

Child sexual abuse is any sexual contact between an adult and a child under 18 years of age. Child sexual abuse runs the gamut from inappropriate fondling and touching, to masturbation, to oral sex, to penetration of the anus or vagina with fingers or a penis. These and other forms of sexual behavior are considered evidence of child sexual abuse despite the child's consent or sexual precociousness. Often sexual abuse starts off as normal hugging, kissing, and playful behavior. It then progresses to more intimate touching, manual and oral stimulation, and finally intercourse. The perpetrator often tells the child that he or she is not doing anything wrong but "Don't tell anyone because they might not understand." The perpetrator often uses bribes and rewards to get the child to conceal the illicit behavior. Or, physical threats or threats of desertion scare the child into silence. Children also may not report abuse because of fear and guilt. They sense that something is wrong but can't bear the shame of others finding out. Often, fear of reprisals from the perpetrator or other family member stands in the way of the victim's reporting abuse. In many cases, even when children report the behavior to a parent, they are not believed.

Child sexual abuse involving nonfamily members is generally referred to as **child molestation.** Child sexual abuse involving genetically related family members is called **incest.** Often, the perpetrators are adults who fall between the two forms, such as steprelatives, the mother's boyfriend, or a caregiver brought into the house to watch the children. As we discussed in Chapter 9, a *pedophile* is an adult who is sexually aroused by children and initiates contact with them out of sexual desire. A nonpedophilic **child molester** is not motivated by sexual desire but, rather, by power, the desire to control, or out of affection.

Child sexual abuse Any sexual contact between an adult and a child who is under 18 years of age

Child molestation Abuse of a child by nonfamily members

Incest Child sexual abuse involving genetically related family members

Child molester One who makes indecent sexual advances to children

Intellectual and Emotional Wellness

As adults, we have the intellectual and emotional maturity to make informed choices regarding when and with whom we want to be sexual. Although "age of consent" is a gray area chronologically, theoretically it is the age where intellect and emotion work together in the mature person to make informed choices regarding their behavior. Society has long believed that children must be "protected" sexually from sexual predators until they are mature enough to make informed decisions regarding their behavior. Sexual predators are often very smart and develop elaborate plans for deceiving, luring, and trapping their victims. They observe and note their victim's behavior, patterns, and weaknesses. Their cognitive abilities, although they may be high-level, are without the self-regulating moral/ethical controls that most of us have.

Preconditions Related to Child Sexual Abuse

Child sexual abusers tend to be shy and lonely, and they have poor interpersonal skills with other adults (Bauman, Kasper, & Alford, 1984). They are conservative in their political and sexual beliefs, tend to be religious, and lack knowledge about sex (Segal & Marshall, 1985). **Child molesters** are more likely to be victims of child sexual molestation themselves, alcoholics, and have severe marital difficulties (Johnston, 1987). Preconditions related to child sexual abuse have been identified (Finkelhor, 1984); these are explored in the following sections.

Motivation to Abuse   Three key variables influence the perpetrator's motivation to abuse: (a) emotional congruence, (b) sexual arousal, and (c) blockage of alternative forms of sexual arousal. Whereas adults typically are attracted to, and seek emotional connections with, other adults in emotional congruence, pedophiles are drawn to children for this fulfillment. This may be a result of the perpetrator's arrested emotional development, a need to feel powerful and in control, or a reenactment of his own childhood abuse.

Typically, adults are sexually aroused by other adults and find children's bodies immature and nonarousing. Pedophiles feel the opposite. They are sexually aroused by children and not by adults. In addition to the perpetrators' own modeling of sexual relations experienced in their youth or their own childhood trauma, it may be influenced by erotic portrayals of children in advertising and media or exposure to child pornography.

Sociopath A manifestly antisocial psychopath

Psychosis A severe form of mental disorder or disease affecting the total personality

A subgroup of child sexual abusers is **sociopaths** who have **psychoses** or other forms of mental illness. These abusers obtain gratification not only from sexual activity but also from inflicting pain and suffering on their victims.

Blockage refers to child sexual abusers' inability to use other forms of sexual release and gratification. The abusers may be unable to form adult sexual relationships and be sexually naive. Their strict upbringing and sexual values may block their ability to use masturbation and fantasy as outlets for their sexual desire.

Internal inhibitions Natural impulse control against adult–child sexual relations

Internal Inhibitions Against Abuse   Child sexual abusers find ways to overcome **internal inhibitions** against adult–child sexual relations. Whereas other adults may be curious or fantasize about this activity, they stop short of actually doing it because of the strong cultural and social restrictions against such behavior. They have well-developed impulse control. Child sexual abusers, however, lack these inhibitions. Furthermore, they are more likely to use alcohol and drugs to overcome any inhibitions they do have.

External Inhibitions Against Abuse   **External inhibitions** against abuse include influences of family members, neighbors, friends, social connections, and household privacy. The greatest inhibitor of sexual abuse is the mother. Child sexual abuse is much more likely to occur in households where the mother is absent or neglectful, has emotional or physical problems, or is a victim of marital abuse.

In cases where the mother herself was a victim of child sexual abuse or is disengaged from her husband, she will turn her back on, or even use, her daughter as a buffer between herself and her husband (Browning & Boatman, 1977). This behavior clears the way for the father, stepfather, mother's boyfriend, or other dominant man to gain access to the child.

Children who are socially isolated (having few close friends or neighbors) also are more likely to be victimized. Household sleeping arrangements and crowding, too, may create opportunities for abusers to gain ready access to victims.

External inhibitions
Impulse control against abusing children, as influenced by surrounding people and environment

Social Wellness

As we have just described, sexual predators do not have strong social relationships. Starting with their dysfunctional relationships with their own parents, sexual predators have not developed mature, egalitarian relationships based on caring, respect, and tolerance. From those who harass, to those who rape, to those who abuse children, a common thread is immature, dysfunctional, unsatisfying social relationships. Those who engage in coercive sex often have limited experience with relationships based on love and caring, trust, respect, mutuality, sharing, and commitment. Their relationships are exploitive, self-centered, and destructive. They use power differentials in relationships to take advantage and inflict pain and suffering. Their relationships are really not relationships at all. They are artificial arrangements set up to trap and abuse.

Children's Resistance   Child sexual abusers prey on any perceived child weaknesses. They are canny in using coercion, threat, punishment, or force to overcome any resistance a child may use. Children who are emotionally insecure, deprived, needy, and unsupported are prime victims for the abuser's offers, pleas, bribes, and threats. Children who lack education about sexual abuse and do not have good communication skills and caring adult support systems are easier for the abuser to manipulate.

Risks for Child Sexual Abuse

In a study of approximately 800 college students conducted in 1984, eight risk factors were related to an increased likelihood of childhood sexual abuse (Finkelhor, 1984):

1. Have a stepfather
2. Ever lived with mother alone
3. Not close to mother
4. Mother never finished high school
5. Sex-punitive mother
6. No physical affection from father
7. Income under $10,000 a year (although low income by itself is not a risk)
8. Two friends or fewer in childhood

The incidence of childhood sexual abuse was virtually nonexistent in subjects who did not have any of these risk factors. In contrast, two-thirds of the subjects reporting five or more of the risk factors were victims of childhood sexual abuse. The risk factor that was the greatest predictor of child sexual abuse was having a stepfather. This doubled a woman's risk of ever being abused. These findings confirmed those of Russel (1990), who found that 1 in 40 victims of child sexual victims were abused by their biological fathers versus 1 in 6 by stepfathers.

The second greatest predictor was having a sex-punitive mother. This type of mother was likely to scold or punish her daughter for asking questions about sex or engaging in behavior such as masturbation.

Hyde (1994) has speculated about child abuse being related to male psychosexual development. She asserts that men are socialized to be sexually attracted to partners who are smaller and younger than they are, whereas women receive the opposite messages. Women usually are sexually involved with, and attracted to, partners who are larger and older than them.

Incidence of Child Sexual Abuse

The actual number of cases of child sexual abuse is unknown. Like rape, child sexual abuse is often unreported for many reasons. However, following a sustained 15-year increase from 1977 to 1992, reported cases of child sexual abuse have been decreasing since then (Jones & Finkelhor, 2001). Numbers of cases of reported child sexual abuse reached an estimated peak of 149,800 in 1992. Since that time, cases declined 2 to 11 percent each year through 1998 (Jones & Finkelhor, 2001). In 1998, estimated cases of child sexual abuse reached a low of approximately 103,600, which represents a total decline of 31 percent over that 6-year period (Jones & Finkelhor, 2001). This sustained decline in the number of cases contrasts significantly with the 1980s, when the United States experienced 10 percent annual increases in the number of cases of child sexual abuse (Jones & Finkelhor, 2001).

Explanations for the Decline   Wilson (2001), reporting in the Office of Juvenile Justice bulletin, identifies several reasons for the decline in child sexual abuse cases. The past two decades have seen a dramatic increase in public information and information about child sexual abuse. There has been an increase in child abuse prevention programs. The increase in awareness and prevention has led to the arrest and incarceration of more sex offenders. With the onset of Megan's Law (which we will discuss in detail later), new laws have been passed in many states to increase and improve the monitoring of sex offenders (Jones & Finkelhor, 2001).

The decline in child sexual abuse parallels declines in other criminal offenses that may be related to victimizing children. As we mentioned previously, the number of cases of all violent crime, rape, sexual assault, and other types of female victimization are down nationally. Factors that may be related to the declines in these crimes could also be related to the declines in child sexual abuse (Jones & Finkelhor, 2001).

Effects of Child Sexual Abuse

Several factors have an impact on the future well-being of the victim. Four factors are related to the need for long-term treatment and the prognosis for the child (Krugman, Bays, Chadwick, Levitt, McMugh, & Whitworth, 1991). The closer the victim's relationship to the perpetrator, the longer the abuse, the more violent the contact, and the more intrusive the relationship, the greater is the need for treatment and the poorer the hope for an effective outcome.

As adults, child sexual abuse victims report extremely sad, pain-filled childhoods. They recollect feelings of betrayal, fear, and loss of innocence, painting a

case study 16.5

Lucy: A Victim of Child Abuse

Lucy, 16, single, identifies as Latina.

A 16-year-old girl was referred to the STD clinic by her high school nurse. The report showed a classic macular/papular rash on her hands and feet and a blood test confirming secondary syphilis. This girl, Lucy, probably used drugs, had a few boyfriends, and was a dropout candidate. Dr. Blonna saw these kids all the time. Here he relates Lucy's case.

When I first interviewed Lucy, I knew from the start that this was not a cut-and-dried case. She was young, fresh-faced, and preppy-looking in her Catholic schoolgirl's pleated skirt and white socks.

Lucy was quiet, almost sunken in her posture. She averted eye contact, obviously embarrassed. After my usual introduction, explaining why I needed to talk to her, I began to explain the nitty-gritty of sexually transmitted diseases and how they are spread. By the time I got around to asking her about her sexual contacts, she was on the verge of tears.

Lucy's initial response to my asking for the names of her sexual contacts was "There's only one— my boyfriend, Hector." When pressed for Hector's address and telephone number, Lucy hemmed and hawed, said she didn't know where he lived or went to school, and tried to move the interview along. Finally, I had enough and said, "Look, I know you're lying to me. What's going on here?"

It took but a second for Lucy to break down and the floodgates to open up, her tears pouring forth in a torrent followed by shakes, sobs, and near hyperventilation. She couldn't contain herself any longer. Between gasps of air and body-wracking sobs, she told her story. There was no boyfriend Hector. Rather, there was a 45-year-old man, Luis. Luis was the boyfriend of her mother, Maria. He mostly lived with them and had free rein to come and go. It seemed that he liked to come around when Maria was still at work and Lucy and her younger sister were home from school.

Luis had started sexually abusing Lucy about 5 years ago. It started out with her sitting on his lap and his fondling her. It progressed to his exposing himself to her, demanding fellatio, and, for the past couple of years, vaginal intercourse. When it began, Lucy was confused, but Luis told her not to say anything to her mother. Lucy thought her mother knew what was going on because there were times when Lucy didn't want to be left home with Luis, but her mom made excuses for him and didn't let Lucy leave.

When Luis began to force fellatio and intercourse on Lucy, he warned her not to tell her mother or he'd leave them or, worse, hurt her mother and little sister. Lucy was beginning to worry about her little sister. She'd seen the way Luis was eyeing her sister lately, and Lucy didn't want her to have to go through the same thing that she did.

I'm not sure how the story ended. I brought Lucy downtown to the child welfare agency that afternoon. I had to fill out forms and was still there when they returned with her little sister, afraid but unmolested. The social worker told me that they were removing Lucy and her sister from the home, arresting Luis and probably Maria, and would find a safe home for the girls. The last image I have of Lucy is her sitting on the wooden bench in the child welfare office, her arm around her little sister, smoothing the pleats on her school uniform, looking much older and more tired than her 16 years.

Critical Thinking

Social workers and other mental health professionals are trained to pick up on cues like the ones Lucy presented. Should these people be held liable for missing the same cues? Why?

Use your Virtual Workbook to explore your answers to these questions at **http://health.wadsworth.com/blonna1.**

picture of a lost childhood (Felitti, 1991). Victims of child sexual abuse often have difficulty forming intimate relationships as adults. They have feelings of shame and guilt, depression, a lack of trust, and revulsion at being touched, and they often are alcohol and other drug abusers (Frazier & Cohen, 1992). When victims are able to form relationships, they are often characterized by a lack of emotion and sexual interest and gratification (Jackson, Calhoun, Amick, Maddeve, & Habif, 1990).

Megan's Law

Megan's Law Legislation requiring notification that a sex offender has been released and is residing in a community

On October 31, 1994, the New Jersey State Legislature enacted the Registration and Community Notification Laws (RCNL), also known as **Megan's Law.** The law is named after Megan Kanka, who was lured into the house of a neighbor, whose son, a convicted sex offender, raped and murdered her. Only one family, neighbors of the perpetrator, had any knowledge of him living on the block. Megan's Law requires that certain convicted sexual offenders must register with law enforcement authorities and provide for community notification depending on the degree of risk that they represent to the community. The law applies to those who have been convicted of specified sexual offenses and has a grandfather's clause that includes offenders who were convicted of similar offenses prior to the passage of the law.

The degree of risk that offenders pose to the community is measured by a "tiered system" (Brooks, 1996, p. 54).

Tier 1 applies where the risk of reoffense is low. Under Tier 1, all law enforcement agencies likely to encounter the offender must be notified as well as the victim(s) and his or her family.

Tier 2 applies where the risk of reoffense is moderate. Under Tier 2, all law enforcement agencies and schools (public and private) likely to encounter the offender must be notified as well as the victim(s) and his or her family. The statute also requires notification to organizations in the community, including religious and youth organizations, likely to encounter the offender. Under the court's decision, individual determinations must be made concerning which institutions or organizations own or operate an establishment where children or women are cared for and are "likely to encounter" the offender. The notice to all such organizations must specifically direct them not to notify anyone else.

Tier 3 applies where the risk of reoffense is high. The statute requires that, in addition to the individuals, organizations, and institutions required to be notified by Tier 2, notification as to Tier 3 offenders must be sufficient to reach members of the public likely to encounter the person registered (individuals residing within a half-mile radius of the offender's home).

Over 40 states rushed to enact Megan's Laws of their own, and in May 1996, President Bill Clinton signed into law a federal version of the legislation. The federal version of Megan's Law was a revision of the Federal Violent Crimes and Law Enforcement Act of 1994. The revised law, entitled Megan's Law, required all states wishing to continue to receive federal funding for law enforcement to comply with its identification and notification of sex offenders criteria (*Economist*, 1997). The law came under intense scrutiny from civil libertarian groups, who claimed it denies convicted sex offenders their constitutional rights to privacy and protection (Brooks, 1996).

The various versions of Megan's Law all contain provisions for identifying convicted sex offenders and ranking them on the aforementioned three-tiered scale according to their likelihood to offend again. The level of community notification varies according to the offender's level. Tier 1 offenders must register with local authorities, but their status is not released to the community (Webby, 2003). High-risk residents (all day care center operators; supervisors of Boy Scouts, Big Brothers, Big Sisters; and the like) are notified of Tier 2 offenders. All immediate neighbors and others likely to come in contact with Tier 3 offenders are sent registered letters notifying them of the presence of the offender in their neighborhood (*Economist*, 2002). In addition to registered letters, other means of community notification include posting of pictures and descriptions of sex offenders; mailings to families, community groups, and organizations deemed at risk by local authorities; and postings on Internet bulletin boards.

Critics of Megan's Law legislation claim that, in addition to being unconstitutional, it does not work. Just knowing that a sex offender lives on your street is not sufficient to protect your children (Webby, 2003; Bai, 1997). Neighbors of Megan Kanka, for instance, knew that at least one sex offender (the roommate of Megan's killer) already lived on their street (Knight Ridder/Tribune Services, 2003).

Other critics cite that the placement of convicted sex offenders on the tiers often arbitrarily places many people convicted of sex offenses other than child sexual abuse in the highest-risk tiers (Tiers 2 and 3) unnecessarily. Countless lawsuits have been brought against states because of the nature of the tiering and notification processes.

As we go to press, two cases are being reviewed by the United States Supreme Court. In the first case, *The Connecticut Department of Safety v. Doe*, John Doe, a convicted sex offender, successfully sued the state of Connecticut for labeling him at risk for committing a reoffense and posting his name and personal information on the Internet. The lower court in Connecticut ruled in Doe's favor by stating that he had a right to a hearing to determine his risk of becoming a reoffender before being posted on the Internet (National Conference of State Legislators [NCSL], 2002).

The second case, *Otte v. Doe*, is from Alaska and revolves around similar issues. This case attempts to resolve the issue of whether a state has to conduct individualized risk assessments of individuals before their names and personal information are posted on the Internet (Rushkin, 2002).

The resolution of these two cases should help clear up some of the confusion associated with assessing the risks that sex offenders pose to a community and how that risk should be categorized (tiered) and disseminated (community notification) (NCSL, 2002).

In New Jersey, sex offenders are allowed to challenge their tiering. They have 14 days from being notified of their tier designation to challenge it in court. There have been 1,620 cases involving 3,515 specific objections of tier designations since passage of Megan's Law in New Jersey. These 1,620 cases have resulted in 672 tier changes. In 528 cases, a Tier 2 or Tier 3 placement was downgraded to a Tier 1, eliminating the need for community notification (New Jersey Law Network, 2003).

There is no way to identify potential child abusers and isolate them from children. Preventing child sexual abuse must revolve around empowering children by teaching them the warning signs of inappropriate adult sexual behavior and the escape and communication skills necessary to protect themselves. Parents and other adult caregivers must convey to their children a sense of approachability. Children must feel free to discuss their concerns without fear of reprisal.

Strategies to Prevent Child Sexual Abuse

Parents, teachers, and other helpful adults might use the following strategies to help prevent child sexual abuse:

1. *Provide sex education.* One of the cornerstones of any good school-based sexuality education program is a child sexual abuse prevention component. The unit should be comprehensive and cover issues including self-esteem, communication skills, inappropriate adult physical contact, refusal skills, and escape skills. This unit should be presented early in the child's curriculum, as most sexual abuse begins before 8 years of age.

2. *Become an approachable parent.* Open lines of communication early with your children. Continually underscore the fact that your children can come to you with any question involving sex. Do not punish your children for asking questions.

3. *Discuss inappropriate sexual behavior with your children.* Let your children know that you do not approve of any adult–child sexual contact (explain kissing, hugging, and so forth). Tell them that you would never punish them for telling on another adult (no matter how close their relationship—stepfather, baby-sitter, coach). Differentiate "good touch" and "bad touch" while letting your children know that they have the right to want "no touch."

4. *Let your children know they can decide how, when, and by whom they want to be touched.* Do not force them to hug, kiss, or be affectionate with adults with whom they do not want to behave this way. This reinforces their trust in their intuition about other people's sexual behavior.

5. *Discuss refusal skills.* Have your children practice how to say no in an assertive way. Teach them how to refuse an offer to engage in any behavior in which they do not want to be involved.

6. *Discuss escape skills.* Teach your children how to escape from potentially dangerous or abusive situations. Tell them it is OK to yell, scream, hit, and run away from any adult who does not stop touching them when asked to. Help children identify trusted friends, neighbors, and family members with whom they can seek shelter.

7. *Discuss telling.* Your children have to understand that they absolutely must tell you if they have been approached or touched inappropriately by any adult, no matter how close that person's relationship is with you. Children need to understand that this isn't tattle-telling and is the best way to deal with the situation.

Personal Assessment

16.1 Temper Test

Directions: A number of statements that people have used to describe themselves are given here. Read each statement and then circle the appropriate number to indicate how you generally feel.

	Almost Never	Sometimes	Often	Almost Always
1. I am quick-tempered.	1	2	3	4
2. I get annoyed when I don't receive recognition for doing good work.	1	2	3	4
3. I have a fiery temper.	1	2	3	4
4. I feel infuriated when I do a good job or study hard and get a poor evaluation or test score.	1	2	3	4
5. I am a hot-headed person.	1	2	3	4
6. I get furious when I'm criticized in front of others.	1	2	3	4
7. I get angry when others' mistakes slow me down.	1	2	3	4
8. I fly off the handle easily.	1	2	3	4
9. When I get angry, I say nasty things to anyone around me.	1	2	3	4
10. When I get frustrated, I feel like hitting someone.	1	2	3	4

Total Points: _____

Scoring:

Add the points (1–4) from each item together to get your total score, somewhere between 10 and 40. A man who scores 17 or a woman who scores 18 is just about average. If you score below 13, you're well down in the safe zone. A score above 20 means you may be a hothead—scoring higher than three-quarters of those tested. If these tendencies cause you to take out your anger on anyone else, professional help is advised.

16.2 Personal Alcohol Use

Go to www.intox.com. Click on the "Drink Wheel" on the right side of the screen. Complete the test using the amount and the type of alcohol you usually drink when partying. If you do not drink, use a friend's drinking behavior to complete the assignment.

What were your BAC (blood/breath alcohol concentration) results?

Scroll down and click on "Pharmacology and Disposition of Alcohol in Humans" and "Stages of Alcohol Intoxication." Read the information contained in these links.

What did you learn from this activity?

Thought Questions

1. What sexual acts are covered by the umbrella term *coercive sex*?

2. What conditions are necessary to meet sexual harassment criteria?

3. What is a "hostile environment" in a sexual harassment case? Give an example of a hostile environment.

4. How does power over a subordinate factor into sexual harassment?

5. What are three variations of rape? Is it considered a sexual act? Why or why not?

6. What are three risk factors for acquaintance rape?

7. What are three ways to reduce the risk for acquaintance rape?

8. What are some personality characteristics of a typical child molester?

9. What is the difference between a child molester and a pedophile?

10. What is Megan's Law?

Test Yourself!

1. *Coercive sex* is best defined as
   a. another name for rape.
   b. begging and pleading for sex.
   c. any nonconsensual sexual behavior.
   d. using coercion to set up sexual liaisons.

2. The Sexual Victimization of College Women study found that
   a. date rape is very rare among college women.
   b. about 35 out of every 1,000 college women were rape victims during the time of the study.
   c. about 3.5 out of every 1,000 college women were rape victims last year.
   d. about 3.5 out of every 10,000 college women were rape victims last year.

3. College women are most often raped
   a. in off-campus residences by strangers.
   b. in on-campus residences by strangers.
   c. in off-campus residences by intimate partners.
   d. in on-campus residences by intimate partners.

4. Under Rohypnol, a central nervous system depressant, victims
   a. relax, pass out, are sexually victimized, and suffer from amnesia.
   b. relax, lose their inhibitions, and want sex.
   c. relax, become sexually aroused, and solicit sex.
   d. relax, pass out, and are usually left alone.

5. Under the 1996 Drug-Induced Rape Prevention and Punishment Act,
   a. penalties for Rohypnol and GHB use were made much harsher.
   b. penalties for Rohypnol and GHB use were brought into line with other drugs such as marijuana.
   c. penalties for Rohypnol and GHB use were lessened since they are most often taken for personal use, not major distribution like other drugs such as marijuana or cocaine.
   d. penalties for Rohypnol and GHB use were left unchanged.

6. Which behavior should you avoid if you find yourself the victim of an attempted stranger rape?
   a. Run away if you can.
   b. Try to reason with the perpetrator.
   c. Fight back
   d. Scream, yell, curse.

7. The two criteria needed to prove work site–based sexual harassment are
   a. a hostile environment and unwanted sexual attention.
   b. sex is made a condition for employment.
   c. sex is made a condition of promotion.
   d. hostile sex is part of the work environment.

8. Recent EEOC rulings governing sexual harassment have omitted which of the following groups?
   a. Hispanic women
   b. Homosexuals
   c. White males
   d. African American women

9. Most adults are attracted to, and seek emotional and sexual connections to, other adults. Pedophiles
   a. are attracted to, and seek emotional and sexual connections to, other adults and children.
   b. are attracted to adults but seek emotional and sexual connections to children.
   c. are attracted to, and seek emotional and sexual connections to, children.
   d. neither are attracted to nor seek emotional connections to the children they desire sexually.

10. Megan's Law was recently
    a. struck down in Alaska and Connecticut.
    b. watered down due to cases in Alaska and Connecticut.
    c. upheld due to ruling related to cases in Alaska and Connecticut.
    d. overturned due to cases in Alaska and Connecticut.

Media Menu

You can link to the following online tools by visiting
http://health.wadsworth.com/blonna1.

 InfoTrac Activity

Quittner, J. (2002, December 10). Left out of the law: In the eyes of the court, just about everyone can be a victim of sexual harassment—except, perhaps, out gay men and lesbians. *The Advocate*, pp. 26–30.

 Web Resources

National Center for Victims of Crime

www.ncvc.org

A nonprofit organization providing resources and advocacy to victims of crime. The site offers safety strategies for victims of domestic violence and stalking, highlights of laws and public policy impacting crime victims at state and federal levels, information on crime victims, and finding a lawyer. Access to a virtual library with full-text publications, a directory of publications, recommended reading, bibliographies and a book review, plus links to victim-related sites.

National Organization on Male Sexual Victimization

www.malesurvivor.org

A group started in 1988 by mental health providers who wanted to better understand and treat adult male survivors of childhood sexual abuse. A section on prevention and education talks about how to prevent abused boys from becoming abusive men.

Rape Abuse and Incest National Network (RAINN)

www.rainn.org

A nonprofit organization's hotline providing 24-hour counseling service to survivors of sexual assault. This site also offers information, statistics, and a list of local crisis centers.

Sexual Assault Prevention

www.cc.ysu.edu/rape-prev-info

A site sponsored by the University Counseling Center, Youngstown State University, Youngstown, Ohio. It provides information on prevalence, aftereffects, and treatment of rape and sexual assault and links with a specific focus on higher education.

University of Illinois at Urbana-Champaign, Counseling Center

www.odos.uiuc.edu/Counseling_Center/friends.htm

A site that provides a guide for friends, family, and partners of sexual assault and abuse survivors. Articles address statistics, responses to recent sexual assault/abuse, phases, how to help the survivor, additional suggestions for the romantic partner of a survivor, feelings a victim may experience, how to help oneself, books to read, and other resources.

References

American Academy of Family Physicians. (2003). What to do if you are raped [Online]. Available: http://familydoctor.org/x1976.xml.

American Psychiatric Association. (2000). *Diagnostic and statistical manual of mental disorders* (4th ed., text revision). Washington, DC: Author.

Bai, M. (1997). A report from the front in the war on predators: Years after Megan's murder, her law is still on trial. *Newsweek, 129*(20), 67.

Bauman, R., Kasper, C., & Alford, J. (1984). The child sex abusers. *Corrective and Social Psychiatry, 30*, 76–81.

Benson, D., & Thomson, G. (1990). Sexual harassment on a university campus: The confluence of authority relations, sexual interest, and gender stratification. *Society for the Study of Social Problems, 29*(3), 236–251.

Benton, W. (Ed.). (1996). *Webster's new international dictionary*. Toronto: Encyclopedia Britannica.

Brooks, A. (1996). Megan's Law: Constitutionality and policy. *Criminal Justice Ethics, 15*(56), 51.

Browning, D., & Boatman, B. (1977). Incest: Children at risk. *American Journal of Psychiatry, 134*(1977), 69–72.

Brownmiller, S. (1975). *Against our will*. New York: Simon & Schuster.

Burgess, A. W., & Holmstrom, L. L. (1974). Rape trauma syndrome. *American Journal of Psychiatry, 131*, 981–985.

Cate, R. M., & Lloyd, S. A. (1992). *Courtship*. Newbury Park, Calif.: Sage.

Chmielewski, C. M. (1997). Sexual harassment meets Title IX: New federal rules to combat sexual harassment and place schools at the battlefront. *NEA Today, 16*(2), 25.

The Economist. (1997). Pointing the finger at Megan's Law. *342*(8004), 27–29.

The Economist. (2002, November 16). A scarlet letter: Megan's Law, changing the law for sex offenders. *365*(8299).

Equal Employment Opportunity Commission. (2003). Sexual harassment charges: EEOC and fair employment practices agencies (FEPA) combined, FY 1002-FY 2001 [Online]. Available: www.eeoc.gov/stats/harass.html.

Federal Bureau of Investigation. (2001). *Crime in the United States, 2000.* Washington, DC: U.S. Department of Justice.

Felitti, V. (1991). Long-term medical consequences of incest, rape, and molestation. *Southern Medical Journal, 84,* 328–331.

Finkelhor, D. (1984). *Child sexual abuse: New theory and research.* New York: Free Press.

Fisher, B. S., Cullen, F. T., & Turner, M. G. (2000). *The sexual victimization of college women.* Washington, DC: U.S. Department of Justice.

Fisher, B., Koss, M. P., Gidycz, C. A., & Wisnewski, N. (1987). The scope of rape: Incidence and prevalence of sexual aggression and victimization in a national sample of higher education students. *Journal of Counseling and Clinical Psychology, 55,* 162–170.

Frazier, P., & Cohen, B. (1992). Research on the sexual victimization of women. *Counseling Psychologist, 20,* 141–158.

Frieze, I. H. (1983). Causes and consequences of marital rape. *Signs, 8,* 532–553.

Gleason, N. A. (1994, May). College women and alcohol: A relational perspective. *Journal of American College Health, 42*(6), 279–289.

Higher Education Center. (2003). Sexual assault: Alcohol and other drugs [Online]. Available: www.edc.org/hec/pubs/factsheets/fact_sheet1.html.

Hyde, J. S. (1994). *Understanding human sexuality* (5th ed.). New York: McGraw-Hill.

Jackson, I., Calhoun, K., Amick, A., Maddever, H., & Habif, V. (1990). Young adult women who report childhood intrafamilial sexual abuse: Subsequent adjustment. *Archives of Sexual Behavior, 19,* 211–221.

Johnson, C. B., Stockdale, M. S., & Saal, F. E. (1991). Persistence of men's misperceptions of friendly cues across a variety of interpersonal encounters. *Psychology of Women Quarterly, 15*(3), 463–375.

Johnston, S. (1987, February). The mind of the molester. *Psychology Today,* 60–63.

Jones, L. M., & Finkelhor, D. (2001, January). The decline in child sexual abuse cases. *Juvenile Justice Bulletin.* Washington, DC: Bureau of Justice Statistics, Office of Juvenile Justice and Delinquency Prevention.

Jones, T. S., & Remland, M. S. (1992). Sources of variability in perceptions of and responses to sexual harassment. *Sex Roles, 27*(3–4), 121–142.

Kaufman, L. (1997). A report from the front: Why it's gotten easier to sue for sexual harassment. *Newsweek, 129*(2), 32.

Knight-Ridder/Tribune Services. (2003, January 13). Public must be involved to make Megan's law work. *San Jose Mercury News,* p. 7485.

Koss, M. P. (1992). The underdetection of rape: Methodological choices influence incidental estimates. *Journal of Social Issues, 48,* 61–75.

Koss, M. P. (1996). The measurement of rape victimization in crime surveys. *Criminal Justice and Behavior, 23*(1), 55–69.

Krugman, R., Bays, J., Chadwick, D., Levitt, C., McMugh, M., & Whitworth, J. (1991). Guidelines for evaluation of sexual abuse of children. *Pediatrics, 87,* 254–260.

LeLand, J. (1996). A kiss is just a kiss: Where should schools draw the line between normal childhood behavior and sexual harassment? *Newsweek, 128*(17), 71–72.

Malamuth, N. M., Sockloski, R. J., Koss, M. P., & Tanaka, J. S. (1991). Characteristics of aggressors against women: Testing a model using a national sample of college students. *Journal of Consulting and Clinical Psychology, 59,* 670–781.

Marano, H. E. (1996). Why they stay: A saga of spouse abuse. *Psychology Today, 29*(3), 56–66.

Montgomery, R. L., Benedicto, J. A., & Hammerke, F. M. (1993, December). Personal U.S. social motivation of undergraduates in using alcohol. *Psychological Reports,* 960–962.

Muram, D., Miller, K., & Cutler, A. (1992). Sexual assault of the elderly victim. *Journal of Interpersonal Violence, 791,* 70–76.

National Conference of State Legislators. (2002, July 16). *Connecticut Department of Public Safety vs. Doe.* Law & Justice Committee [Online]. Available: www.ncsl.org/statefed/doe.htm.

New Jersey Law Network. (2003, February 18). New Jersey law [Online]. Available: www.njlawnet.com/megan.html.

Office of National Drug Control Policy. (2002a). Gamma hydrobutyrate (GHB) [Online]. Available: www.whitehousedrugpolicy.gov/publications/factsh/tgamma/index.html.

Office of National Drug Control Policy. (2002b). Rohypnol [Online]. Available: www.whitehousedrugpolicy.gov/publications/factsht/rohypnol/index.html.

Quittner, J. (2002, December 10). Left out of the law: In the eyes of the court, just about everyone can be a victim of sexual harassment—except, perhaps, out gay men and lesbians. *The Advocate,* pp. 26–29.

Rantala, R. R., & Edwards, T. J. (2000, July). *Effects of the NIBRS on crime statistics.* Bureau of Justice Statistics Special Report (NJC 178890). Washington, DC: U.S. Department of Justice, Office of Justice Programs.

Rennison, C. M. (2001). *Criminal victimization 2000: Changes 1999–2000 with trends 1993–2000.* Bureau of Justice Statistics, National Crime Victimization Survey. Washington, DC: U.S. Department of Justice.

Ruskin, L. (2002, November 12). Sex registry goes to court; John Doe: Alaskans say law amounts to retroactive punishment. *Anchorage Daily News.*

Russel, D. E. H. (1990). *Rape in marriage.* Bloomington: Indiana University Press.

Sanday, P. (1987). The socio-cultural context of rape: A cross-cultural study. *Journal of Social Issues, 37*(4), 5–27.

Segal, Z., & Marshall, W. (1985). Heterosexual social skills in a population of rapists and child molesters. *Journal of Consulting and Clinical Psychology, 53,* 55–63.

Stockdale, M. S. (1993). The role of sexual misperceptions of women's friendliness in an emerging theory of sexual harassment. *Journal of Vocational Behavior, 42*(1), 84–101.

Task Force of the National Advisory Council on Alcohol Abuse and Alcoholism. (2002). *A call to action: Changing the culture of drinking at US colleges.* NIH Publication 02-5010. Washington, DC: National Institute on Alcohol Abuse and Alcoholism.

United States Congress. (1996). The Drug-Induced Rape Prevention and Punishment Act of 1996. 21 USC 841(b)(7).

Webby, S. (2003, January 13). Lack of funding, personnel hinder enforcement of Megan's Law. *San Jose Mercury News,* p. 1058.

Wechsler, H., Davenport, A., Dowdell, G., Moeykens, B., & Castillo, S. (1994). Health and behavioral consequences of binge drinking in college. *Journal of American Medical Association, 272*(21), 1672–1677.

Weschler, H., Eun, L. J., Kuo, M., Sebring, M., Nelson, T. F., & Lee, H. (2002). Trends in college binge drinking during a period of increased prevention efforts: Findings from four Harvard School of Public Health college alcohol study surveys, 1993–2001. *Journal of American College Health, 50*(5), 203–217.

Williams, L. (1984). The classic rape: When do victims report? *Social Problems, 31,* 459–467.

Wilson, J. J. (2001, January). Explanation for the decline in child sexual abuse cases. *Juvenile Justice Bulletin.* Washington, DC: Bureau of Justice Statistics, Office of Juvenile Justice and Delinquency Prevention.

Glossary

Abortion Termination of an established pregnancy through surgical or nonsurgical techniques

Abstinence Self-restraint or self-denial, as in not engaging in sexual activity

Abstinence-based curricula School programs that advocate not having sex before marriage

Acquaintance rape Forced intercourse by a person, other than a spouse, whom the victim knows

Active listening Listening with understanding and providing feedback

Actual-use effectiveness The percentage of women who get pregnant while using a contraceptive method for 1 year

Adhesions Spider-web-like bands of scar tissue that painfully bind internal organs to each other or the abdominal wall

Adolescence Time period representing the psychosocial transition from childhood to young adulthood

Afterbirth The placenta, umbilical cord, which has been cut at the baby's abdomen but attached to the placenta, and membranes expelled after the birth of a child

Aggressiveness Pursuing one's own wants and needs without regard for the rights of others

AIDS The acronym for *acquired immunodeficiency syndrome*, the end result of HIV infection

Allurin A chemical released by a mature ovum that attracts a sperm to enable conception

Amenorrhea Absence of menstruation at some time after a female has reached menses

Amniocentesis Removal of the amniotic fluid

Amniotic fluid The transparent liquid contained in the amniotic sac that protects the fetus from injury and helps maintain an even temperature

Amphetamine A central nervous system stimulant that is administered by ingestion, injection, snorting, or inhalation

Androcentrism A position of viewing the world with the male at the center

Androgens A group of naturally occurring steroid hormones produced by both men and women

Androgynous Expressing characteristics and traits considered stereotypically male and female

Anilingus Oral stimulation of the anus

Anorgasmia An inability to achieve orgasm

Anus The opening of the bowel, through which fecal matter is eliminated from the body

Areola The brownish or pink ring of tissue surrounding the nipple of the breast

Assertiveness Pursuing one's own needs and wants without infringing on others

Assisted reproductive technology (ART) Infertility interventions in which a laboratory is involved with the union of the sperm and egg

Associational brain functions Connecting together individual sensory inputs

Autoeroticism The dimension of the sex life defined by sexual desire and/or gratification experienced by a person without the direct participation of another

Autoinnoculate To self-inflict the spread of disease from one body part to another

Autonomic nervous system The part of the peripheral nervous system that is automatic and involuntary

Aversion therapy A behavior modification technique that pairs an aversive stimulus with the behavior targeted for change

Balanitis Inflammation of the glans penis

Barrier methods Nonsurgical contraceptive measures that prevent the sperm and egg from uniting

Bartholin's glands Small glands adjacent to the vaginal opening that secrete a mucus-like lubricant during arousal

Basal body temperature (BBT) The lowest body temperature of a healthy person during waking hours

Behaviorism A stimulus-response theory of personality development grounded in the belief that human personality evolves as a result of the interaction between exposure to stimuli and the responses that this exposure evokes in the person. Watson is credited with the theory, expanded later by Skinner.

Binge drinking Having four or more drinks at one sitting

Biological essentialism The position that biology is destiny and our biology explains our nature

Biological immaturity The incomplete anatomical and physiological development associated with early adolescence or preadolescence

Biological/anatomical sex Categorizing individuals based primarily on their reproductive organs, chromosome makeup, and hormone levels; traditionally, one sex is labeled male and the other female

Birth control The broadest term covering all methods designed to prevent the birth of a child

Bisexuality Forming sexual relationships with both men and women

Blastocysts Spherical clusters of cells, also known as *preembryos*, that form shortly after conception

Blood alcohol concentration (BAC) A measurement of percentage of alcohol in blood; also termed *blood alcohol level* (BAL)

Body composition The fat and nonfat components of the human body; important in assessing recommended body weight

Body language Sending intentional or unintentional messages through body postures and movements

Bonding The close physical emotional attachment between infants and their primary caregiver(s)

Breech position A birth position in which the buttocks or foot rather than the baby's head presents at the cervix

Brothel A house of prostitution

Cannula A tapered, strawlike tube used in the vacuum aspiration method of abortion

Carriers Individuals who have a given disease and are capable of passing it on but have no apparent symptoms

Celibacy Abstaining from sexual intercourse

Central nervous system The brain and spinal cord

Cervical interepithelial neoplasms (CIN) Tumors or growths within the cervical membrane tissues

Cervix The neck of the uterus, which extends into the inner end of the vagina

Cesarean delivery (c-section) The surgical form of childbirth in which an incision is made through the abdomen and uterus to deliver the baby

Chancre A painless, indurated primary lesion of early syphilis

Chancroid An STD named for the irregular and painful genital lesions it produces, caused by the bacterium *Haemophilus ducreyi*

Chat rooms Live e-mail discussion lines in which a person can communicate with others by typing messages

Childbirth Labor and delivery

Child molestation Abuse of a child by nonfamily members

Child molester One who makes indecent sexual advances to children

Child sexual abuse Any sexual contact between an adult and a child who is under 18 years of age

Chlamydia trachomatis The most prevalent sexually transmitted bacterial pathogen, causing the STD chlamydia

Circumcision Surgical removal of foreskin of penis

Clitoris A small, highly sensitive, organ located at the top of the labia minora

Cohabitation Living together without being married

Coitus Vaginal intercourse

Communication The process by which information is exchanged between individuals through a common system of symbols, signs, and behaviors

Companionate love Feelings that include deep attachment, commitment, and intimacy

Complementary relationships Relationships based on differences

Congenital syphilis The disease acquired by the fetus in the womb and present at birth

Connective tissue Tissue that supports or binds other tissue

Contraception Methods designed to prevent conception

Corpus luteum The follicle after it has released its ovum and begins to produce progesterone

Covert sensitization A type of behavior modification in which an aversive fantasy is paired with the paraphiliac fantasy in an attempt to extinguish it

Cowper's glands Bulbourethral glands, located below seminal vesicles, which produce preejaculatory fluid that lubricate vas deferens and urethra and protect sperm that are being ejaculated

Cryptorchidism Undescended testicle(s)

Culture The sum of the learned set of rules governing the behavior of people, often focused on the influences of race, class, religion, and ethnicity

Cunnilingus Oral stimulation of the clitoris or vulva

Cystitis Bladder infections

Cystoscopy Direct visual examination of interior of urethra, urinary bladder, and kidneys by inserting a cystoscope (optical viewing tube) into the urethra

Cysts An abnormal condition of fluid-filled sacs that can burst and cause pain and scarring

Declarative statement A verbal initiating technique that does not require a response to a message

Decoding The use of knowledge, memory, language, context, and personal history and experience to interpret a message

Dialogue An exchange of information in communication

Dilation and evacuation (D&E) A second-trimester abortion procedure in which the cervix is first dilated, and then the fetus removed by suction and curretage

Discharge A secretion from a bodily orifice, such as the urethra or vagina, which may or may not represent an infection

Domestic partnerships Registered relationships between gay and lesbian couples

Dyadic sex Referring to the sexual behavior of a couple, the two people in a relationship

Dysmenorrhea Painful menstruation

Dyspareunia Genital pain associated with sexual intercourse

Dysuria Burning upon urination

Ectopic pregnancy Implantation of an egg outside the womb

Effacement Thinning of the cervix during first stage of labor

Ego Rational, analytical facet of human mind, according to Freudian theory

Ejaculatory inevitability The first step in male ejaculation; beginning of smooth-muscle contractions that trigger release of ejaculate

Electromyographic Refers to measurement of muscle tension through electrical sensors at skin surface

Embryo A fertilized egg up to 8 weeks gestation

Emission The release of secretions from various organs and glands that produce male ejaculate

Emotional well-being A component of wellness that refers to being in touch with one's feelings, having the ability to express them, and being able to control them when necessary

Encoding Selecting the signs, symbols, emotions, and words to transmit a message

Endemic A 20 percent level of ongoing infection within a specific population

Endometriosis A condition in which pieces of the endometrium migrate to the fallopian tubes, ovaries, or abdominal cavity

Endometrium The inner blood lining of the uterus

Environmental well-being A component of wellness that reflects our ability to function in our immediate environment, such as home, school, and work, as well as being able to deal with the world at large

Epidemic Levels of infection in populations that exceed those normally expected for that population

Epidemiological Dealing with incidence, distribution, and control, as in STDs

Epidemiological synergy The distribution of disease caused by the effects of infection with more than one condition

Epididymis A comma-shaped structure that sits along top of each testicle and serves as storage chamber for immature sperm

Epididymitis Inflammation of the small oblong body that rests upon and beside the surface of the testes

Epidural anesthetic An injection of a drug into the spinal cord during labor to dull pain

Episiotomy A surgical procedure that facilitates childbirth by enlarging the vaginal opening through cutting the perineum

Erectile dysfunction A disturbance or disorder related to obtaining an erection

Erection Filling of the penile spongy tissue with blood during vasocongestion, resulting in a hard, erect, penis

Erogenous Capable of producing sexual excitement

Erotic Devoted to arousing sexual love or desire

Ethyl alcohol A grain alcohol that is a central nervous system depressant

Exhibitionism Deriving sexual pleasure from exposing one's genitals to unsuspecting strangers

External inhibitions Impulse control against abusing children, as influenced by surrounding people and environment

Extradyadic sex Referring to sexual behavior outside the primary relationship. This term replaces *extramarital sex*, which is confined to heterosexual marriages.

Extramarital sex Usually refers to coitus, sexual intercourse, outside marriage

Fallopian tubes Conduits connected to the uterus through which the egg passes into the uterus during ovulation. Fertilization usually takes place at the outer third of the tube.

Family planning The conscious effort of deciding to have a family, including when to have children, how many, and how far apart to space them

Family practitioners Physicians who offer comprehensive health care, including monitoring pregnancies and delivering babies

Feedback A verbal or nonverbal response sent from a person receiving a message to the person sending that message

Fellatio Oral stimulation of the penis

Female climacteric A syndrome experienced by women between about 45 and 55 years of age as a result of declining levels of estrogen production associated with menopause

Feminist theory Theories that argue that personality and identity are socially constructed. What is "correct development" for boys is different from what is deemed "correct development" for girls.

Fertilin A protein on the plasma membrane of the sperm that enables it to bind with the ovum

Fertility awareness Natural family planning

Fertilization/conception Union of the sperm and ovum

Fetal alcohol syndrome Effects on embryo and fetus of pregnant woman's alcohol consumption; symptoms include facial abnormalities, mental retardation, and nervous system damage

Fetishism Deriving sexual pleasure from inanimate objects

Fetus A fertilized egg from 8 weeks after conception to birth

Fibroadenomas Benign, solid tumors associated with fibrocystic breast disorder

Follicle An egg sac in the ovary

Frotteurism Deriving sexual pleasure from rubbing up against unsuspecting and unwilling victims

Gametes The reproductive cells—sperm and ova

Gender dysphoria The condition in which one's anatomy is inconsistent with one's gender identity

Gender identity One's personal perception and sense of being male, female, or blended

Gender polarization The belief that males and females are fundamentally different, with mutually exclusive scripts

Gender role The ways we express our gender identity—including appearance, clothing, movement, and life choices

Genital herpes An infection caused by exposure to the herpes simplex virus type 1 or type 2 through sexual contact

Genital warts An STD caused by the HPV or human papilloma virus

Gestation The period of time representing pregnancy and development of fetus from conception to birth

Glans penis The end of corpus spongiosum, which is composed of the head of the penis and the urethral opening

Gonads The primary endocrine glands in men (testes) and women (ovaries) that influence sexuality

Gonorrhea A sexually transmitted disease caused by the bacteria *Neisseria gonorrheae*

G-spot An area in the upper, rear section of the vagina named after Ernest Grafenberg, who claimed it to be an erogenous zone

Guanosine triphosphate A chemical that controls the muscular and vascular changes of erection

Gynecology The medical specialty focused on women's reproductive health

Gynecomastia Enlargement of one or both breasts in men

Hallucinogens A class of drugs that distort the perception of reality by altering the perception of all sensory inputs

Health Total mental, physical, and social well-being, not merely the absence of disease

Healthy sexuality The safe and open exploration and development of our potential as human beings

Hemispheres The two halves of the cerebrum, each controlling the functions of the opposite side of the body

Hepatitis B virus (HBV) A disease caused by contact with infected blood; often associated with unprotected sex with multiple partners

Heterosexuality Forming sexual relationships with members of the other sex

HIV The acronym for *human immunodeficiency virus,* the infection that leads to AIDS

Holistic health The process of moving toward optimal functioning across the physical, social, spiritual, emotional, and intellectual dimensions

Homologous structures Body parts that develop from the same embryonic tissue (for example, the female clitoris and the male penis)

Homosexuality Forming sexual relationships with members of the same sex

Hooking up A sexual encounter between two people who may or may not know each other well and are not seriously dating

Hormonal releasing factors Chemicals secreted by the hypothalamus that trigger the pituitary to release specific hormones

Human chorionic gonadotropin (hCG) A hormone secreted during pregnancy that shows up in the urine of pregnant women; the basis for determining pregnancy using home kits

Human papilloma virus (HPV) A condition spread through direct contact with an infected person's genital warts during sexual contact

Humanism A theory of personality development proposing that human personality development is shaped by innate desire and need for maximizing personal growth

Hydrocele Accumulation of fluid in any sac, cavity, or duct

Hymen The membrane that covers the introitus

Hypoactive sexual desire disorder A dysfunction characterized by very low or complete absence of sexual desire

Hypothalamus The part of the brain that correlates activities between the nervous centers and the pituitary gland

Hypoxyphilia Deriving sexual pleasure from activities that involve oxygen deprivation

Hysterectomy Surgical removal of uterus. In practice, a hysterectomy often is accompanied by surgical removal of fallopian tubes and sometimes also the ovaries

Hysterosalpingograms Tests that determine whether the fallopian tubes are open

Hysterotomy A surgical procedure in which the fetus and placenta are removed surgically through an abdominal incision

"I" language Taking responsibility for feelings by saying "I feel . . ." versus "You make me feel . . ."

Id Pleasure-seeking, guilt-free facet of human mind, according to Freudian theory

IDU The acronym for *injectable drug user*

Illogical thinking Thought based on inaccurate or irrational perception of information

Immunocompetence The level of efficiency of the immune system

Implantation The attachment of a fertilized egg to lining of uterus

Incest Child sexual abuse involving genetically related family members

Incidence The number of new cases of a disease during a specific time period

Incidence rates Rates of new infection used to measure the likelihood of becoming infected

Infantilism Deriving sexual pleasure from being treated like an infant

Infertility The inability to conceive after 1 year of unprotected intercourse

Inhibited male orgasm A persistent or recurrent delay in or absence of orgasm following a normal excitement phase

Intellectual well-being A component of wellness referring to the ability to process information effectively and rationally

Internal inhibitions Natural impulse control against adult–child sexual relations

Intersexual An individual possessing some degree of both male and female internal or external reproductive structures; the preferred term, replacing earlier labels of *hermaphrodite* and *pseudohermaphrodite*

Intimacy Connectedness to another person characterized by mutual caring, openness, self-disclosure, honesty, attentiveness, sharing, commitment, trust, empathy, and tenderness

Introitus The vaginal opening

In vitro fertilization (IVF) A procedure in which ova are removed from the woman's body and fertilized with sperm in a laboratory; the embryo is surgically implanted into her uterus

Labia majora The larger, outer vaginal lips

Labia minora The smaller, inner vaginal lips

Lactation The process of producing and secreting milk from the breasts

Laparoscope A medical instrument made up of a tube with a light that permits examination of reproductive structures, requiring only a small abdominal incision

Lochia The uterine discharge that is released over a period of weeks after childbirth

Lymph nodes The main drainage and filtration sites in the lymph system

Macro-environment The environment that extends beyond the micro and includes one's city, state, country, and the world at large

Male climacteric A syndrome experienced by about 5 percent of men in their 40s and 50s, characterized by diminished interest in sex, loss of appetite, fatigue, and inability to concentrate

Mammary glands Glands within the breasts that produce milk for lactation

Masturbation Individual or mutual stimulation of genitalia by hand or using other objects

Megan's Law Legislation requiring notification that a sex offender has been released and is residing in a community

Menarche The onset of the menstrual cycle in girls

Menopause The absence of a period for 12 consecutive months, without surgery or medical treatment

Metacommunication Communication about communication

Micro-environment The part of one's environment that is immediate and includes living situation, campus, neighborhood, home, and work site and family, friends, and associates who populate these places

Minilaparotomy A female sterilization procedure in which the fallopian tubes are cut to block transport of the egg

Mirroring Restating the message exactly, including body language

Monogamy Commonly used to refer to having one sexual partner, whether married to that person or not

Morbidity The relative incidence of a disease

Mortality The number of deaths during a specific time period

Motor Relating to nerve impulses going out to muscles

Myomectomy A surgical procedure that removes fibroid tumors without removing the uterus

Myometrium The muscular, middle layer of the uterus

Myotonia Involuntary skeletal muscle contractions

Nongonococcal urethritis (NGU) An infection in the urethra of males, usually caused by chlamydia bacteria

Nontraditional relationships Any relationships other than a monogamous, legal marriage between a man and a woman

Nuclear family A family made up of the mother, father, and their children

Obscenity Material that is abhorrent to moral virtue and accepted norms of social behavior

Obstetrics A medical specialization focused on pregnancy and childbirth

Occupational/vocational well-being A component of wellness that reflects our ability to use our unique skills/talents to work that is meaningful and rewarding. Our values are expressed through involvement in paid and nonpaid activities that are personally rewarding for us and make a contribution to the well-being of the community at large.

Oedipal complex A psychoanalytical term (named after Oedipus in Shakespeare's play) that describes the internal struggle that 3- to 4-year-olds face as they begin to identify more with their opposite-sex parent

Open-ended questions Sentences that require information from the other person

Opportunistic infection An infection that is able to develop as a result of the body's weakened immune status

Orgasm The stage of sexual response characterized by ejaculation in males and involuntary muscular contractions followed by relaxation in both males and females

Orgasmic disorders Dysfunctions related to the orgasm phase of sexual response

Outercourse Nonpenetrative sexual activities such as massage and masturbation

Ovarian cycle A three-phased period of time covering maturation of a follicle, release of ovum, and secreting role of corpus luteum

Ovaries Two almond-shaped structures that contain and release ova and secrete the hormones estrogen and progesterone

Ovulation The release of an egg from the ovary

Paraphilia An unusual or atypical sexual behavior that becomes the focal point for an obsessive preoccupation or need

Paraphrasing Restating a message in one's own words

Passionate love Feelings characterized by intense longing for another, infatuation, ecstasy when reciprocated, and emptiness when not shared by the other

Passive listening One-way listening; provides no feedback

Pedophilia Engaging in sexual activity with or fantasizing about prepubescent children

Performance anxiety Fear, worry, or panic associated with one's perceived sexual behavior

Perimenopause A period of gradually declining estrogen levels produced by the ovaries

Perimetrium The outer lining of the uterus

Perineum In men, the erogenous area of skin extending from the base of testicles to the anal opening; in women, the area of muscle and skin between vagina and anus

Peripheral nervous system All nerves coming off of the spinal cord

Personality The collection of values, attitudes, and behavior that make us who we are

Pheromones Body chemicals that attract potential sexual partners

Phimosis A condition where a tight foreskin cannot be retracted fully

Physical well-being A component of wellness reflected in how well the body performs its intended functions

Pelvic Inflammatory Disease (PID) A generic term that can apply to any STD that produces the characteristic symptoms of infection; used to describe infection of the uterus, fallopian tubes, or ovaries resulting in fever, malaise, pain, and other symptoms

Placenta An organ that attaches to the uterine wall and serves as a conduit for oxygen and nutrients to pass to the developing fetus

Pornography A depiction of lewd material or erotic behavior designed to cause sexual arousal

Postabortion syndrome (PAS) A controversial term referring to supposed long-term negative psychological effects of abortion

Posttraumatic stress disorder (PTSD) A syndrome developing after exposure to an extremely traumatic event. Symptoms include anxiety, sleeplessness, eating disorders, depression, and hyperactive nervous system.

Pragmatics The relationship between communicators

Premarital sex Usually refers to coitus, sexual intercourse, before marriage

Premature ejaculation The persistent or recurring early onset of orgasm and ejaculation

Premenstrual syndrome (PMS) A condition preceding menstruation, characterized by a myriad of physical and psychological symptoms

Prevalence rates Rates of prevailing infection used to measure the extent of the overall threat faced by the public

Primary sex characteristics Growth of the sex organs

Prior learning Factors relating to childhood development

Prodrome Stage of a communicable disease that follows the incubation period, with nonspecific, possibly flulike symptoms

Promiscuity Frequent and indiscriminate change in sexual partners

Prostaglandins Hormones that can cause muscle contractions and have been associated with menstrual pain

Prostate gland A chestnut-sized gland connected to neck of the bladder and vas deferens, which secretes alkaline fluid and enzymes that are part of ejaculatory fluid

Prostatitis Inflammation and irritation of the prostate gland

Prostitution The exchange of sexual services for money

Protease inhibitors A group of antiviral drugs used to prevent replication of HIV-infected cells

Psychoanalytic theory Also known as Freudian theory (after its founder, Sigmund Freud), describes personality development as outgrowth of interaction of id (pleasure-seeking, guilt-free), superego (the conscience, influenced by society and parents), and ego (rational, analytical mind driven by logical thinking)

Psychosexual development The blending of sexual aspects of one's development with other psychological factors

Psychosis A severe form of mental disorder or disease affecting the total personality

Psychotropic drugs Substances that are mind altering

Puberty Biological transition from childhood to young adulthood

Pubic lice *Phthirius pubis;* small insects (metazoan) that infest the host's pubic hair

Queer theory Theories that look to explain sexual orientation and sexual identity without relying on heterosexuality as the norm

Rape Illicit sexual intercourse without consent

Rates Statistics calculated by dividing the number of cases of disease by the population at risk of infection

Refractory period The time from last orgasm to the next beginning of excitement

Reproductive readiness Pubertal development resulting in full growth of genitalia and onset of fertility

Rohypnol A depressant drug also known as the "date rape drug," because it causes loss of memory and makes women vulnerable to uninvited sexual intercourse

Role model A person whose behaviors are imitated by others

RU-486 Known as the "abortion pill"; mifepristone, a drug used to induce menstruation by blocking the absorption of progesterone and thereby preventing the uterine lining from supporting an embryo

Safe zone A fertility awareness concept that factors ovulation and length of time sperm and eggs can live as a time to avoid intercourse

Scabies A condition caused by the *Sarcoptes scabiei* parasite, which burrows under the skin and lays eggs

Scrotum A double-chambered pouch of tissue that hangs loosely from the base of the penis, containing the testicles

Secondary sex characteristics Physical traits that develop during puberty and signal sexual maturity; examples are developed breasts, armpit and pubic hair, and coarse facial hair

Self-esteem A way of looking at oneself; may be high or low

Seminal vesicles Small structures connected to vas deferens, which release fluids that nourish and buffer sperm as they are ejaculated

Sensate focus Nongenital pleasuring used to heighten sensuality without sexual activity

Sensory Relating to nerve messages coming into the brain

Sensuality Experiencing things through all five senses

Serous fluid A fluid that has the characteristics of serum

Sex surrogate A person who acts as a substitute sex partner during therapy

Sexologists Specialized researchers of sexual subjects from a variety of disciplines including psychology, biology, medicine, nursing, and health

Sexology The discipline that scientifically studies sexuality

Sexual aggression Any form of forced sexual contact, including but not limited to intercourse, without the person's consent

Sexual aversion disorder A disorder characterized by disgust and active avoidance of any genital sexual contact

Sexual coercion Any nonconsensual sexual behavior that occurs as the result of arguing, pleading, and cajoling and includes, but is not limited to, force

Sexual differentiation The processes by which the embryo/fetus develops into a male or a female; internal and external genitalia develop in distinct ways, as does the brain

Sexual dysfunction A disturbance or disorder in desire, excitement, orgasm, or resolution of the sexual response cycle

Sexual harassment Unwelcome sexual advances, requests for sexual favors, and other verbal or physical conduct of a sexual nature in the workplace or educational setting

Sexual lifestyle The interaction between types and numbers of current sex partners

Sexual masochism Deriving sexual pleasure from being humiliated or forced to suffer pain

Sexual orientation One's propensity for romantic and erotic attachments. *Heterosexuality* refers to attaching to a partner with different anatomy; *homosexuality* refers to a same-sex partner; *bisexuality* refers to attaching to both men and women

Sexual sadism Deriving sexual pleasure from inflicting pain or humiliation

Sexual victimization Depriving a person of free choice and forcing him or her to endure, observe, or comply with sexual acts

Sexuality A broad term referring to all aspects of being sexual

Sexually transmitted diseases (STDs) Diseases that are spread from person to person through sexual contact

Social well-being A component of wellness that involves connection to others through various types of relationships

Sociopath A manifestly antisocial psychopath

Somatic nervous system The part of the peripheral nervous system under voluntary control

Somatotropic drugs Substances that are body altering

Sonogram The picture of the fetus produced by an ultrasound screening

Spectatoring Becoming an outside observer of one's own sexual encounter while it is occurring

Spermatogenesis Sperm production

Spiritual well-being A component of wellness that involves feeling connected to something beyond oneself

Spirochete A mobile, flexible, corkscrew-shaped bacterium of the genus *Spirocheta*, one type of which causes syphilis

Statutory rape A person older than the legal age of consent having intercourse with a partner who is younger than the legal age of consent

Sterility The permanent inability to reproduce

Sterilization Techniques (vasectomy and tubal ligation) that prevent sperm from reaching ova

Stranger rape Forced intercourse by a person who is unknown to the target person

Suction curettage A surgical abortion procedure that removes the embryo and placenta from the uterus through suction and use of a curette

Superego The conscience, influenced by society and family, according to Freudian theory

Symmetrical relationships Relationships based on equality

Synergistic effect An enhanced, unpredictable drug effect caused by combining two or more substances

Syphilis An STD caused by the spirochete bacterium *Treponema pallidum*

Teratogenic effects Side effects of drugs and other substances that cause birth defects

Testes Two almond-shaped male gonads responsible for sperm and hormone production

Testosterone The main hormone associated with sexual desire; the most notable androgen, recognized for fueling aggressiveness in males

Thalamus The part of the brain that relays all inputs to the cerebral cortex

Theoretical effectiveness The lowest expected percentage of women who will get pregnant while using a given contraceptive method

Thriving Pattern of normal weight gain, neuromuscular development, and other developmental attributes of infants

Toxemia A highly dangerous condition during pregnancy when high blood pressure occurs

Transactional analysis (TA) Eric Berne's communication model based on three ego states—parent, adult, and child

Transcend To rise above or extend beyond ordinary limits

Transgendered The preferred term to describe individuals whose gender identity and gender role encompass both masculine and feminine qualities.

Transsexualism (a gender identity disorder) A strong and persistent cross-gender identification

Transudation The production of vaginal lubrication because of sweating of vaginal tissue engorged with blood during vasocongestion

Transvestic fetishism Deriving sexual pleasure from wearing women's clothing

Tubal ligation A female sterilization procedure in which a surgical instrument is used to cut and tie back the fallopian tubes to block passage of the ova and thereby prevent fertilization

T-zone Transformation zone of the cervix, where columnar epithelial tissue of the uterus meets with squamous tissue of the vagina

Urethra The tube through which urine (and semen for males) passes from the bladder to outside the body

Urethral opening The opening to the urethra, lying behind the clitoris and in front of the vaginal opening

Urethritis Inflammation and irritation of urethra

Uterine fibroid tumors Noncancerous solid growths on the endometrium or in the walls of the uterus

Uterus Also called the womb, a fist-sized muscular structure that houses the developing fetus during gestation

Vacuum aspiration An induced abortion procedure in which uterine contents are removed by suction; used for early abortions

Vagina A tubular organ connecting to the uterus, which serves both reproductive and erotic functions

Vaginismus Painful, involuntary contractions of the outer third of the vagina during attempted penetration

Vaginitis Inflammation and irritation of the vagina

Varicocele An enlarged vein in the scrotum impairing blood flow

Vas deferens A tube extending from testicles to prostate gland, where it converts into urethra; responsible for transporting sperm and other ejaculatory fluid

Vasectomy A male contraceptive method resulting in sterilization by cutting and tying off the vas deferens

Vasectomy The surgical sterilization of the male that involves cutting and tying off the vas deferens

Vasocongestion The movement of blood flow into the genitals resulting in a variety of responses including erection in men and lubrication in women

Vesicles Fluid-filled blisters

Vestibule The area within the labia minora that includes the hymen, introitus, and urethral opening

Viability A gestational weight of the fetus of at least 500 grams and/or age of 24 weeks of age

Viagra The drug sildenafil, prescribed for the treatment of erectile disorder

Voyeurism Deriving sexual pleasure from observing unsuspecting individuals undressing or engaging in sexual activities

Vulva The external female genitalia

Wellness The state of optimal health and well-being

Widowhood The period of time between loss of spouse and remarriage

Women's movement A force to gain full educational, social, and economic opportunities and rights for women equal to those that men are traditionally understood to have

Yes/no questions A verbal initiating technique involving a question that requires only a yes or no response

Index

NOTES:

NOTES:

NOTES:

NOTES:

NOTES:

NOTES:

NOTES:

NOTES:

NOTES:

NOTES:

NOTES:

NOTES: